Surgeon, Scientist, Soldier

The life and times of Henry Wade
1876–1955

Dugald Gardner

The ROYAL
SOCIETY of
MEDICINE
PRESS Limited

THE ROYAL
COLLEGE of
SURGEONS
EDINBURGH

Founded 1505
From here health

© 2005 Royal Society of Medicine Press Ltd
1 Wimpole Street, London W1G 0AE, UK
Tel: +44 (0)20 7290 2921
Fax: +44 (0)20 7290 2929
Email: publishing@rsm.ac.uk
www.rsmpress.co.uk

British Library Cataloguing in Publication Data
A catalogue record for this book is available from the British Library.

ISBN 1-85315-661-2

Distribution in Europe and Rest of World:
Marston Book Services Ltd
PO Box 269
Abingdon
OXON OX14 4YN, UK
Tel: +44 (0)1235 465500
Fax: +44 (0)1235 465555
Email: direct.order@marston.co.uk

Distribution in the USA and Canada:
Royal Society of Medicine Press Ltd
c/o BookMasters, Inc.
30 Amberwood Parkway
Ashland, Ohio 44805, USA
Tel: +1 800 247 6553 / +1 800 266 5564
Email: order@bookmasters.com

Distribution in Australia and New Zealand:
Elsevier Australia
30–52 Smidmore Street
Marrickville NSW 2204
Australia
Tel: + 61 2 9517 8999
Fax: + 61 2 9517 2249
Email: service@elsevier.com.au

Designed and typeset by Phoenix Photosetting, Chatham, Kent
Printed and bound by Replika Press Pvt Ltd, India

Contents

Drawing of Henry Wade presented after his death to the Royal College of Surgeons of Edinburgh by his sister Margaret Callander Wade. The artist is not known.

Dedication

Dedicated to the memory of Thomas Gardner MD, FRCSEd whose
foresight and wisdom first took his son, the author, to the City of
Edinburgh, to its Medical School and to the Royal College of Surgeons
of Edinburgh.

Foreword

In this compelling account of the life of an early twentieth century surgeon, Dugald Gardner has painted on a broad canvas, illuminating the 50th anniversary of the death of one of the most distinguished of the Fellows of the Royal College of Surgeons of Edinburgh with insight and scholarship. He demonstrates in Henry Wade the Listerian ideal of devotion and humility in the care of patients combined with remorseless dedication to science, reminding contemporary surgeons that there is more to earthly existence than the knife and the cautery, the computer screen and the microprobe.

Gardner's subject, Henry Wade, was born into the life of a large family reared circumspectly in a late nineteenth century Scottish manse. Wade enhanced surgery, promoted science and endured war. He enjoyed five lives: he was at once a scientist and pathologist expert in the biology of cancer, a master of the complex and exacting field of surgical urology, a military surgeon in the tradition of Dominique Larrey, a museum conservator of distinction and an antiquarian. To each of his five lives he brought the severity and intensity of his Scottish inheritance and to each he devoted his academic knowledge, his practical skill, a thoughtful thrift and economy with words but a generosity of spirit. Experience taught him the politics of a Royal College and the mental and physical stamina needed to endure committees. Tragedy scarred Wade's personal life, but he sustained his loss with apparent equanimity and sought solace in the garden of his ancient home in East Lothian and in antiquarian studies. His many honours indicate the height with which he was regarded by his peers and the esteem with which he was held when first a member and then the President of a College Council. The feelings were reciprocated, and his bequests to the College were only a token of his regard for a body to which he had given so much over a period of 50 years.

To forget the misjudgements of the past is a sure recipe for repeating them in the future. Few biographies have been written of the lives of Presidents of Royal Scottish surgical Colleges. In the present scintillating account, it is evident that, in a fulfilling life, Henry Wade exemplified not only what *is* best in medicine but what *can be* best for medicine. *Surgeon, Scientist, Soldier* is particularly apposite: it coincides with the celebration of the 500th anniversary of the Incorporation of Edinburgh Barber Surgeons, mirroring the ideals that they set themselves and the struggles they endured.

John Allan Raymond Smith, PhD FRCSEng FRCSEd
177th President of the Royal College of Surgeons of Edinburgh
2005

Preface

Henry Wade was the archetypal surgeon. He lived from 1876 to 1955, a time of transition in the world of medicine. His career spanned the reigns of six monarchs, so an account of his life is an account of his surgical times. He was at once scientist, master surgeon, military man, antiquarian and philanthropist. During the half century before his birth, surgery had been transformed by the advent of anaesthesia, by an understanding of infection and by laboratory science. Benefiting from these discoveries, Wade was destined to achieve renown in cancer research, war surgery, teaching and the surgery of the urinary system.

This tribute arose when Sir Robert Shields, President of the Royal College of Surgeons of Edinburgh, introduced me to the trust documents of Pilmuir House, East Lothian, the home of Henry Wade, surgeon, for 26 years. By happy coincidence, the book commemorates the 50th year of Wade's death and the 500th anniversary of the Incorporation of Barber Surgeons of Edinburgh.

For men and women of the twenty-first century, life without the possibility of surgery is unthinkable. The struggle against disease is unending, and many battles are fought in operating theatres. But only a small minority of men and women choose to become surgeons. These exceptional few are unusual individuals: their art and science call for extraordinary learning and humanity, manual dexterity and skill, confidence and physical stamina and, above all, the quality of *Aequanimitas* – the innate gift of rising above the turmoil of suffering, guiding, inspiring and acting without personal or emotional involvement. These are attributes described throughout the ages – never better than by Celsus and, nearly 2,000 years later, by the physician, William Osler.

> 'He should be youthful, or in early middle age, with a strong and steady hand, as expert with the left hand as with the right, with vision sharp and clear, and spirit undaunted; so far void of pity that while he wishes only to cure his patient, yet is not moved by his cries to go too fast or cut less than is necessary.'

> (Aulus Cornelius Celsus, circa 40 AD)

> 'No quality takes rank with imperturbability – coolness and presence of mind under all circumstances, calmness amid storm,

clearness of judgement in moments of grave peril, immobility, impassiveness, or, to use an old and expressive word, *phlegm.*'

(William Osler, in his valedictory address, University of Pennsylvania, 1st May 1889)

Wade became an Edinburgh medical student in 1893. Lister's startling discoveries were fresh in the minds of his contemporaries, yet the majority of surgeons still operated without masks or gloves. Bacteria were known, but the application of the microscope to the diagnosis of disease had hardly begun. The existence of filterable viruses was suspected but not proven. Immunization against typhoid was predicted but not yet practised. There were no remedies for syphilis, tetanus, influenza or poliomyelitis. Great numbers of children died in childhood, and men and women were fortunate to reach the age of 40 years. But dramatic changes were pending. When Wade returned from the Great South African War in 1902, he found that the uncrowned King Edward VII had narrowly survived an operation for appendicitis, that new hospitals for infectious and mental diseases were opening and that the miraculous new Röntgen (X)-ray apparatus seemed likely to revolutionize the surgical scene. The transmission of malaria had been elucidated, a concept of blood groups was emerging and chemotherapy was showing signs of turning from theory to reality.

Following in Lister's footsteps, Wade mastered anatomy, trained in the medical sciences, qualified as a surgeon, became Conservator of the world-famous Museum of the Royal College of Surgeons of Edinburgh and embarked on an ambitious programme of cancer research. Apprenticed to eminent teachers, he spent nearly three years as Assistant Pathologist to the Royal Infirmary of Edinburgh, learning diagnostic laboratory methods and acquiring a deep understanding of disease. He rose to become a young consultant, but the realization of ambition was interrupted when patriotism drew him like a magnet to the war of 1914. It was during this conflict that his enthusiasm of photography came to the fore. He made nearly 1,000 photographs of his experiences in the armed forces. A small selection has been incorporated in this text; the remainder are translated into a commentary synthesized from his notes. They are shown as yellow tinted boxes in Chapters 7 and 8. Returning to peacetime Britain after an absence of five years, he established his own nursing home and made himself the leading Scottish figure in the rising speciality of urology. In 1935, he was elected President of the Royal College of Surgeons of Edinburgh. In 1946, he was knighted for his contributions to medicine.

Such was the variegated nature of Wade's life, so far-reaching the ramifications of his work and travels, that I would be foolish to claim that I have recorded and analyzed every detail of them. Inevitably, I have placed reliance on figures and statistics: in comparing surgical practice in the first decade of the twentieth century with the second and third, records such as those detailing the number of patients admitted to hospital and the proportion of these operated upon must be allowed to speak for themselves. An arithmetical approach has also been inevitable in dealing with wartime casualties, and I make no apology for the occasional use of tables and graphs. After all, did not Sir William Petty say in 1690:

> 'Instead of using only comparative words and intellectual arguments, I have taken the course…to express myself in terms of Numbers, Weights, or Measure, to use only arguments of sense, and to consider only such causes, as have visible foundations in nature.'

In the present work, subjects of particular interest or of a specialized nature are displayed against a grey background. There are inevitable omissions of fact and commissions of misinformation and for every one of these errors I accept full responsibility. I use Chapters 3, 9, 10, 11 and 12 to describe Henry Wade's professional life in surgery; Chapters 4, 5 and 6 to summarize his contributions to biological science; and Chapters 2, 7 and 8 to outline his military ventures. Chapters 13 and 14 deal with the political matters that occupied much of his later years, while Chapters 1, 15 and 16 centre on his early and later times, those in which family and personal concerns played a dominant part.

When Wade left the Royal Infirmary of Edinburgh in 1939, aseptic surgery had become the norm, chemotherapy had been introduced, immunization against tetanus was standard practice and a blood transfusion service had been established. After the tragically early death of his wife, he devoted himself to his beloved Pilmuir House, East Lothian, where he lived out his final years as antiquarian and historian. By the time of his death in 1955, he realized that spectacular advances in anaesthesia now enabled safe operations on the brain, lungs, blood vessels and heart; that paediatric, orthopaedic and plastic surgery had become specialities; and that transplantation, robotic and keyhole procedures could be foreseen.

It was a new age.

DL Gardner
2005

Acknowledgements

Innumerable friends and colleagues have helped with the collection of the records that relate to Wade's life and times, and I am deeply grateful to them. If, peradventure, I have failed to acknowledge each kindly individual, I can only anticipate their frustration by sincere apology.

I owe much to Ms Marianne Smith, Librarian to the Royal College of Surgeons of Edinburgh, for her unremitting and benevolent help and advice, and I thank the Assistant Librarians, Mr Steven Kerr and Mr Andrew Morgan; the former Assistant Librarians Ms Gillian Johnstone, Mr Simon Johnston and Mr David Collier; and the former Archivist, Ms Alison Stevenson, for their generous aid. I am also grateful to Mr Iain Milne, Librarian to the Royal College of Physicians of Edinburgh and his colleagues. The University of Edinburgh Library enabled the identification of photographs of Henry Wade and his 1907 MD thesis, while Mr Arnott Wilson gave invaluable help in examining the papers relating to the Chairs of Clinical and Systematic Surgery of the University. The Librarians of the Royal College of Physicians of London assisted in the search for Wade papers, and I acknowledge the invaluable assistance of Mr W Todd of the Map Division of the National Library of Scotland; Mr Paul Taylor, Librarian to the Peebles Library; and the librarians of New College, Church of Scotland, who assisted with an understanding of the Falkirk United Presbyterian Church.

Mr Peter Clapham, of the History Department, Callendar House, Falkirk, together with the staff of Register House, Edinburgh, facilitated my study of the Wade family inheritance, while the archivists to the Edinburgh City Council displayed the records of the Royal High School. The archivist to the Cumberland Infirmary identified the papers that relate to Wade's time in that hospital. Mr John Renshaw gave invaluable help in explaining the design of the 1832 Playfair building of the Royal College of Surgeons of Edinburgh and of the changes in the building structure that took place during Henry Wade's lifetime; correspondingly, the staff of the Royal Commission on the Ancient and Historical Monuments of Scotland gave invaluable advice as did those of Register House, Edinburgh.

I am grateful to the former tenants of Pilmuir House for allowing visits to the house. Mrs E Fraser-Tytler very kindly advised me on the history of her family. I am equally grateful to Mr GH Rust of Morton Fraser, solicitors, for permitting access to the documents of the

Pilmuir Trust, while Mr J Kerr, Secretary of Gullane Golf Club, provided valuable guidance in tracing Henry Wade's membership of that club.

The reports of the 1901 and 1903 Royal Commissions on the South African War were consulted with the assistance of the Library of the Wellcome Centre for the History of Medicine. An understanding of Wade's service with the Scottish Yeomanry was helped by Mr Alan Carswell, Curator of the Castle Museum, Edinburgh. The archivist to the Royal Scots Fusiliers provided comparable guidance. The Imperial War Museum, London, offered advice with regard to the South African war of 1899–1902, and the Public Records Office assisted in a search for the citation for Wade's Distinguished Service Order.

The archives of the Royal Infirmary of Edinburgh contain the records of the innumerable patients under Wade's care during the years 1924 to 1939. I am indebted to Dr Michael Barfoot, Lothian Heath Services Archivist, and Mrs Julie Hutton and Ms Alison Gardiner for facilitating access to these records. Permission to study these papers was granted by Professor Peter Donnelly, Director of Public Health and Health Policy for the Lothian NHS Board.

Access to the minute books of the Section of Urology of the Royal Society of Medicine that recorded the transactions during Henry Wade's time as President of that Section was facilitated by the Society's library. Many records that relate to the origins of the National Health Service are held by the Department of Health for Scotland: I thank the Division of Health Statistics, Trinity Park House, Edinburgh, for access to them. Mrs Susan Lawson of the offices of the British Medical Association, Scottish Division, kindly facilitated my reading of the minutes of the Scottish War Committee.

Dr Helen Dingwall, Historian to the Royal College of Surgeons of Edinburgh, gave generously of her time in reading and commenting on my manuscript. Her recent account of the history of the College, _A Famous and Flourishing Society_, has been of immeasurable help in understanding the early history of that body. Dr Morrice McCrae, Historian to the Royal College of Physicians of Edinburgh, Dr Sara Barnes and Sheena Jones read and criticized my manuscript expertly. To the late Mr JH Annan, the late Mr Noel Gray, Mr AA Gunn, Mr IF MacLaren, Dr Neil Maclean, Dr AHB Masson, Mr JE Newsam and Ms Robyn Webber – all Fellows of the Royal College of Surgeons of Edinburgh – I owe thanks for their generosity in commenting on parts of the work.

Mr Max McKenzie, ABIPP, made many of the photographs with his customary skill. The photographic help of Mr John H Simmons of the University of Edinburgh Library is acknowledged, together with that of Mr W Hopkinson of the University of Edinburgh's Department of Medical Photography and his colleagues Ms Louise Henderson and Ms Nicky Greenhorn. Mr David Gardner provided invaluable photographic assistance.

Ms Sadie Maskery undertook the expert scanning of some of Wade's histological sections and illustrative material. Miss Jennifer Clarke of the Publications Department of the Royal College of Surgeons of Edinburgh offered much help with the scanning and preparation of images, while her colleague, Mr Mark Baillie, provided invaluable technical advice and support.

Professor John Edgar de Burgh Norman, AO FRCSEd, Sydney, Australia, made it possible to find an image of a live duck-billed platypus, *Ornithorhyncus anatinus*.

I am indebted to the Scottish Society of the History of Medicine for their financial support of my studies and to the Royal College of Surgeons of Edinburgh for making possible the publication of this book at a time when the College is celebrating its Quincentenary, and I express my thanks to Natalie Hayeem and her colleagues at the Royal Society of Medicine Press for their unfailing courtesy, tolerance and generous skill during the gestation of this volume.

In the course of the past 20 years, I have been privileged to view the sombre panorama of the Gallipoli peninsula and the island of Thasos. I have also been fortunate in being able to admire the historical beauty of Jerusalem and many other parts of Israel that were seen by Wade. An invitation to Baghdad permitted travel in and around that ancient city. These ventures, together with journeys to archives in Falkirk, Haddington, Edinburgh, London and Melbourne, have facilitated the present tribute.

The completion of this work would not have been possible but for the selfless, tolerant and unstinting support of my wife Helen and my family during a period when matters of greater importance were inevitably uppermost in their minds.

DL Gardner
2005

Abbreviations

Abbreviations are defined in each chapter when they are first used.

BMA	British Medical Association
CM	Minutes of the meetings of the Royal College of Surgeons of Edinburgh
CRec	Case records from the Royal Infirmary of Edinburgh
EEF	Egyptian Expeditionary Force
EMCS	Edinburgh Medico-Chirurgical Society
FA	Field ambulance
HWP	Henry Wade papers
MC	Museum committee
PCM	Minutes of the President's Council of the Royal College of Surgeons of Edinburgh
RAMC	Royal Army Medical Corps
RCPEd	Royal College of Physicians of Edinburgh
RCPSG	Royal College of Physicians and Surgeons of Glasgow
RCSEd	Royal College of Surgeons of Edinburgh
RCSEng	Royal College of Surgeons of England
RIE	Royal Infirmary of Edinburgh
RIEM	Minutes of the meetings of the managers of the Royal Infirmary of Edinburgh
RIEMM	Minutes of the Committee of medical managers of the Royal Infirmary of Edinburgh
RRIE	Annual reports of the Royal Infirmary of Edinburgh
RSM	Royal Society of Medicine
SCMWC	Scottish Central Medical War Committee
SHMB	Scottish Horse Mounted Brigade
SYP	Serving Young Practitioners Sub-Committee

CHAPTER 1

Early years – the tale unfolds

1876–99

Fame is not achieved by sitting on feather cushions
or lying in bed.

(Dante Alighieri: *Inferno,* Canto XXIV 1307)

This is the story of a simple man who became a famous surgeon, a scientist of repute and a war hero. Henry Wade was neither born great nor had greatness 'thrust upon him'. He achieved greatness through the good fortune of high intelligence, practical skills, an aptitude for conscientious hard work and, from time to time, a proper disrespect for overbearing authority. He was not, in the strict sense, a scholar. Nevertheless, he attained distinction in the corridors of the University of Edinburgh, and in the Presidencies of a Scottish Royal College and a Section of the Royal Society of Medicine. He was a man of action rather than of words and a challenge for any biographer as he is not known to have kept a diary. His forte was the compilation of visual rather than written images: he was a skilled and imaginative photographer. Coming from a staunchly devout royalist family, his inborn instincts and duty took him twice to great theatres of war. His strong physique proved invaluable not only on the battlefields of South Africa, Gallipoli, Egypt, Palestine and Syria but in the exacting struggles he waged in surgical operating theatres, where, for 50 years, he fought to transform and save innumerable lives. Faced by tragedy, he rose above mere mortal toil and ended his days an antiquarian and philanthropist.

Falkirk

Wade was a native of Falkirk, Scotland.[1,2] The ancient town envelopes the Roman Antonine wall built across southern Scotland in 142 AD.

The name Falkirk signified *Faw Kirk* – a speckled church. A battle of Falkirk was fought in 1298 between the levies of William Wallace and those of King Edward I. In 1745, an engagement between the Jacobites of Bonnie Prince Charlie and those of the English, the second battle of Falkirk, lasted 20 minutes. Later, the Seven Years War exploded. The struggle by Prussia, Hanover and Great Britain against Austria, France,

Chapter Summary
Chapter Summary
• Falkirk
• Henry Wade's family
• School
• Medical school
• New Royal Infirmary of Edinburgh
• Teachers and teaching
• Graduation and qualification
• Resident House Surgeon and House Physician

Sweden and Russia led to an insatiable demand for munitions. Falkirk and nearby Carron became the sites for the manufacture of canons and canonballs.[2] Iron ore was mined nearby: coalfields were close, limestone quarried locally and timber brought from the Highlands. The deadly *Carronade* became the weapon of choice for the world's navies.

Within 10 years of its foundation, the Carron ironworks employed more than a thousand men. The new industry manufactured every form of industrial and domestic metal work. Transport was demanded to carry these products to world markets. The construction of a canal began in 1768. Following the path of the Roman wall, the waterway ran from the Clyde in the west to the Forth, at Grangemouth, in the east. Soon, it was used by great numbers of barges. In 1818, a second Union canal began. With locks, aqueducts and a tunnel, it was completed in 1822. Men of ill repute as well as those of peace adopted the canal for their own purposes, and the murderers William Burke and William Hare found it a convenient channel for carrying bodies from Ireland for dissection in Edinburgh.

Although emigration depleted the population, a relative increase was seen in the numbers of people living in central Scotland. A loss of Scots to England and to the Empire was balanced by the immigration of Irish. But disease was rampant and malnutrition commonplace among the poor. Although the death rate declined, so did the birth rate. Tuberculosis was endemic, poliomyelitis frequent. The existence of bacteria was suspected but viruses were wholly unknown. Measles, whooping cough, typhus and cholera decimated the community each year. Appendicitis remained a mystery, and there was no understanding of the causes of cancer.

Change was imminent, however, as living conditions slowly improved. Life expectation rose from around 40 years in 1871 to 50 or more years in 1910–12. Gradually, Falkirk was transformed from a modest rural community to a thriving industrial centre of 16,000 people. Rail transport started in 1841, complementing the waterways. The electric telegraph arrived. The telephone followed in 1876, and the scene was set for twentieth century life. Horse-drawn transport was customary, but 'penny farthing' and then 'safety' bicycles emerged, and, in large cities like Manchester and Edinburgh, electric tram cars could be seen gliding along metal rails. Motor cars rushed upon the scene in 1893 and motorcycles in 1901 – the year in which electric street lighting succeeded gas. Urban areas fared well but there was a price to pay and, in 1908, the rent for a single room became more than five shillings, today's equivalent of 25p.

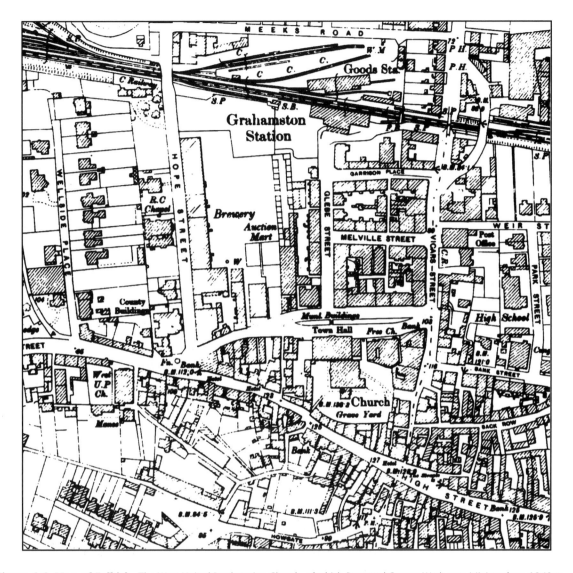

Figure 1.1 Map of Falkirk. *The West United Presbyterian Church, of which Reverend George Wade was Minister from 1862 to 1892, is on the south side of West Bridge Street. The 'Old' Manse is beside the church. Falkirk High School (right) is midway between the High Street and Grahamston Station (upper centre). The railway line (top), West Bridge Street and High Street all run from east to west, emphasizing the importance of communication between Edinburgh and Glasgow. (Courtesy of the Trustees of the National Library of Scotland)*
    Figures 1.1, 2.1, 7.2, 7.15, 8.1 and 15.2 are reproduced by courtesy of the Trustees of the National Library of Scotland

Henry Wade's family

Henry Wade was born on Monday 18th December 1876 in the Manse of the Falkirk West United Presyterian Church.[3-8, A]

For the people of Europe, 1876 was a year of promise and hope. The arts prospered, Bayreuth acclaimed the *Ring* cycle, Renoir completed *Le Moulin de la Galette* and Schliemann revealed the glories of Troy. Commerce flourished, and new railways and roads were built. The chemical industry transformed science, revolutionizing medicine, printing and agriculture. It was also a year of anxiety. Ambitious Prussia threatened European stability, Bulgarians had been massacred as Serbia declared war on Turkey, and the Boers of South Africa were increasingly unhappy with British rule. But it was no more than seven days before Christmas, and Wade's father, the Reverend George Wade, was preoccupied with his parish duties. There were services to take, meetings to attend, sermons to prepare. There may even have been time to buy presents for his already large family and many friends. It is no surprise to learn, therefore, that the arrival of his youngest son, Henry, was not registered until 8th January 1877, and this is often shown as the year of his birth.

Wade's paternal grandfather, also George, married Mary Duff. Wade's father was born in Dublin on 27th March 1832. At the age of seven, he moved with his family to Irvine, where he was educated at the Academy. Subsequently, he attended the University of Glasgow, studied at the United Presbyterian Hall, Edinburgh, and spent a year

Figure 1.2 Falkirk West United Presbyterian Church *as it is today*

at the University of Halle, Germany. He became an accomplished German scholar, travelling in Italy before returning to Scotland. Placed on a probationer's list within the Presbyterian Church, he received calls to St Andrews, Strathaven and Falkirk,[B] accepting the Ministry of the Falkirk West United Presbyterian Church in 1856 at the early age of 24 years.[8] The church stood prominently in the High Street, the 'Old' Manse (1860) next to the church.

Henry Wade's mother was Eliza Callander,[C] the daughter of Captain Thomas Callander, a native of Falkirk, and of Mary Russell, daughter of James Russell of Blackbraes. Eliza Callander and George Wade were married on 17th July 1860. He was 28 years old, she 22. She gave her address as 1 Grey Place, Greenock. Both her father and George Wade's own father had been sea captains and 'shipmasters', and it may be surmised that their shared interests encouraged the meeting of the young people.

Figure 1.3 The 'Old' Manse (built 1789, enlarged 1860) of the West United Prebyterian Church at Falkirk

Figure 1.4 Elders of the Falkirk West United Presbyterian Church in session in 1862. *The Minister, the young Reverend George Wade, is seated at the extreme left*

Wade was the youngest child of a large inheritance. There were nine children, five sons and four daughters. The evidence suggests that the Wades were a united, contented and vigorous family. The paths chosen by George Wade's sons were among those open to the children of well-educated, modestly affluent Scottish families: the church, law and medicine. None of the Reverend Wade's sons decided to follow him into the church: two practised as solicitors and one, James, elected to emigrate at a relatively early age.

- Henry's eldest brother, George, graduated MB, CM (p 16) from the University of Edinburgh in 1887 at the age of 21. In 1894, he advanced to the higher degree of MD. He worked in Hawick in the Scottish Borders. In 1913, he migrated to Tasmania, subsequently practising at Port Cygnet, New South Wales. He died in 1938 aged 73. A son, also George Wade, served in the First World War in the 7th Argyll and Sutherland Highlanders. Attached to the Machine Gun Corps (MGC), he was lost when the troopship *Ivernia* was torpedoed off the coast of Marseilles in 1915.
- Thomas Callander Wade was an outstanding scholar at the Royal High School, Edinburgh. In 1885, his last year, he was in the mathematics class. He became a distinguished student of law, graduating LLB, and subsequently an examiner in law for the University of Edinburgh. He practised as a solicitor with Russel and Aitken, Falkirk. His account of the Falkirk United Free Church is a valuable source of details of the Wade family.[8] He died from cardiac failure, aged 78 years, on 28th July 1945 at Pilmuir House, Haddington, the home of his brother Henry (Chapter 15).
- Henry Wade's third brother was Grahame Hardie Wade, born in 1874. Like the other boys, he attended the Royal High School, Edinburgh. In the session 1888–9, the year in which he was in the fourth class on the classical side, there were 265 pupils. He excelled at arithmetic, algebra and Euclid, studied law and became a partner in Logie and Fisher, Writers, Glasgow. A Captain in the 7th Argyll and Sutherland Highlanders, the same regiment as his nephew, he was only 42 when he was killed in action near Ypres on 25th April 1915. His grave is in the Seaforth Cemetery, Cheddar Villa.
- James Russell Wade was Henry's youngest brother. He left for the Transvaal in 1894 at the age of 24 years. James served in the Great South African or Anglo–Boer War (p 23) as a trooper, then as Acting Sergeant Major in Thorneycroft's Mounted Infantry. Fluent in Dutch and Kaffir, he joined the Army Intelligence Department. As Chapter 2 suggests, his presence in South Africa may have contributed to Henry Wade's decision to volunteer for service in that country in 1900. After the war, James developed an extensive and successful business as an artesian well contractor. He corresponded with his widowed mother[D] and his younger brother (Appendix 1.1).

Circumstances took two of George Wade's daughters to Australia. A third, displaying the ambitions of the suffragettes, struck out into pharmacy and the armed forces, while his fourth daughter remained in Scotland, struggling with ill health and leading the secluded life of a frail Edinburgh spinster.

- Henry's eldest sister, Mary Russell Wade, settled with her mother at Broomage House, Larbert, after the death of the Reverend George Wade obliged them to leave Falkirk. She did not marry. Henry arranged to take her into his own early home at 32 Alva Street, Edinburgh, when she became terminally ill. She died from rheumatic heart disease in 1908 at 6 Manor Place. She was 46.
- Henry's second sister Eliza junior, born in 1864, was 27 at the time of her death in 1890. She had left Scotland to marry Dr Eric Sinclair, Medical Superintendent of the Gladesville Mental Hospital, New South Wales. There were two sons, both of whom graduated in medicine and practised in Australia. Henry Wade always felt a particular responsibility for his nephews; however, he had little opportunity to help and advise them until 1922.[E]
- Catherine Agnes Wade was born on 13th December 1871. She migrated to New South Wales after the death of her sister, to be with one of the nephews, Callander W Sinclair.
- Margaret Callander Wade lived in Larbert. She was Henry Wade's youngest sister and was born on 18th May 1875. He kept in close touch with Margaret, and, through her, with his mother. Margaret Wade qualified as a pharmacist. She had charge of the dispensary of the First Scottish General Hospital at Aberdeen during the First World War, then of the dispensary of the Second and Third Scottish General Hospitals at Stobhill. Moving to the Royal Naval Hospital at Larbert, she was recorded in the navy list as an officer of the Royal Navy. A surviving letter[F] shows that she wrote to her brother in 1920 (Appendix 1.2). In old age, she suffered greatly from rheumatoid arthritis. She died aged 86 on 22nd August 1961 at her home. The death certificate was witnessed by her niece, Elizabeth Singer, who lived at 6 Learmonth Gardens, Edinburgh.

Early in 1890, an exciting message reached the Old Manse, Falkirk. The telegram told Reverend George Wade and his wife Eliza of the birth, in Australia, of their first grandchild. George Wade had not been well. Now 58, he had dedicated his life to the welfare of a devoted congregation. When the wonderful news came, he and Eliza decided that the time had come for a well-earned rest. With the agreement of the church, they decided to sail to Australia to see the baby, the child of Eliza junior. Arriving at Sydney, they were met with tragedy: a second telegram told them of the death of their daughter in childbirth.

Returning to Scotland, the Reverend George Wade never recovered. He died from pneumonia on 24th July 1892 at Buccleugh Street, Melrose, the home of his eldest son Dr George Wade. Years later, Henry Wade and his sister Margaret presented a forecourt to the Falkirk West Church in memory of their father. Their mother, Eliza Wade, lived to the age of 89 and died on 12th March 1927 at her home: Woodcroft, Larbert. While Reverend and Mrs Wade were absent in Australia, the General Census of 1891 was conducted. The census revealed that 10 people, including the domestic servants, were present at the Falkirk home when the recording officer called; only Catherine was not listed. She had already left for Australia.

Figure 1.5 Reverend George Wade, *Henry Wade's father, at the time he visited Australia in 1890*

Figure 1.6 Memorial
erected by his family to the memory of Reverend George Wade

School

To his family and friends, Henry Wade was 'Harry'. Left-handed, his manual dexterity proved invaluable in later life. He was educated at the Falkirk Southern School, where he reached Standard III. When the Falkirk High School opened on 6th September 1886, Harry moved there. Three years later, in 1889 and at the age of 12 years, he migrated again, this time to the Royal High School, Edinburgh. The Reverend George Wade had thought carefully about his sons' education. The railway had come to Falkirk in 1841, and the journey from Falkirk to the Waverley Station, Edinburgh, took barely 30 minutes. A walk of no more than a few hundred yards brought young Harry to the doors of the Royal High School and its magnificent building on the slopes of the Calton Hill.

The Royal High School was the oldest school in Edinburgh. The first building was erected in 1578. At the time of Henry Wade's admission, the Rector was Dr John Marshall, a distinguished classicist. Like the Reverend George Wade, he had spent time in Halle before graduating from Balliol College, Oxford. The style of education the school offered was in accordance with the conventions of the time. Initially, Harry was placed in Class III (classical).[G] He displayed an early aptitude for English, writing and geometry but a more slowly developing liking for Latin and Greek, little skill in arithmetic and only a modest accomplishment in gymnastics. There is no reference to team games such as rugby, although it would be surprising if this competitive sport, so popular in Scotland, was not enjoyed. No science was taught. In the course of the following three years, Harry rose through classes IV, V and VI. He left school in 1893, by which time the size of the establishment had increased to 345 pupils. His father had died shortly before the end of his penultimate year, and Harry's address became 'c/o Mrs Wade, the West Manse, Falkirk.'

Medical school

The reasons Henry Wade chose to become a doctor, following the path set by his elder brother George, remain a matter for conjecture. Well educated, vigorous and intelligent, he had other options. It seems likely, however, that the relatively early death of his father, together with the example of his brother, turned his mind towards the care of the sick. Later in life, moral rectitude, dedication and a firm

Figure 1.7 The Royal High School, Edinburgh. *The magnificent building was erected in 1830 on the slopes of Calton Hill. (From Minto CS. Victorian and Edwardian Edinburgh in old photographs. London: BT Batsford, 1973: Plate 60)*

basis of Christian belief suggest that he might have become a minister of the church as exemplary and inspirational as his father. However, he embarked on a career in medicine and entered the University of Edinburgh in the autumn of 1893.[7,9] He was doubly fortunate and at once enjoyed the twin benefits of a new Medical School[H] and a new teaching hospital – the second Royal Infirmary of Edinburgh, the RIE, which had opened for the admission of patients on 29th October 1879.[10]

In 1870, the University of Edinburgh responded to the explosive growth of medical science by planning an ambitious new building in Teviot Place. It was constructed to the specification of Sir William Turner.[11] The huge new edifice became the envy of the medical world, inviting comparison with the schools of Vienna, Prague, Budapest, St Petersburg, Boston and New York. The teaching of anatomy in the new Medical School began in 1880; the rooms and laboratories were fully occupied by 1884. The course on which Wade embarked had recently been lengthened from four years to five years as a result of the Universities (Scotland) Act of 1889. The change was to take effect from 1895, midway through his student years. In the academic year 1879–80, there had been 1,459 medical students in the University – an increase of nearly 1,000 from 10 years previously.[I] Immediately before the lengthening of the course in the new Medical School, the number grew to more than 2,000 but as the revised arrangements came to be accepted, the numbers fell again to less than 1,400. Nevertheless, in Wade's class of 1894–95, he had nearly 300 colleagues. The great number of students meant that the Medical School courses were largely confined to lectures. Small group education was impracticable. Anatomical dissection formed much the largest part of the practical teaching. Between 600 and 700 first- and second-year students attended the dissecting room, where each 'anatomized' the parts of a 'whole body': anatomization was both a key element in contemporary medical education and a focus for a social exchange that brought students and their teachers together in a surprisingly intimate manner.

New Royal Infirmary of Edinburgh

To appreciate the conditions under which Wade received much of his early training, and in which he spent many years of his later life, it is necessary to outline the nature of his hospital, the RIE. It was among the most modern in Europe. The design of the new RIE, approved by Florence Nightingale, took account of contemporary views on the need for plentiful air and light, an environment thought to minimize the spread of infection. Similar hospitals were being built throughout Europe.[12] Many were huge, and the Eppendorfer Krankenhaus in Hamburg, for example, had 80 separate pavilions. The pre-Listerian concept of the spread of sepsis and gangrene by a 'miasma' conveyed in the air had not yet been entirely overtaken by more recent evidence showing that much infection was spread by direct contact, by food and water or by 'fomites', objects like towels that harboured micro-organisms. The new science of Bacteriology was only beginning to emerge from the shadows.

After years of debate and enquiry, the foundation stone of the new RIE was laid by His Royal Highness the Prince of Wales on 13th October 1870. The hospital was to take the place of the first Royal Infirmary which had opened in 1741.[J] The site chosen for the new building was that of George Watson's Hospital (School), an 11-acre area entitled Heriot's Croft, between Lauriston Place and the Meadows.

Plans for the new voluntary hospital, the second RIE, at first called for the accommodation of 750 patients at an estimated cost of not less than £300,000.[11] The design of the hospital was to follow an old tradition and would be in two parts: a medical 'house' and a surgical 'house'. Every pound needed for the building had to be raised by public subscription. However, by 1872, it was no longer judged necessary to provide beds for a great number of cases of infectious disease, and new plans were prepared that incorporated no more than 500 beds. They would cost less than £185,000. In the final analysis, there were 227 beds for general surgery, 208 for general medicine and 74 for 'special' subjects that included Ophthalmology, Gynaecology, Venereal disease and 'Incidental Delirium'. The cost of the hospital furnishings had not been anticipated and was met by a further public appeal. By the time of its opening,[10] the ultimate cost of the new Infirmary amounted to £351,826/6/8d.

Figure 1.8 New Edinburgh Medical School of 1880

Figure 1.9 Place card *for the laying of the foundation stone of the new Royal Infirmary of Edinburgh. The stone was laid by HRH the Prince of Wales on 13th October 1870 in the presence of a large and distinguished body of people*

Construction of the new RIE began in 1872. The four pavilions of the medical house were built before those for surgical patients. Work on the six pavilions of the surgical house commenced in 1874, while the original, centrally located George Watson's School building was retained to provide administrative offices and accommodation for supportive services. They included the kitchens, the apothecary's shop, the house of the Lady Superintendent of Nurses, the nurses' home and a panelled chapel.[10] Four of the six pavilions of the surgical house were sited immediately next to Lauriston Place; the remaining two faced the medical blocks. The boiler house, laundry, carpenter's shop, pathological department and mortuary were sited at the north-west corner of the grounds. Heating of the hospital wards and rooms was still by open coal fires, of which there were 476, while hospital lighting was provided by 2,400 gas mantles. The telephone had not arrived, and messages were sent by hand or communicated by voice tube. Patients were carried by stretcher (there were not yet any electric carriages) and ambulances, like fire wagons, were horse-drawn. Surgeons came by horse-drawn carriage or, in an emergency, on horseback.

After the opening of the hospital, the volume of medical and surgical work rose quickly and continued to rise.[K] The average daily number of patients in hospital beds in the first year was 469 and the number of patients treated 5,315. By 1903–04, these figures had risen to 810 and 11,125, respectively. The number of outpatients seen annually had also more than doubled, increasing from 15,000 to 33,412. The hospital staff numbered many hundreds. The nurses, of whom 111

Figure 1.10 New Edinburgh Royal Infirmary. *The doors of the new hospital were opened for the admission of patients on 29th October 1879*

were employed, were supervised by the Lady Superintendent of Nurses, Miss Angélique Lucille Pringle. The nursing staff included two day and two night Assistant Superintendents, staff nurses, assistant nurses and probationers. As Logan Turner explained, the hours of work were long – from 7 am until 8.30 pm. Nurses were not well paid and were granted only two weeks' holiday each year.

At first, 11 physicians and 13 surgeons had access to 555 beds. Sufficient space was also needed for teaching. The number of surgeons was as much a reflection of the number of wards available for patients' accommodation as of the number of patients seeking care. It was a time when the admission of women to medicine was still contentious and the practicability of allowing them access to hospital ward teaching was still debated fiercely. Their admission was an important factor in the provision of teaching accommodation.

The senior appointments were contested. In 1898, the surgical staff granted access to beds for patients comprised five Surgeons-in-Ordinary, two Professors of Surgery and two senior consultants, a designation implying an individual who could be called in consultation, not simply a senior surgeon. The term of office of the Physicians – and Surgeons-in-Ordinary – was restricted to 15 years. None might hold office beyond the age of 65 years. In 1898–99, the Surgical Registrar, in effect a coordinator, was WM Hutton. From 1899–1910, the position was held by Wade's close friend and collaborator, ES Carmichael (p 53).

Teachers and teaching

In 1890, the Edinburgh Medical School was at the height of its fame. Wade was taught human Anatomy (the structure of the body), Physiology (the normal function of the body), *Materia Medica* (the nature and use of drugs of every kind), Pathology (the understanding of disease), Forensic Medicine (medicine in relation to the law), Medicine (the province of the physician, comprising the diagnosis and treatment of disease by non-invasive techniques), Midwifery (the subject later termed Obstetrics) and Surgery (the diagnosis and treatment of disease by operative methods). In 1893, Wade benefited from the talents and interests of a galaxy of distinguished teachers.[13,14,L]

Foremost among Wade's teachers was **William Turner**, Professor of Anatomy. In 1903, he became Principal of the University. Turner's colleagues in Physiology were **William Rutherford** and **Edward Albert Sharpey-Schafer**. Rutherford concentrated on research and promoted histology, as the revolution in the microscopy of tissues and cells took effect. He wrote a pioneering work on this subject and developed a novel freezing microtome (p 81). Sharpey-Schafer had established a reputation in Neurophysiology and Endocrine Physiology in London. In Edinburgh, he constructed a laboratory for experimental Physiology, a demonstration theatre, a lecture hall and biochemical and histological laboratories. By 1893, Pathology had assumed an importance it was to keep for the next century. Professor **William Smith Greenfield** was a neuropathologist who initiated a practical class in pathological histology under the direction of **Dr German Sims Woodhead** (p 343). The curriculum was adjusted accordingly. **Thomas Grainger Stewart** taught Wade Clinical Medicine and may also have influenced Wade's choice of training in Pathology: Grainger Stewart had worked as a pathologist in the Old (1741) Royal Infirmary. In 1895, Clinical Pharmacology was still '*Materia Medica*': **Thomas Richard Fraser** held the chair in this subject for 41 years. Wade's instruction in Forensic Medicine was in the hands of no less a figure than **Henry Duncan Littlejohn** (1828–1914) who had become Edinburgh's first Medical Officer of Health in 1862. **Thomas Annandale** taught Wade the elements of surgical practice: Clinical Surgery. Annandale (Logan Turner, 1933) tended to attract public as well as surgical interest.[10] He was 'a familiar figure in the streets of Edinburgh, saluted by policemen on duty and by "cabbies" on the ranks for all of whom he had a cheery greeting'. **John Chiene**, 'Honest John', was one of Wade's most influential mentors. Known for his good humour, scholarship and philosophy, he succeeded James Spence as Professor of Systematic Surgery and established a laboratory for teaching Bacteriology. By the time Wade entered the Medical School, the responsibility for this subject had been taken over by the Department of Pathology. In 1907, Chiene recalled his experiences in a memorable lecture: *Looking back 1907–1860.*[15] His son George Chiene (p 23) followed in his father's footsteps, rising to prominence as a surgeon to the RIE. **Alexander Russell Simpson** taught Wade Midwifery. He was the nephew of the discoverer of chloroform anaesthesia, James Young Simpson, and was Dean of the Faculty of Medicine when Wade accepted his first post as Demonstrator in Anatomy (p 40).

During Henry Wade's third student year, worldwide interest was aroused by the announcement on the 6th January 1896 of Wilhelm Conrad Röntgen's discovery of X-rays.[16] More was to follow. After Antoine Henri Becquerel's observation of radioactivity, Pierre and Marie Curies' search for a new and radioactive element culminated in their isolation of radium (1898) and then polonium. Many other scientific advances were being reported, and in the same year, *Shigella dysenteriae* (the cause of one form of bacillary dysentery) was announced, a sign of a revolution that was to shake surgery to its roots. These were exciting times not only in medicine and science but in the arts, in literature and in the theatre. It was the year in which Emile Zola transfixed the political world with *J'accuse* and Henry James, HG Wells and Oscar Wilde sought fame with *The Turn of the Screw*, *The War of the Worlds* and *The Ballad of Reading Gaol*, respectively. Ominously, it was the year in which Kitchener destroyed an army of 40,000 dervishes at the Battle of Omdurman and Paul Krueger became President of the State of Transvaal, paving the way for the Great South African War of 1899, to which Chapter 2 is devoted.

Graduation and qualification

To practise as a doctor, it was first necessary for Wade to qualify by passing the examinations for one of the degrees or diplomas recognized by the General Medical Council, the GMC. This body was established under the Medical Act of 1858 to regulate the medical

Figure 1.11 McEwan Hall.
The hall became the site of the majority of graduation ceremonies after its completion in 1894

profession. The Act required that all practitioners of medicine and surgery be registered,[M] an obligation that could be met by the possession of a university Doctorate of Medicine (MD), by passing the examinations for the new 'primary, qualifying' degree of MB (Bachelor of Medicine) and CM (Mastership of Surgery), or by the possession of a licentiateship[N] of one of the Royal Colleges or Faculties.[17,18] Wade fulfilled this requirement and qualified in the summer of 1898 by graduating MB, ChB (Batchelor of Surgery, the revised designation) with honours from the University of Edinburgh. His certificate of registration came on August 5th. The graduation ceremony took place in the new McEwan Hall.

Resident House Surgeon and House Physician

Wade was then compelled to fulfil a second criterion before he could be licensed to practise: it was necessary to work under supervision for a year in a recognized hospital usually in a position of Resident House Physician or Surgeon. To obtain a position as 'Resident' in a large modern hospital rather than in a municipal or smaller hospital was desirable, as it provided the best path to successful postgraduate training. In Edinburgh, the RIE offered fewer than 20 such vacancies annually, each tenable for six months. There were five Resident House Surgeons, one for each Surgeon-in-Ordinary. Every year, however, at least 200 medical graduates of the University, as well as many diplomates who had qualified from the School of Medicine of the Edinburgh Royal Colleges, the SMRC (p 246), were eligible to apply for these appointments. How were the fortunate few chosen? The answer lay in clinical and academic performance. Those lucky enough to be chosen as Residents tended to be students who had caught the eye of their teachers because of their knowledge, assiduity, alertness or skills: they were individuals who had attended the hospital wards regularly and had shown responsibility in the care of patients and aptitude in the performance of clinical duties.

Until very recent times, surgeons and their associates were pleased to have the help of senior students in tasks that ranged from the administration of anaesthetics to the performance of pleural aspiration, spinal puncture, the collection of blood needed in tests for anaemia and any necessary analyses of urine. It was in the interests of the senior physicians and surgeons to select the best of the recently qualified graduates or diplomates as Residents: these were the young men, and increasingly young women, to whom the care of patients was passed during the many day and night hours when no experienced physician or surgeon was available within a ward unit to attend the sick and the dying.

In 1898, the conditions under which Residents survived and worked were arduous and demanding. Residents lived in the hospital and were granted 'board and lodging'. But they received no salary and were granted no formal holidays or 'days off'. Yet there was never

Figure 1.12 Resident house surgeons and house physicians, Royal Infirmary of Edinburgh, winter session 1899–1900. *In the list below, brackets provide the names of the surgeons and physicians to whose 'charge' the Residents were attached.*

(**back row**) *Frank R Seager (Dr Byrom Bramwell); James Miller (Dr Alexander James); George Lyon (Professor WS Greenfield); Alfred Shearer (Professor Thomas Annandale); John D Comrie (Dr JO Affleck); WJ Barclay (Professor AR Simpson) and WM Paul (Mr CW MacGillivray)* (**middle row**) *H Wade (Professor Sir Thomas Fraser); JD Lithgow (Mr JS MacLaren); John Jeffrey (Professor Grainger Stewart); Joseph Hunter (Dr Andrew Smart); AW Limont (Mr JM Cotterill); JM Cuthbert (Professor John Chiene) and TD McLaren (Mr CW Cathcart)* (**at front**) *Geo Mackie (Sir John Halliday Croom) and A Cassels Brown (Dr GA Gibson)*

difficulty in filling the appointments. Wade well knew that to obtain such a position would allow him to place his feet on the first rungs of a steep ladder of promotion. In turn, this could lead through intermediary appointments to a post first as Assistant Physician or Surgeon and then ultimately to the pinnacle of a respected profession: the position of full surgeon – Surgeon-in-Ordinary. Many less fortunate students were obliged to seek 'resident' appointments in other parts of Scotland or, very commonly, in England, Wales or Ireland. There were also many openings in the countries of the British Empire, and Edinburgh graduates and diplomates took advantage of these posts in Canada, Australia, New Zealand, the West Indies and South Africa.

Dr Henry Wade's first employment came in the summer of 1898, soon after his graduation.[O] The *Medical Register* showed his address to be Broomage House, Larbert, Sterlingshire [*sic*], where his widowed

Figure 1.13 Henry Wade as Resident House Physician. *Wade's first Edinburgh appointment was to Sir Thomas Fraser, Professor of Materia Medica. The photograph is an enlargement taken from the group photograph* (Figure 1.12)

mother had settled. It is not certain how he occupied the weeks after his graduation, but on 1st October he accepted the appointment of Assistant House Surgeon to the Cumberland Infirmary, Carlisle, a post he held until 23rd April 1899. The contract for this Residency was expected to last until 30th April, but he made two appeals for release from this obligation. The second appeal was granted. The reasons Wade sought early escape from this, his first paid appointment and his first in surgery, are not known. It is reasonable to speculate that it was to allow him to take up another position, the nature of which has not yet been established. Then, in September 1899, he was invited by Sir Thomas Fraser (p 14), to be his House Physician in Wards 25 and 26 of the RIE. They were medical not surgical wards. It was a prestigious but onerous appointment, as Fraser was, by that time, not only Dean of the Faculty of Medicine but Chairman of the Indian Plague Commission, a position that often called him to meetings in other centres. His absences inevitably placed additional responsibilities on his House Physician. When the time came for Wade to leave for South Africa in the spring of 1900, Sir Thomas showed his appreciation for Wade's devotion by giving a 'supper' to mark the occasion and to bid his protégée *au revoir*.

Meanwhile, Henry Wade's concern for his sisters and brothers grew and matured. With the loss of a sister in 1890 and his father in 1892, he assumed a greater responsibility for the welfare and benefit of the others. His generosity, kindly words and solicitude for young Callander W Sinclair in 1922, shown vividly in their exchange of letters, reveal much of a thoughtful and warm character. His elder brother, Thomas, had watched over the legal and financial affairs of their mother. Increasingly, he gave Henry wise advice and guidance. In 1945, Henry arranged for Thomas's care as his health deteriorated.

On 11th October 1899, just as Wade was embarking on his splendid new appointment, world events entirely changed the direction of the young graduate's professional life. The South African Boers of the Transvaal and Orange Free State declared war on Britain. Within six months, the uncertain military scene was compounded by a desperate medical crisis. Epidemic typhoid fever had broken out and the Royal Army Medical Corps had been overwhelmed. The government had been forced to make an appeal for civilian volunteers, particularly for medical and surgical help.

Dutiful and adventurous, Wade decided to enlist.

Figures 1.4 and 1.5 are taken from Wade TC.[8] *Story of the Falkirk West United Free Church*. Falkirk: F Johnston, 1926.

Figure 1.14 Part of the oak table from the Resident's mess of the 1879 Royal Infirmary of Edinburgh. *It was the custom for each Resident to carve his name on the table during his time in post. Henry Wade's name is seen (lower left) next to those of his colleagues – JD Comrie, Alfred Shearer, John Jeffrey and J Hunter. The table, in segments, now adorns the walls of the 2002 'New' Edinburgh Royal Infirmary at Little France*

CHAPTER 2

With the army in South Africa

1900–02

Before the war, and especially before the Boer War, it was
summer all the year round.

(George Orwell, *Coming up for Air*, 1939)

F or young Dr Henry Wade, 1900 marked a point of no return. Well
liked by his influential teachers in the Royal Infirmary of
Edinburgh, the RIE, respected by his 'Chief', Sir Thomas Fraser,
and his influential friends, Wade might have expected to climb
steadily up the challenging and competitive ladder of medical promotion. Had he chosen the immediate pursuit of Internal Medicine or
Surgery, there is little doubt that he could have moved swiftly to
become a Clinical Tutor, the first assistant to a senior consultant.
Within a few years more, he could have expected to be an Assistant
Surgeon or Assistant Physician to the teaching hospital, earmarked for
further advancement. It was not to be.

On 11th October 1899, the South African Boers of the Transvaal and
Orange Free State[1,2] declared war on Britain. Like so many conflicts,
the outbreak of the Great Boer War, or Anglo–Boer War as it is now
often called, was a result of mutual distrust[A] and misunderstanding.
By the spring of 1900, a poorly led British army was facing humiliation. Confronted by military disaster, threatened by epidemic disease
on an unprecedented scale and handicapped by a wholly inadequate
medical service, the government sought volunteers from the civilian
population and, with increasing urgency, from the medical profession.

Wade's future was now in his own hands. He responded loyally to
the government's call. It is easy to suggest that the reason he acted in
this way was an innate desire for adventure but there were other factors. His decision was almost certainly influenced by the fact that family ties were weakening. Wade's future had seemed to lie with medical
school teachers and clinicians. Now it was in the less predictable
hands of politicians and generals.

Chapter Summary
- The military scene
- The medical
  services
- The hospitals
- Transport
- Wounds
- The medical crisis
- Henry Wade's
  experiences
- A retrospect

The military scene

By the time of Wade's arrival in South Africa in the late spring of 1900, after a voyage of some three weeks, the military scene[3] was desperately uncertain. Before the outbreak of war, the army had been in a weak state, small by European standards and inexperienced in the disturbing conditions of modern war waged against heavily armed, amateur but skilled and highly mobile opponents. During Queen Victoria's reign, there had been more than 60 campaigns and more than 400 battles[4] but most had been against relatively weak Indian, Asian or African opponents. The British and Imperial Army had not absorbed the lessons of the Franco–Prussian war and had changed little between 1815[B] and 1898: but the musket had given way to a new generation of rifles and machine guns while sophisticated explosives primed shells.

The weakness of the army lay in its inflexibility, its dependence on non-combatants and long lines of communication for supplies and its use of inappropriate clothing and equipment. The health of army recruits remained a matter of great concern. Many were of poor

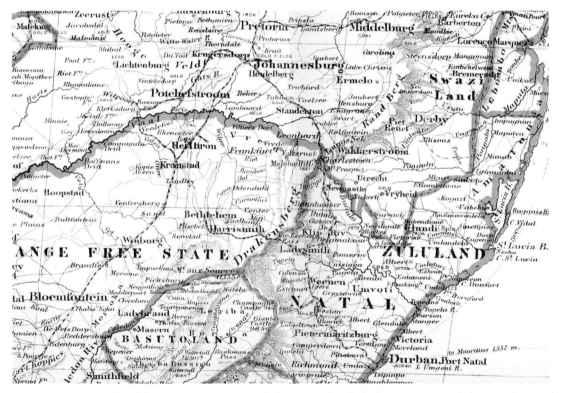

Figure 2.1 Map of South Africa, 1900. *Railways were the key to British and allied strategy. Originating in Cape Town and in Port Elizabeth, two tracks ran northwards, an eastern line through Beaufort to Kimberley and Mafeking, a western through Colesberg to Bloemfontein, Johannesburg and Pretoria. Originating in Durban, the railway divided at Ladysmith before reaching northwards to Johannesburg. (Copyright, see p 3)*

physique. Late into the Victorian era, new recruits were still 'broken' by harsh discipline and bullying.[4,5] Nevertheless, the soldiers' courage was rarely questioned. Regimental honour, tradition, comradeship and high standards of duty ensured a first-class militia. Although the British at first had only 10 field guns[4] and were unaccustomed to the Boer style of 'sniping' with high velocity rifles at long range, in one respect the army was strong: it was highly disciplined.

The medical services

The challenge of dealing with the sick and wounded fell on the recently formed Royal Army Medical Corps (RAMC).[6–9] However, the scale of the South African conflict soon exceeded anything that had been anticipated.[10] At the outset, the army garrison in South Africa amounted to no more than 10,000 men. They were strengthened by 5,600 arrivals from India.[C] The dispatch to South Africa of a further 50,000 men soon exhausted the entire Medical Department. Eventually, the average daily 'ration strength' reached the huge total of 208,226. Yet at first, no more than 21 medical officers were present in the Western Cape Colony Force and 39 in the Eastern Natal Force.

A call for army volunteers, advertised on 7th October 1899, quickly extended to the British and Colonial civilian medical professions. The Royal surgical Colleges attempted to help.[D] A spirit of national loyalty led to a flood of offers. By the end of the war, the enormous total of 589 physicians and surgeons had served in medical units in South Africa.[11–17] They were supported by nearly 20,000 'other ranks' (ORs). The surgeons who volunteered included Sir William MacCormac,[12] W Watson Cheyne, Sir Frederick Treves,[17] Professor John Chiene[18] and Professor Alexander Ogston.[19,E] The Royal Colleges played an active part in recommending further surgeons qualified to assist. Among them were Mr GL Cheatle, Mr George Chiene[20,F] (son of John Chiene), Mr AD Fripp and Mr David Wallace.[G]

In March 1900, Wade became a 'civilian surgeon'. His brother James had already joined Thorneycroft's Mounted Infantry.[H,I] Volunteers were not commissioned officers and were engaged for one year in the first instance. A Regimental Medical Officer's pay was no more than £365 per annum. By contrast, the civilian surgeons received the pay of a Major, a rank equivalent to a Captain and, as Wade asserted graphically 'the dress of a Hindu dispenser'.[21] On some transport ships, military discipline was unjustifiably strict. On others, physical and mental health were encouraged and there were opportunities for card and other games – a practice later recorded by Wade in the photographs he made of his voyage to the Mediterranean in 1915 and described by Gardner on a comparable journey to the German East African campaign of 1917 (Gardner T. *Diary of the East African campaign, 1917–1918*, unpublished observations).

Wade reached Number 1 General Hospital, Wynberg, Cape Town in April 1900 at the moment when the medical staff was grappling with devastating outbreaks of enteric (typhoid) fever and dysentery (p 32). Within three weeks, he was sent 'up country' by rail to Number 9 General Hospital, Bloemfontein – described in Burdett Coutts' dramatic report of 29th May 1900 as 'The Tainted City of Pestilence'. Almost at once, Wade began to see ox-drawn wagons rumbling from the town, with the dead sewn into their blankets. Wade joined the Royal Scots Fusiliers as their Medical Officer – a position he held for 14 months. For the last few months of his tour of duty, he acted as a surgeon to the Number 2 General Hospital at Pretoria, where his colleagues included Charles Gordon-Watson and Frank Gairdner. All in all, Wade lived on the open veldt for one year and 10 months.[21]

The hospitals

At first, the small number of military hospitals, together with the limited number of medical officers and surgeons, led to great difficulties. At the outbreak of war, there were permanent hospitals at Wynberg, Ladysmith and Maritzburg – their size corresponding only to that of the permanent garrisons. In response to public outcry, an enormous public effort and the contribution of great sums of money resulted in the dispatch to South Africa of 11 Voluntary Hospitals. They included the Langman, with which Conan Doyle was associated, the Van Alen, the Imperial Yeomanry, the Welsh, the Irish, the Scottish Roman Catholic and the Edinburgh.[22] As they began to arrive, the number of hospital beds increased greatly. In January 1900, only 2,834 beds were available. In May of that year, the number had increased to 10,856, still insufficient to meet the demand. Each hospital was compelled to form an enteric division set aside for the enormous numbers of cases of gastrointestinal infection (Table 2.1).

Figure 2.2 View of Imperial Yeomanry Hospital, South Africa, 1900

Table 2.1   Hospital admissions for diseases other than battle wounds during the early part of the South African War (Royal Commission, 1901)

Disease	Admitted	Died	Mean annual rate (%)
Dysentery	33,108	1,343	6.9
Enteric fever (typhoid)	57,684	8,022	10.4
Malaria	25,156	85	4.5
Pneumonia	2,591	466	not known
Rheumatic fever	24,460	25	4.4
Enteritis, typhlitis, colitis	1,738	46	not known
'Diarrhoea'	18,716	20	not known

Transport

The demands placed by the war on the Merchant Navy were very great. By March 1900, 1,700 tons of equipment had been dispatched for the Imperial Yeomanry Hospital alone. In the field, the key to the successful treatment of the wounded was rapid transport. In 1898, there were few good roads in South Africa. To take advantage of those that could be used, Thorneycroft steam lorries proved reliable. With them, 45 steam road transport 'trains' were employed. However, the railways remained central to military strategy. There were three steam-drawn ambulance trains. Rail lines not only defined the movement of large bodies of British and allied troops: they served to evacuate the wounded. For the enemy, the practices were quite different. In the

Boer tradition, long columns of oxen enabled the transport of their supplies across the veldt. Both combatants, however, relied heavily on horses. By 31st January 1902, the war had assimilated 216,863 horses – bought from every part of the world – together with 94,030 mules.

In the field, Wade learnt a lesson which he applied successfully in the First World War (Chapters 7 and 8). The lives of many wounded were lost on account of long and difficult journeys from the front line to hospital. Blood loss and shock were particular threats to victims of compound fracture and abdominal injury, a principle well understood by Napoleon's Surgeon General Dominique Larrey (p 324) (Appendix 2.1) and reiterated by Frederick Treves (p 53). A rigid British wooden ambulance drawn by horses, mules or oxen compared unfavourably with a swift, light Indian Army tonga.

Wounds

Wade and his fellow volunteer surgeons learned quickly by bitter experience. They were confronted by two classes of weapon and therefore two classes of wound: those caused by small arms fire[J] (by far the most common[11]) and those caused by shells. Bayonets were relatively rare causes of injury. During his time as a battalion Medical Officer, the casualties with which Wade dealt were largely those caused by rifle fire. The Boers were expert marksmen. Later, in Pretoria, Wade's surgical skills were tested to the full as he was obliged to deal with wounds of a more serious character. He was fortunate in

Figure 2.4 The first stage in the evacuation of the wounded – *carrying an early casualty over the Doom Spruit, South Africa 1900*

Figure 2.5 The ambulance wagons *used by the army in 1900 differed little from those employed in the Crimean campaigns of 1854–55*

Figure 2.6 Hospital transport crossing the Vet River drift, 1900

Figure 2.7 Steam traction engines *(steam sappers) were employed whenever possible. Here, the engine is hauling trucks at Six-mile Spruit on the way to Pretoria, South Africa 1900*

Figure 2.8 Bridge building and a train

working under the direction of some of the country's most eminent surgeons.

War surgery in South Africa was fundamentally different from that of the later 'Great' War of 1914–18.[13,15–17,21] Suppurating wounds were almost unknown so that wound healing was generally 'by first intention'. Even in the case of abdominal wounds, it became a saying – McCormac's dictum – that 'those with abdominal wounds died if operated upon, those who were left alone, survived'. The reasons wounds healed well attracted much attention. First, it was observed that the wounded often lay unattended for hours or days in a dry environment in the bright sun. By contrast, dressed wounds frequently became infected. Second, in striking contrast to their way of life in barracks, the troops were 'clean living' and well nourished. A third reason related to the nature of the missiles used. In the early months of their campaigns, the Boers used hard-nosed and humane Mauser bullets with a flat trajectory, fired with very considerable accuracy over distances of 500–600 yards. Shell injuries often suppurated, but bullet wounds seldom became septic.

Injuries caused by the new high velocity rifle bullets characteristically had a small entrance wound and a slightly larger exit wound where the force of the missile tore tissues apart. The relatively small entrance and exit wounds healed with surprising ease. In Wade's words, 'the entrance wound could be covered by a shilling, the exit wound by a florin'. There were complicating factors: high velocity bullets did not always travel in a perfect trajectory: bullets often 'tumbled' or 'wobbled', pursuing an uneven path that caused enhanced tissue injury. Tumbling and irregular paths were more frequent when ricochets occurred. Moreover, wounds were often multiple – a reflection of a high rate of fire and skilled marksmanship. The abdomen and thighs were especially vulnerable.

As many as 50% of the wounded died from primary haemorrhage. Apart from manual pressure or the application of tourniquets or haemostatic forceps, haemorrhage could not be controlled except by surgery. Recurrent haemorrhage was frequent as blood pressure rose. Secondary haemorrhage was relatively infrequent because of the rarity of sepsis. Wounds of limb bones and joints, often affecting peripheral nerves, were frequent. Blood vessel injuries often resulted in traumatic arteriovenous aneurysms. Head and neck injuries were life threatening, and the lives of those with vertebral column and spinal cord injuries could rarely be saved. Primary amputation was uncommon, and many of the wounded who required amputation were returned to Britain. However, head injuries were frequent, and trepanning was often used. Abdominal wounds were complicated by the effects of dehydration, and there was a mortality of 70%, to which the difficulty of making antiseptic solutions contributed. Occasionally, gunshot wounds of the kidneys, liver or spleen could be treated successfully. Chest wounds might recover, and thoracotomy was exceptional. The overall death rate was 34%.

A specimen in the Museum of the Royal College of Surgeons of Edinburgh, the RCSEd, is a bone derived from a wound suffered at the Battle of Magersfontein on 11th December 1900. The case was reported by David Middleton Greig,[23] who presented the specimen to the museum during his distinguished years as Conservator (pp 102,112). Paraphrasing his words:

'The patient was a 28 year old private struck by a Mauser bullet fired from a distance of only 50 yards. He had been resting on his elbows with both hands raised to adjust his helmet. The bullet entered 32 mm to the right of the 7th cervical spinous process and made its exit through the 9th rib 40 mm behind the posterior axillary line. Haemoptysis was immediate. He lay where he was for 36 hours before being carried to the Orange River where the wound was treated four days after the injury. Two weeks later, he was transferred to the base hospital at Wynberg. Both wounds suppurated but had healed by February 1901. Thereafter, he developed a troublesome cough with great pain on any exertion at the wound of exit [sic] which was hyperaesthetic. His breathing was shallow and accompanied by a spasmodic twitching of the muscles of the right face and neck. The symptoms were considered to be due to implication of the intercostal nerves in the cicatrix [scar] or callus [site of bone healing] and were permanently relieved by excision of these portions of the ribs.'

Greig noted that the 9th rib had been completely fractured and the ventral (anterior) fragment displaced caudally. It had united along its upper border by the formation of a false joint, a pseudarthrosis, between the ventral (anterior) and dorsal (posterior) fragments, which were otherwise separated.

With few exceptions, such as the attack at Diamond Hill, in which the Early of Airlie was killed, intense shell fire was unusual. Where there was shell or shrapnel injury, death was frequent. Extensive laceration and/or destruction of the head or limbs or the laying open of the thorax or abdomen were among the consequences. High explosives maimed and disrupted. As a result, only a small proportion of hospital surgery dealt with the consequences of shell fire, and Makins described the surgery of shell injuries as 'uninteresting'.[13] Many shell injuries were 'mere lacerations'. Among the survivors, however, severe injuries were mutilating and 'not congenial to modern surgeons'. By this, Makins clearly intended to convey that amputation, so frequent in Napoleonic and Crimean times, was infrequently employed and only as a last resort when a more conservative approach to limb injury was impracticable.

An indication of the scale of the surgical supplies required for the war, and thus of the early expectations of the medical services, can be gained from the list of items held in the besieged town of

Ladysmith.[24,K] The presence of only eight pairs of large scissors and 17 small pairs, with 13 sets of dressing trays, two and a half sets of retractors, 11 sets of orderlies' dressing instruments, six sterilizers and six Spencer Wells forceps does not suggest that great surgical activity was anticipated, but this view is contradicted by the finding that there was a total of 83 tourniquets, of which 23 were of a 'field' type (Appendix 2.2).

The South African campaign was among the first in which properly equipped X-ray units were used. Hall-Edwards gave a clear account of the difficulties he encountered in using his simple apparatus in the Imperial Yeomanry Hospital at Deelfontein.[25,L] The principal problems were the heat of the water during the hot season and the incessant dust storms, which could turn X-ray plates into a 'new form of sandpaper'.

The medical crisis

No proper understanding of the surgical scene that Wade confronted in South Africa in 1900 is possible without mention of the dreadful medical impasse (Appendix 2.3).

Many recruits to the army were unfit.[14] In 1898, syphilis, gonorrhoea, tuberculosis, alcoholism and parasitic disease accounted for great numbers of sick soldiers before hostilities began. Psychiatric

Figure 2.9 An operating theatre, South Africa, 1900

abnormalities could result from the habit of chewing cordite.[M] In the field, 'veldt sore' was cutaneous diphtheria. Tonsillitis was very frequent, and rheumatic fever accounted for nearly 24,400 casualties. Among the causes of ophthalmic disorders was the frequent exposure to dust. There were many ear infections. Storms could be severe and lightning injury accounted for 1,528 burns, 206 hospital admissions and 16 deaths. Sunburn affected the legs of the Scottish regiments severely, because they wore kilts. Heat stroke was not well understood. There were 25,156 cases of malaria.

Water- and food-borne infections, particularly acute bacterial dysentery and typhoid (enteric fever), were responsible for many more deaths than missile wounds. Epidemics, the result of the contamination of food and the defective chlorination of water, were frequent. Immunization by anti-typhoid vaccines was optional and was accepted by only a small proportion of British officers and men, so that although 9,365 men died from water- and food- borne infections, during the entire war there were only 7,792 deaths from military causes.

An epidemic of enteric fever exploded after the capture of Bloemfontein by Lord Robert's troops. The disease broke out when the army surrounded the Boers at the Modder River. The principles of preventing food- and water-borne infection were well understood. The handbooks issued to medical officers gave excellent and detailed information on the methods to be used for sterilizing water: for example, by boiling.[7] Why, then, did the waters of the Modder River prove so punishing? The answer may lie in the shortage of wood for fires. The country was barren scrub. The iron boilers carried with the supply trains could not be heated, the water could not be sterilized and enteric fever spread with lightning rapidity.

Wade had decided wisely to accept voluntary inoculation with the new typhoid vaccine that had been offered to personnel during the voyage from Britain.[N] As war threatened, the possibility of immunizing the army actively[O] against enteric fever (typhoid) was considered fully and responsibly.[26] Almroth Wright's methods for the preparation of a vaccine had been published in full in 1897. Close to the army, he had been Professor of Pathology at the Army Medical School at Netley. In Britain, there was still resistance to the concept of compulsory vaccination. Serving officers and men were not compelled to accept immunization, and there is little doubt that this influenced the attitude of the troops to the offer of an anti-typhoid vaccine. Only 16,000 of a total of 305,000 troops accepted the procedure during the war. There was no hint of the disasters to come, although behind these medical problems lay a serious deficit in laboratory facilities (p 47). The Widal test, so valuable in the diagnosis of enteric fever, had not been adopted, and Britain lagged behind Germany, France and Russia in the provision of this form of service. The consequences became clear. At the siege of Ladysmith, typhoid affected 2% of 1,705 inoculated soldiers and 14% of 10,529 not inoculated. In the final

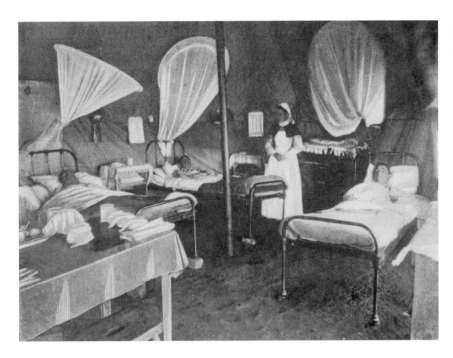

Figure 2.10 An 'enteric' (typhoid fever) ward *of the Imperial Yeomanry Hospital, 1900*

analysis, 105 (10.05%) of every 1,000 serving personnel contracted typhoid. In the campaigns of 1914–18, after immunization had become obligatory, the corresponding figure was 2.35%.

Henry Wade's experiences

After being on the move for 14 months, Wade was transferred to Number 2 General Hospital, Pretoria, where he remained for eight months. He described how the wounded were brought in from an engagement at Noitgedacht in which troops from General Clement's Brigade suffered badly.[21] Abandoned by the retreating Boers, many wounded lay unattended for long periods. A few had their wounds dressed by the regimental cook. Although wounded himself, he crawled to the assistance of the other men and bound their injuries with cloths from the cookhouse. Later, it was remarked that the wounds of those left alone healed well. By contrast, those dressed by the cook suppurated profusely. Nevertheless, the cook's bravery was recognized properly by the award of the Distinguished Conduct Medal.

In one incident, at Helpmaarker Farm, in the Orange Free State, Wade was attached to the Queen's Town Volunteers.[21] His unit was surrounded for three days by General Olivier's Commando. On the second afternoon, the fighting stopped momentarily, and Wade walked to a nearby farm and attended to the Boer wounded. Afterwards, he sat with the South Africans in a circle in the farm kitchen – Commander Haasbrook on his right, the adjutant on his left, each with their Mauser carbine between their knees and their little *sjambok*, or cowhide whip, hanging over the side of their rifles. Wade's horse had been taken away and given a feed of oats and hay, and the enemies sat and quietly discussed the war and other questions until it was time to return and continue the siege.

Unhappily, many later events showed a less civilized aspect of war. At Groenkop in November, the Boers under De Wet broke with convention by using expanding bullets. The resulting injuries were horrific. At the infamous Battle of Elands River in September 1901, the Boers unwisely replaced their own tattered clothes with those of captured British troops. The decision was endorsed by Jan Smuts, but it turned the Boer fighters into traitors. Any who were caught were shot. Among those sufficiently unwise to wear khaki was young Denys Reitz, son of Paul Krueger's Foreign Secretary, the author of the ultimatum that presaged the outbreak of war in 1899. He survived, plundered the tents, selected a tunic from the dead 17th Lancers and said: 'We were like giants refreshed. We all had fresh horses, fresh rifles, clothing and supplies'.

Wade recorded that it was unacceptable for either side to shoot at wounded men. One day, a British trooper from Howard's Scouts was brought into the hospital for Wade's care and told Wade an unusual story. Shot in the chest by a marksman of the opposing Boer Scouts,

Figure 2.11 A youthful Henry Wade sitting beside his horse *during the fighting in South Africa*

Figure 2.12 Henry Wade and Norman Wilson outside their tent

the trooper lurched forward into the upright, sitting position characteristic of those with thoracic gunshot wounds, gasping for breath.
This attitude deceived a young Boer, who was about to shoot the
unfortunate trooper again, but from close range, when his rifle was
knocked from his hand by an older Boer who called out 'We do not
shoot the wounded'. A few days after this episode, a young wounded
Boer was admitted to the same hospital. He had a gunshot fracture of
the thigh. To the great surprise and joy of the Howard's trooper whose
life had been so nearly at an end, this was the same marksman whose
rifle had been knocked away. The Boer was Peters. He came from
Pretoria. His mother and a sister came to visit him. At first, not surprisingly, they were hostile and strained. Later, however, as Wade
recalled, 'we all became the very best of friends'. Peter's family asked
whether they might plant two trees – one on each side of the Indian
pattern hospital tent in which their young relative had been nursed.

When Wade left Pretoria in the spring of 1902, the trees were still
blooming. As Wade said later, 'if I ever return to that country I would
go to the outskirts of Pretoria where the [railway] lines from the South
join the rail to Komati Port and Delagoa Bay, to see whether the two
tall trees are alive and flourishing'.[21]

The story of Howard's Scouts caught Wade's attention. Like the greater part of the army in South Africa, the troops had enlisted voluntarily. They were engaged for one year or for the duration of the war, whichever should be longer. At the end of the period of enlistment, a volunteer was free to return home or to negotiate terms upon which he might be permitted to remain in the service. Howard's Scouts began in Canada as a battery of artillery. They were dispatched to the Western (Kalahari) desert where they were not treated well. After an initial year, they returned to Cape Town where they held a meeting. The men stated that they would stay if commanded by their second-in command, Major Howard, and on condition that they were made into scouts. The new unit formed in this unorthodox way was attached to General Smith Dorrien's Division. They were nicknamed 'Smith Dorrien's Bloodhounds'.

Figure 2.13 Henry Wade and Major Nesbit *leaving the operating theatre as one of their patients is carried out*

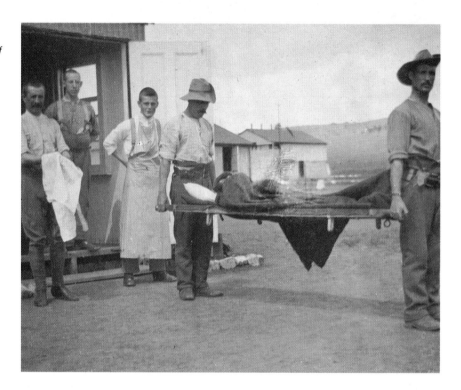

A retrospect

Wade was ever ready to acknowledge the contribution made to the Boer cause by Denys Reitz. Young Reitz served throughout the Great South African War.[27] Wade treasured a copy of his book. Many years later, he presented it to the Library of the RCSEd. On at least one occasion, Reitz was in action against the Royal Scots Fusiliers when Wade was their Medical Officer. It was of the greatest interest to Wade that, at the end of the South African campaign, Reitz and his brother left to become transport riders in Madagascar. It required the diplomatic

Figure 2.14 Henry Wade, Norman Wilson and friend *playing cards outside their tent during the South African campaign*

skills of General Smuts to persuade them to return. Later, by a quirk of history, many British and South African Boers who had fought against each other from 1899 to 1902 found themselves together in action against the Germans at Delville Wood in 1916. Denys Reitz shared the distinction of commanding a battalion of the Royal Scots Fusiliers. They were the same regiment of which a battalion was commanded by Winston Churchill, whose exploits in South Africa brought him worldwide notoriety.[28,29]

The campaigns in South Africa, and especially those fought before the introduction by General Kitchener in 1901 of a catastrophic 'scorched earth' policy, were at first conducted in a spirit of sportsmanship rare in more recent wars. Wade remarked that, in war, this attitude might appear foolish and quixotic. Yet, in a long view, it was a wise policy and gained its own ultimate reward. As he said, the fighting was 'clean'. It was like a dangerous athletic contest – a game of life and death played with a very high standard of 'honour'. In this 'game', however, 518 British and Allied officers had been killed or had died of their wounds. Of the unfortunate other ranks, 5,256 had been killed, 21,292 wounded while 835 had died from their wounds.[10] In addition to these great numbers of battle casualties, 404,126 individuals were listed as non-battle casualties, and 14,048 of this number had died. Astonishingly, the ratio of non-battle to battle casualties was 15:1. The medical disasters of the war were subjects of the Royal Commissions of 1901 and 1903.[24,30,P,Q] Many comments made to the Commissions were scathing (Appendices 2.3 and 2.4).

Figure 2.15 A Queen's South African medal.
Wade's medal had four clasps: for service at Cape Colony, Witterbergen, the Transvaal and South Africa

Older and wiser, Wade returned to Britain from South Africa in 1902 to resume his medical career. For his part in the South African campaigns, he was awarded the Queen's Medal with four clasps, for service at Cape Colony, Witterbergen, the Transvaal and South Africa.

Figures 2.2–2.10 are taken from *The Imperial Yeomanry Hospitals in South Africa 1900–1902* volumes 1–3. Ed Countess Howe. London: Arthur L. Humfreys, 1902. Figures 2.11–2.14 are from the Pilmuir Trust Archives, by permission of the Trustees.

CHAPTER 3

Surgeon in the making

1903–14

In truth, the anxiety of a surgeon, before an important
operation, is the greatest any man can suffer.

(Charles Bell, *Illustrations of the Great Operations of Surgery*, 1821)

The operation was at once begun; it was necessarily slow;
and chloroform – one of God's best gifts to his suffering
children, was then unknown.

(Dr John Brown, from *Rab and his Friends* in *Horae Subsecivae*, 1862[A])

Within a month of leaving South Africa, after a sea voyage of three weeks, Henry Wade was again in the land of his birth. 'Auld Reekie', the ancient city of Edinburgh, was as cold, damp and smoke laden as it had been when he left to fight 'for Queen and Country'. His life had altered beyond recognition. He was a veteran, accustomed to battlefield disease, injury and death in every guise. His ambition was to master surgery, but the transition from war to peace was harsh. Youthful and bronzed, Wade wrote that the contrast in existence between the South African veldt and the Edinburgh dissecting room 'took all my will power to survive'.

These were exciting times for ambitious medical graduates. The list of Nobel Prize winners in Medicine and Physiology gives some idea of the advances that were occurring. A strong emphasis was on discoveries made by laboratory methods. In the coming years, the award of the 1909 prize to Theodor Kocher for his work on the thyroid gland and the 1913 prize to Alexis Carrel for his studies of the circulation would ensure that Surgery remained close to the growing edge of knowledge.

A future in surgery?

This chapter describes the steps that set Wade on the path to a position of seniority in surgery. Chapter 4 recounts his years of research into the nature of cancer, while Chapter 5 deals with the period from 1906 to 1908, when he served as an Assistant Pathologist to the Royal Infirmary of Edinburgh, the RIE.

Chapter Summary
- A future in surgery?
- Qualifying as a surgeon
- Learning surgery
- Edwardian surgery
- Royal Infirmary of Edinburgh before 1914
- Surgical diagnosis
- X-rays in diagnosis, radium in treatment
- Anaesthesia
- Antisepsis and asepsis
- Operative surgery
- Chemotherapy
- Resuscitation
- Blood transfusion
- Assistant Surgeon to Leith Hospital
- Assistant Surgeon to the Royal Infirmary of Edinburgh

The random threads of Wade's life began to converge in 1902, and he was obliged to decide in which direction his medical career was to go. Was it to be surgery, centred on the skills he had used in South Africa, or medicine, a profession less dependent on manual dexterity? The choice was surgery. Wade was sufficiently astute to appreciate that to succeed in Edinburgh, a 'hotbed of genius',[1] he would need high levels of learning and much experience. To practise clinical surgery successfully called for a mastery of three fundamental disciplines: Anatomy (the structure of the normal human body), Physiology (the function of the normal human body) and Pathology (the understanding of disease). To gain this breadth of postgraduate learning, it was usual for Edinburgh's medical graduates to study in the Departments of the University of Edinburgh Medical School or in those of the Extramural Medical School of the Edinburgh Royal Colleges, the SMRC, that are described in Chapter 13.

On his return from the army, therefore, Wade chose to begin in the University Department of Anatomy under the influential guidance of Professor Sir William Turner. In 1902, Wade became a Demonstrator in Anatomy. The principles of Anatomy could be learned from books, but the subject was best mastered by dissection. The financial reward was small, although long hours in the dissecting room could pay rich surgical dividends in later life: a safe approach to a constricted bile duct, a bladder tumour or an inflamed appendix demanded a full knowledge of the structure of the human body. In the same way that Anatomy was the gateway to successful operative surgery, Pathology was the path to precise diagnosis and the choice of treatment. In 1903, Wade moved to the Department of Pathology where he was taught by Professor WS Greenfield.[B] It was a subject in which he had already been strongly influenced by a young teacher, Dr Robert Muir,[C] who was later to inspire a whole generation of Scottish pathologists.

Qualifying as a surgeon

A professional qualification in surgery was now essential. Wade realized that he must pass the examinations for the Fellowship of a surgical Faculty or Royal College.[D] A surgical Fellowship was an essential qualification for the proper practice of surgery in Britain. It was possible to enter for the examinations of the sister Colleges or Faculties of London, Glasgow or Ireland but the Edinburgh diploma was the criterion by which the prowess of a young surgeon would be judged in Scotland and, indeed, in many of the countries of the Dominions and Empire.

Wade applied himself assiduously. To enter for the Fellowship examinations of the Royal College of Surgeons of Edinburgh, the RCSEd, he needed sponsors who would vouch for both his education and his aptitude and character. It was important early in any professional career to have the loyal support of influential individuals. Wade

Figure 3.1 Royal College of Surgeons of Edinburgh. *The engraving depicts the college towards the end of the nineteenth century*

Figure 3.2 Francis Mitchell Caird. *Henry Wade acted as Clinical Assistant to Caird, who was one of his sponsors for election to the Fellowship of the Royal College of Surgeons of Edinburgh in 1903*

chose Sir William Turner (p 14) and Mr Francis Mitchell Caird[E] (pp 270,274). Turner had become the University Principal. Caird would soon be President of the RCSEd.

Challenged by demanding questions, Wade satisfied the examiners between 30th April and 1st May 1903. On 30th July, after a petition had been hung in the College Library for the obligatory three months, Wade's name was advanced for election by the quarterly meeting of Fellows. The ceremony was presided over by Sir John Halliday Croom (pp 270,279). The election was successful, and he was allowed to take his seat. He was now Mr Henry Wade, FRCSEd. At the time of his success, the Council Minutes show his home address to be 3 Randolph Place, Edinburgh.

Learning surgery

Surgery is a manual skill, whether it is the arduous task of removing a gigantic sarcoma from a shoulder or the laser-assisted microsurgery of a myopic eye. Writing of the importance of practical, clinical education as opposed to reading medical texts, Osler drew an analogy between *learning about* navigation by studying charts and *practising* navigation by going to sea.[2]

Figure 3.3 David Percival Dalbreck Wilkie. *David Wilkie, one of Wade's closest friends and associates, was co-founder of their Private Clinic in 1921. Wilkie was successful in his application for the Chair of Surgery of the University of Edinburgh in 1924, when Wade was also an applicant*

Soon after he took up the position of Demonstrator in Anatomy, Wade was invited by Francis Caird to be his Clinical Tutor in the RIE and to assist with the teaching of surgery in the Medical School. Wade's position was that of Junior Extramural Clinical Surgery Tutor. Within a few months, Caird supported Wade again, when the young surgeon applied for the Conservatorship of the Museum of the RCSEd (p 91). The apprenticeship to Caird lasted from 1903 to 1906, their association for Caird's lifetime. It was in the class of 1903–04 that Wade first met David Wilkie who was to become Wade's friend, colleague and business partner.[F] The association between the two young surgeons was very close (Chapters 9 and 15).

In his new post, Wade was privileged to assist master craftsmen while gaining valuable practical experience. Nevertheless, there was financial stringency. During the years in which he was Clinical Tutor (1903–06) and assistant to Caird, Wade survived on a pittance. At the beginning of the twentieth century, a Clinical Tutor received no salary from a voluntary hospital such as the RIE. A Tutor earned a little from assisting his 'Chief' in private surgical work and might make something more from tutorial classes organized outside the hospital.

Edwardian surgery

At the turn of the nineteenth century, advances in surgery were relatively much greater than in medicine.[3] However, the majority of surgeons were still 'generalists', and specialism, the act of specializing, was only starting to emerge. Wade, like his many colleagues, would pride himself on remaining a 'general' surgeon. However, the frequency and nature of the diseases that surgeons were being called upon to treat were changing. Life expectation was increasing, infant mortality falling. In 1898, the death rate in Scotland was 18.4 per 1,000 population per year, the number of deaths from tuberculosis more than 7,000. Forty years later, as Wade approached retirement from the RIE, the corresponding figures were 11.8 and 3,400.

During the last years of the nineteenth century, the Listerian revolution of antisepsis and asepsis was approaching its climax. For the first time, it had become reasonably safe to operate on the internal organs of the body. To excise a prostate gland or treat a compound fracture by a means other than amputation were now ethical practices. There were still innumerable cases of bone and joint tuberculosis but appendicitis, perforated peptic ulcer and gall bladder disease were now the common objects of operative surgery. As a result, the frequency of surgery was rising quickly. In turn, surgeons were daring 'boldly to go where no man had gone before'. Technical innovation began to make incurable disease curable and untreatable lesions treatable, a trend in which Edinburgh surgeons benefited from European innovation and from the advances taking place in the United States.[4] Together, these changes were placing severe demands on a hospital designed in the previous century.

Royal Infirmary of Edinburgh before 1914

Wade's early surgical training benefited greatly from the fact that he found himself working in one of the largest and most modern voluntary hospitals in the country. The new RIE still comprised two functionally distinct parts: a Medical Hospital and a Surgical Hospital. It was governed by a Court of Contributors and regulated by a Board of Management. Although the governance was cumbersome, a medically qualified Superintendent with considerable disciplinary power determined logistical efficiency and ensured financial thrift.

The hospital presented a very different appearance from the building of 1879.[G] The wards held in reserve in case of epidemic infection had been freed. The Town Council had assumed responsibility for the prevalent 'infective fevers', although a small 'cottage' was retained for their treatment in the grounds of the RIE. Together with the removal of the Dental Hospital to Chambers Street and the Royal College of Physicians of Edinburgh (RCPEd) laboratory to Forrest Road, these acquisitions allowed the construction of accommodation for new 'special' clinical subjects.

During the 25 years since the Lauriston Place hospital opened (p 13), there had been great changes in the buildings.[5] Sufficient money had been raised to buy the sites of the Children's Hospital and George Watson's College Junior School. In 1883–84, facilities for the diagnosis and treatment of ear, nose and throat diseases (Otolaryngology) and the cure of skin disorders (Dermatology) had been provided. Now wards were opened for these purposes. Beds were set up for the management of 'incidental delirium' and for venereal disease, while special provision was made for diseases of women (Gynaecology, 1885) and the eye (Ophthalmology, 1887). A red stone 'Jubilee' pavilion, with wards for Gynaecology was opened in 1898. The surgical outpatient department was rebuilt, and a small operating theatre was constructed in association with it. Accommodation was found for the Medical Electrical Department beneath the operating theatre of the Professor of Clinical Surgery and in 1903–04, the basement of the south east surgical pavilion was reconstructed as a centre for what would become the Department of Radiology.

Advantage was taken of the emergence of the telephone, and a system was installed throughout the hospital. In 1897, the 2,690 gas

Figure 3.4 Ward 8 of the RIE in 1914

burners that provided light within the hospital were replaced by electric lamps. A new boiler house was constructed, and many of the 476 open coal fires that heated the hospital imperfectly were replaced by 'central' heating. After vigorous discussion, a new laundry was built within the hospital grounds rather than in the open country. The kitchen was reconstructed and new plumbing and drainage systems completed.

The number of patients operated on in the RIE before and during Wade's time may be judged from Table 3.1 and compared with those quoted by Chiene.[6] The proportion of patients who *entered* hospital for surgery had increased quickly. Surgical patients remained in hospital for two, three or more weeks. In 1904, a ward for the treatment of casualties facilitated the work of the three Resident House Surgeons appointed to the Outpatient Department, as well as the instruction offered to students. Not surprisingly, the cost of hospital treatment continued to rise.

A revolution in nursing had taken place after the scandals of the Crimea.[7] Wade and his colleagues acknowledged the benefits. In the 1890s, Bell recorded that 'the students of this generation know only of wards and beds perfect in cleanliness, even in luxuriousness of bright detail, of thoroughly educated and equipped women who act as staff nurses, night nurses, and probationers, have each her own work under efficient supervision and wisely arranged hours and methods'.[8,H] The impact of Florence Nightingale's reforms had penetrated throughout the hospital system. Now the steady rise in the work of the hospital led to an increased demand for nursing staff. In the course of the next 30 years, the numbers rose from about 100 to more

Table 3.1 Surgical operations conducted in the Royal Infirmary of Edinburgh during the years 1879–85 and 1899–1906.[8] The greatest change was in the frequency of abdominal surgery, made possible by advances in antisepsis and asepsis. Of the cases of abdominal surgery, 210 were appendicectomies. The first appendicectomy was performed in 1893. A rush for this operation began in 1901 and had peaked by 1904

Operation	(1879–85)	(1899–1906)
Surgical beds	241	379
Operations	752	2,805
Mean annual operation rate	107	400.5
Operative deaths (%)	7.2	6.7
Amputations	107	118
Excisions of joint	58	108
Mastectomies	40	101
Operations on tumour	114	353
Abdominal surgery	1	429
Operations on veins	5	109
Operations on nerves	19	33
Genitourinary surgery	50	321
Hernias (radical cure)	21	233
Strangulated hernias	7	29

than 400. With this increase came the need for additional residential accommodation. In 1898, an entirely new building constructed of red brick was opened. It had 121 rooms and its appearance led to the epithet 'Red Home'.

Surgical diagnosis

Effective surgery was only practicable when diagnosis was prompt and precise. In the years before the First World War, surgeons had few technical aids. The recognition and identification of disease still rested on a patient's description of his or her symptoms, together with the signs elicited by palpation, percussion, auscultation and, occasionally, smell.

The assistance to diagnosis offered by laboratory and radiological methods was not yet dominant: understanding of the mechanisms of any disease was usually incomplete. For example, the vitamins had not yet been discovered so that rickets, with its secondary deformities, was one of many diseases of 'uncertain aetiology'. However, novel techniques were coming into use. Thus disease could now be

Figure 3.5 The new nurses' home. *The new home, the 'Red Home', was opened in 1898 to accommodate 150 nurses*

recognized by the microscopic examination of tissue samples. By 1903, it had become possible to discriminate between the lesions of individual infections, neoplasms, malformations and injuries by the histological methods outlined in Chapter 5. The first golden age of the new science of Bacteriology was already drawing to a close (Chapter 3). Isolation of the tubercle bacillus now enabled an understanding of the 'white plague'.[9] Ogston (p 23) had described the streptococcus and the pathogenic staphylococcus.[10] Kitasato had isolated the tetanus bacillus,[11] and Welch had identified the pathogen causing gas gangrene.[12] However, Gradle wrote perceptively: 'we have scarcely progressed beyond the certainty that various diseases are really due to bacterial invasion of the body'.[13] A close association existed between Edinburgh and the countries of the Empire, and consequent familiarity with the problems of tropical surgery resulted in great interest when Ronald Ross identified the mode of transmission of the parasite that caused malaria.[14] In the year before Wade entered medical school, another revolution was occurring that presaged the birth of Virology. Ivanowski had demonstrated that the sap of a diseased tobacco plant could transmit tobacco mosaic virus,[15] even after the fluid had passed through a filter of too fine a pore size to permit the passage of any known bacterium.[16] The agent could not be seen with a light microscope.[17]

Surgery had begun to benefit from the new science of Immunology and the concept of immunity.[18] The practical benefits of immunization against the agents of diphtheria and tetanus stemmed from the discovery of their toxins.[19] Immunization against typhoid (p 83) was promoted by Wright and Leishman[20] but immunization against the toxins of *Clostridium perfringens*, the principal agent of gas gangrene, came later. In the study of blood diseases, Haematology, rapid progress had been made. Ehrlich and Lazarus epitomized the advances that had occurred in understanding normal blood and bone marrow cells.[21] Nevertheless, simple iron deficiency anaemia was not explained fully and it would be more than 20 years before a way of correcting pernicious anaemia could be demonstrated. By 1905, an outline of the coagulation mechanism had been elucidated but in Wade's early years tests neither for excessive thrombosis nor for excessive bleeding were used commonly. Chemistry had begun to be practised within the hospital but the apparatus employed was necessarily simple. Many tests, such as those for blood in stools and protein in urine, were performed in 'side rooms' that adjoined the hospital wards. As specialized laboratories were constructed, the complexity of tests increased. Initially, the substances detected and measured were simple and included glucose, urea and albumin. More sophisticated analyses soon followed.

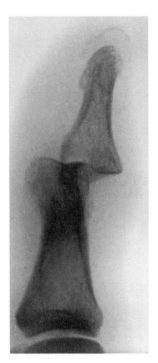

Figure 3.6 X-ray of dislocated finger made in 1904 by DFD Turner. *The Department of Radiology evolved from the Department of Medical Electricity that had been established in 1890*

X-rays in diagnosis, radium in treatment

During Wade's student days, the discovery of X-rays, radioactivity and radium revolutionized surgical diagnosis and treatment.[22–24] Many hospitals, including the RIE, extended their electrical departments in order to exploit these discoveries. The Infirmary Electrical Department was opened in 1898. It was expanded in 1904 and entirely reconstructed in 1924. The first Medical Electrician was Dawson Fyers Duckworth Turner (1857–1928),[I] who had previously published work on medical electricity in diagnosis and treatment.[25] Progress was swift. The new techniques of bismuth meal and infusion pyelography (p 231) were among many contrast techniques that exploited increasingly complex and powerful new equipment. Radiotherapy was born: small quantities of radium were becoming available for the treatment of cancers and an Edinburgh centre for this new discipline was soon to emerge (Chapter 10, p 190).

Anaesthesia

By the time of Wade's initiation into civilian surgery, the use of alcoholic fumes, hemlock, Mandragora root, hypnosis, mesmerism, animal magnetism and compression had lapsed into history.[26,J] Opiates were, of course, in general use but cannabis (hashish) had not assumed the significance it has today.

In the early years of the twentieth century, Anaesthetics had not yet become a recognized speciality. Many operations were undertaken in private houses, and, after a lecture, Caird would often ask a student, House Surgeon or Clinical Tutor to assist in the operation or to administer chloroform, the usual anaesthetic. In return, the assistant received a fee. By 1901, the surgeons of the RIE had still failed to agree to the appointment of an anaesthetist. Instead, Tutors in Anaesthetics were chosen. The attempt to create a position with the same privileges granted to physicians and surgeons was refused by the Managers of the RIE. In 1911, a medicolegal case brought the whole question to the fore and the Managers were compelled to accept that 'assistance in the supervision of anaesthesia should be afforded to each surgical charge'.[27] They met this obligation by delegating the responsibility to the seven surgical Clinical Tutors who were granted an honorarium of £15 each per annum.

Sedatives were employed widely, morphine frequently. The first barbiturate, veronal (1903), and phenobarbitone soon became popular. **Local anaesthesia** was adopted when possible. Operating on frozen or chilled tissues, cryosurgery was of value for procedures such as the incision of an abscess. A spray of ethyl chloride might also be employed, the same agent that was employed in freezing microtomy (p 81). Cocaine, isolated in 1859, came into use for laryngeal surgery and ophthalmology in 1884 and for **infiltration anaesthesia** in 1885. Stovaine followed in 1903 and novocaine in 1905. Sensation could be abolished by injections near nerves, around the dura mater or into the spinal fluid itself, within the subarachnoid space. Indeed, **epidural anaesthesia** had been explored as early as 1885. When spinal puncture became a diagnostic technique, **spinal anaesthesia** soon followed. Again, cocaine was used. The less toxic tropacocaine, stovaine and novocaine were adopted and their use is described in Wade's case records.

For almost all major surgical procedures, **general inhalational anaesthesia** remained the norm. By 1903, ether and chloroform had found universal acceptance although the inflammable nature of ether restricted its use when a cautery was to be employed. The safety of chloroform remained contentious. The vapour might provoke ventricular fibrillation, especially if adrenaline was injected intravenously. Ethylene dioxide was a less potent but safer alternative. Nitrous oxide, laughing gas, was often chosen for minor procedures and dentistry and when chloroform and ether were too hazardous. There is no evidence to show that cyclopropane, synthesized in 1882, was used by Wade or those who assisted him.

It was sometimes necessary to introduce a gas or vapour directly into the larynx[28] or trachea by **intubation**. Where there was a cancer of the pharynx, for example, such a technique was unavoidable. Wade's notes show that he adopted this method on many occasions. The practice of intubation was not confined to surgery and, by 1893, intubation of the larynx was often used to treat diphtheria.

Antisepsis and asepsis

After years of debate, the control of wound infection by antisepsis was a principle thoroughly accepted by Wade and his colleagues. Farsighted surgeons realized, however, that the key to success lay not simply in eradicating micro-organisms from patients' skin but in preventing bacteria reaching this site. This was the basis of asepsis and was championed by pioneers, among whom Macewen was prominent.[29]

The simplest part of the doctrine of asepsis lay in the design and manner of use of operating theatres. Fresh air, clean working surfaces, the disinfection of any object or material entering the theatre and the destruction of anything that was contaminated were some of the accepted aims that lay behind the design of the theatres used in 1903. Until 1886, the sterilization of instruments was by moist heat, boiling or by dry heat, in an oven. In that year, von Bergmann introduced steam sterilization, and autoclaves, devices that use steam under pressure, began to appear. The procedures of sterilization were carried out in the anaesthetic room adjoining the operating theatre. There was no central hospital facility. Instrument design required that crevices be abolished. Gone were the beautifully engraved ivory handles of earlier days. Instead, stainless steel became the medium for a unitary structure.

As Wade entered the world of surgery, it was customary for the operator to wear a gown and an apron. The use of caps was frequent but the adoption of masks was only starting.[30] The routine scrubbing of a surgeon's hands before an operation was not normal practice until the end of the nineteenth century. Indeed, as late as 1903 it was sometimes doubted whether the effort should be made. Oil of turpentine, mercuric chloride (corrosive sublimate) and ethyl alcohol were among the agents chosen to inactivate bacteria or to remove them from the skin. However, it became clear that scrubbing the hands with soap and water was indeed the best protection and this was Wade's normal practice. As early as 1825, protection for the hands during anatomical dissection had been proposed. Subsequently, it seemed likely that India rubber gloves 'would be impenetrable to the most malignant virus'.[31] The wearing of fine gloves might also diminish the hazards of puerperal fever, and a glove was devised that would protect an accoucheur against syphilis. Although there are conflicting claims, Halstead is generally credited with the introduction of rubber gloves into surgery.[32,33]

Operative surgery

Between 1878 and 1907, the number of operations performed annually in the RIE increased fourfold. Not only were four times as many patients seen but the proportion of patients subjected to surgery rose from 30% to 45%. There were continual improvements in the success of the many new operations and a corresponding reduction in operative mortality.[34–36] The range of conditions treated by surgical operation after the new RIE had become established (1899–1906) is indicated in Table 3.1, where a comparison is made with the numbers treated as the new RIE first came into use (1878–85).

Throughout his life, Wade prided himself on being a 'general' surgeon able, should the occasion arise, to meet any demand on his services. The evidence for his claim lies in the cases he reported to the Edinburgh Medico-Chirurgical Society (EMCS) between 1907 and 1914 and in the ward books of the RIE.

Orthopaedic surgery was advancing quickly but, as Chapter 11 explains, the subject was not yet a recognized specialty in Edinburgh and would not be so for many years. By 1903, however, the operative treatment of fracture with the use of screws and plates had been adopted. Tendon transplantation had been introduced. Bone sarcomas had been resected, internal derangements of the knee joint rectified and hindquarter amputation practised. The upper and lower jaws had been excised safely and the correction of deformities attempted. The Thomas splint had revolutionized the treatment of compound fracture of the femur (p 154). Wade demonstrated his interest in orthopaedic surgery when he described a boy aged 4½ years after excision of the ulna for acute osteomyelitis.[37] He recounted an instance of 'anthracoid cellulitis' in a man of 19 years with osteomyelitis,[38] and

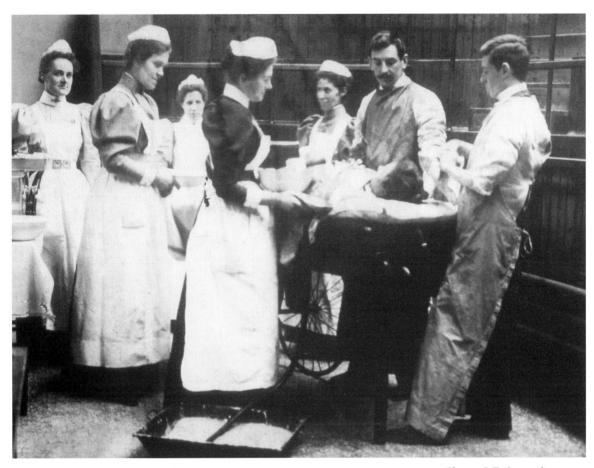

Figure 3.7 Operating theatre of the RIE in 1893.
The photograph illustrates both the overall design of the theatre and the dress worn by the staff at that time

in the same year he took part in a discussion on methods of treating simple fractures.[39] The history of a patient who sustained a fracture of the right humerus proved of particular interest and importance.

In Wade's words[40,K]:A man aged 27 years had fallen playing football in August 1913. He had numbness, immobility and pain in an arm. An X-ray showed a pathological fracture of the upper end of the shaft of the humerus. The fracture had healed satisfactorily, although stiffness persisted and movement was restricted.

Two years later, the emergence of a swelling led to the diagnosis of myeloid sarcoma, although the tumour was not examined microscopically. An exploratory operation revealed a centrally situated tumour. The head and upper portion of the shaft of the humerus, including six inches of bone, were excised. Before the operation, an amputation for senile gangrene had been performed on a man aged 67 years, and a six-inch long segment of the lower end of the femoral shaft was removed under aseptic conditions. This bone graft was implanted in

continued

continuity with the glenoid cavity of the younger man. No plates or screws were used to secure the implant because of the danger of ischaemia. Subsequent review showed new bone fixing the graft in position. Wade believed that the new bone had arisen in part from the bone cells of the implanted femur. The patient successfully resumed his occupation as a mill worker within two months of the graft.

Re-examination in November 1919 confirmed that the implanted bone remained firmly united to the recipient's humeral shaft.

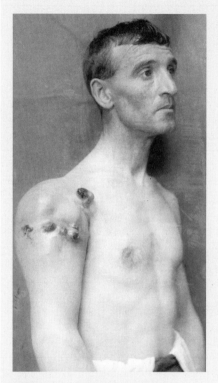 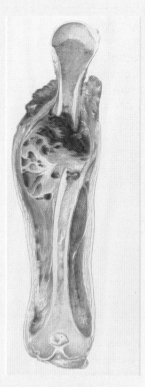

Figure 3.8 'Myeloid sarcoma' following fracture. *In 1912, this 27-year-old man sustained a pathological fracture of the right humerus. Two years later, a swelling described as a 'myeloid sarcoma' appeared. Wade replaced the affected bone with an allograft*

Figure 3.9 'Myeloid sarcoma' from patient described in Figure 3.8. *The patient survived six years.[40] The tumour then 'assumed invasive characteristics'. The figure illustrates the bone retrieved post-mortem*

In 1913, Wade made another important contribution, the significance of which was not known to him for many years.[L] A boy of barely 16 years acquired a motor bicycle and crashed in Lothian Road, Edinburgh. He sustained a compound fracture of the tibia. Admitted to hospital, the casualty officer recommended amputation. Wade demurred and the leg, treated conservatively, recovered. The patient was Norman Dott.

Vascular surgery was in its infancy, although cardiac wounds had been sutured successfully and sympathectomy had been tested for the relief of defective arterial blood flow. **Surgery of the chest and lungs** was little further advanced. An early bronchoscope had come into use and part of a lung infiltrated by a sarcoma of a rib had been excised successfully. Indeed, a whole lung had been removed. Thoracotomy, rib resection and thoracoplasty had become possible treatments for tuberculosis. **Otolaryngology** was advancing, aided by the direct vision laryngoscope. Foreign bodies could be removed from the air passages and cancers of the larynx excised.[M] Tonsillectomy had become fashionable as many common but poorly understood diseases such as rheumatoid arthritis were now attributed to foci of bacterial infection.

A surgical approach to diseases of the **alimentary system** could now be considered. The oesophagus had been resected but many years passed before an oesophageal carcinoma could be removed by opening the chest. In Edinburgh, gastric cancer was much more frequent than it is today, and a carcinoma had at last been removed. Total gastrectomy had proved possible. The stomach had been excised for peptic ulcer, a perforated ulcer sutured and a new operation, gastroenterostomy, designed. Wade made one of his many contributions when he described a woman who had had repetitive attacks of incomplete intestinal obstruction because of the presence of a gastric polyp.[41,42] Operations for intestinal disease were proliferating but the operative mortality remained high until the introduction of blood transfusion and chemotherapy. Intestinal obstruction had been relieved by surgery. In one of the most significant advances in surgery of the post-Listerian era, Fitz had revolutionized understanding of the hitherto mysterious and intractable condition of 'perityphlitis'.[43] He advocated the term 'appendicitis'. Within a few years, this 'new' disease caught the public imagination.[N] By 1901, Treves (p 23) had completed 1,000 operations for the disease.[44] The excision of colon cancers had been followed by the restoration of continuity by end-to-end anastomosis. Colostomy had been practised. Perineal resection now allowed the excision of cancer of the rectum although the alternative abdominoperineal approach had become an elective procedure. Tumour chemotherapy remained a distant dream.

Visceroptosis is a diagnosis of a bygone age. In 1903, the increased frequency of abdominal surgery permitted the observation that the organs of the body were not always in the positions seen in textbooks. In modern times, the discovery of a stomach within the chest, a heart on the right rather than the left, a kidney in the pelvis or a thyroid gland in the mediastinum no longer occasion surprise. The discovery of visceroptosis was sometimes a convenient explanation for otherwise inexplicable symptoms of a minor character. It called for 'correction' and, in the absence of further evidence, Wade and his colleagues were inclined to perform 'nephropexy' and 'gastropexy'.

Hepatobiliary surgery had begun when stones were removed safely from the gallbladder but it was some years before the organ itself could be excised.[45] It then became practicable to remove whole stones from the bile duct rather than simply crushing them. Liver surgery remained a subject for the future although Wade contributed to this new field by describing a case of primary hepatic sarcoma in a child aged four months.[46]

Dramatic progress had been made in **urological surgery**, the subject that became Wade's particular speciality (Chapter 12). He practised many new procedures. Occasionally, his interests in orthopaedic and urinary surgery came together in a single clinical meeting. Thus, in 1910, he demonstrated a patient with osteomyelitis and a boy aged four years and one month after nephropexy for a mobile kidney.[37]

Progress in the recently designated speciality of **Gynaecology** was related to innovations in abdominal and urological surgery. Abdominal hysterectomy for carcinoma, vaginal hysterectomy, oophorectomy and perineal repair were developed. Wade added his voice to the subject by describing the anatomy and histology of an early tubal gestation.[47] Significant advances had been made in the **surgery of the breast**. Operative techniques for breast cancer had advanced and mammoplasty had been used for the reduction of breast tissue. **Endocrine surgery** had progressed quickly. Excision of part of the thyroid gland for the relief of hypothyroidism became practicable. Postoperative hypothyroidism was a recognized danger but pioneer endocrine surgeons were at first unaware of the threat to the parathyroid glands.

Neurosurgery remained in its infancy. Macewen was able to locate a cerebral abscess precisely, an achievement described in his monograph.[48] He had already removed a cerebral tumour successfully.[49] Spinal surgery originated when an extramedullary tumour was resected. The use of bone flaps made the brain more accessible than trephining. The ophthalmoscope had transformed the diagnosis of diseases of the eye, **Ophthalmology**. The removal of cataract, an age-old procedure, had been followed by corneal grafting. Antisepsis had permitted evisceration of the eyeball and keratoplasty. **Plastic surgery** had also advanced. Varieties of skin grafts had been tested and harelip treated successfully.

Chemotherapy

When Wade began operative surgery, chemotherapy was no more than a gleam in Ehrlich's eye (p 343). Ehrlich argued that, just as individual chemical stains could colour particular cells specifically, so selective molecules could bind and inhibit particular micro-organisms, causing the death of the parasite without injuring host cells. In 1909, Ehrlich showed that the 606th compound he had tested (salvarsan, arsphenamine) was active against syphilis.[50] No further practical advances were made until 1935 (p 224). For the greater part of his career in surgery, therefore, Wade did not have the advantage of the agents that are synonymous with modern chemotherapy and antibiosis.

Resuscitation

Septic shock was more frequent in 1903 than it is today. After accident or injury, **haemorrhagic shock** was also common and chloroform was suspected to be a cause of **cardiogenic shock**. In the early years of the twentieth century, the emergency measures available for the treatment of all forms of shock were rudimentary. Some idea of the attempts that might be made to revive a dying individual may be gained from the description of a patient seen by Wade some years later.

A man had been wounded by shrapnel in the left leg during the battles of 1918. A mass of scar tissue remained at the site of injury. An attempt was to be made to excise the cicatrix. Anaesthesia was induced with ethylene and continued with chloroform and ether. The callus was excised and conical 'pinch' autografts applied, taking skin from the left thigh. However, only 3 of the grafts 'took'. Some days later, a second operation was begun but the patient stopped breathing. Artificial ventilation with oxygen and carbon dioxide was started and cardiac massage attempted by abdominal compression. Without avail, strychnine was injected subcutaneously, ether placed on the tongue and adrenaline injected into the heart.

Blood transfusion

Blood transfusion (p 220) was not yet a practicable procedure[51] although the first transfusion from one human to another had been as long ago as 1818. Bold surgeons used person-to-person transfusion in desperate situations. Macewen reported one of Lister's cases in 1869 and one of his own in 1879.[29]

A large urinary bladder stone had been removed from a man aged 24. The operation was followed by severe haemorrhage. The skin of a donor was cleansed with soap and water, rinsed with turpentine and washed with a 1 in 20 solution of carbolic acid. 'The vein [in the arm] having been opened, phlebotomy was carried out on the donor, whose blood was received into a small, warmed, carbolised vessel. From the latter it was at once drawn into a carbolised syringe and slowly injected into the recipient'. The arm to receive the blood was supported above the patient's head so that blood would enter the vein by gravity, to keep any air bubbles in the syringe while allowing air to escape from the vein if any had entered.

The blood groups (p 221) had been discovered in 1905 but their practical importance was not yet appreciated. Before 1914, blood could not be stored safely: the need for panels of donors had not yet arisen.

Assistant Surgeon to Leith Hospital

After the end of his period as Assistant Pathologist to the RIE, on 26th May 1908 (Chapter 5), Wade returned to the whole-time pursuit of surgery. The year marked a turning point in his ambitions. He was appointed Assistant Surgeon to Leith Hospital from 8th November 1908 and in the following year, Assistant Surgeon to the RIE.

It was, coincidentally, a time when international events were of absorbing interest and significance. Lenin had published *Materialism and empiric criticism*, Selfridges store had opened in London, the Girl Guides had been founded and Bleriot had crossed the English Channel by aeroplane. Few foresaw any future association between the advent of the aeroplane and the coincidental annexation by Austria of Bosnia and Herzegovina; fewer still could have predicted that Anglo–German discussions on the control of the railway that linked Constantinople and Baghdad with the Suez Canal, Mesopotamia and the Persian Gulf were any more than rumblings on a distant political horizon. They are matters that emerge again in Chapters 7 and 8.

Figure 3.10 Leith Hospital. *The main entrance to the hospital in 1910. (From Boyd, D. Leith Hospital 1848 to 1988. 1990, Scottish Academic Press)*

Leith Hospital had been founded in 1851. Leith was a busy port and had been a Burgh independent of Edinburgh. As commerce flourished, the population rose to more than 30,000 people. In 1844, 2,272 ships arrived at the docks.[52] To treat the sick, many of whom suffered from accidental injury, typhoid, typhus, measles, cholera or smallpox, a casualty hospital emerged from the fusion of a dispensary and the Humane Society. A Resident House Surgeon was appointed. In its first year, the hospital dealt with 2,344 patients including 122 cases of 'fever' and eight of drowning ('submersion'). The first Consultant Surgeon, Professor James Syme, was designated in 1859.[O] In 1891, 1896 and 1906, there were 308, 477 and 747 surgical inpatients, respectively (Table 3.2). In later years, Wade actively promoted the role of Leith Hospital in undergraduate and postgraduate teaching (Chapter 13).

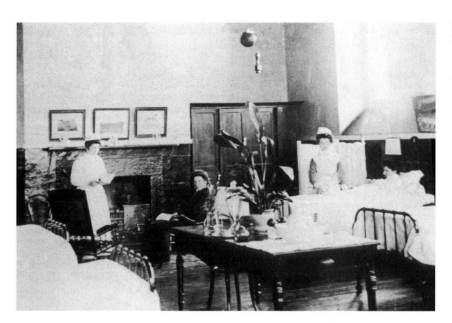

Figure 3.11 A ward in Leith Hospital. *A coal fire at the end of the ward suggests that the photograph was taken between 1890 and 1905*

Assistant Surgeon to the Royal Infirmary of Edinburgh

In the RIE, each surgical 'charge' (Table 3.3) was directed by a Surgeon-in-Ordinary who had with him an Assistant Surgeon, a Clinical Tutor and a Resident House Surgeon. In addition to Caird, others to whom Wade was apprenticed included Thomas Annandale (p 14), John Chiene (p 23), Harold Jalland Stiles[P] and Patrick Heron Watson.[7,Q] Wade was appointed seventh Assistant Surgeon to the RIE on 8th November 1909.[R] He was reappointed in successive years, and, after his return from the war in 1919, his position was renewed and retained until 8th September 1924.

Within two years of his appointment as Assistant Surgeon, Wade's financial affairs had advanced to the point at which he was able to establish a consulting room of his own. In 1911, he purchased the self-contained house at 6 Manor Place, Edinburgh for £2,100 from the Trustees of the late Thomas Francis Spittal Caverhill, MB, CM. A bond for £1,000 was made available to him by Mary Georgina Wade Wilson of Falkirk. The bond was discharged on 28th May 1924, at the time when Wade became Surgeon-in-Ordinary to the RIE. In the meantime, however, he had embarked on and completed an ambitious programme of research into the causes of cancer, studies that are described in Chapter 4.

Table 3.2 Surgical conditions treated at Leith Hospital in 1886.[52] There were two cases each of carbuncle, cellulitis, cut throat, ear disease, eye disease and haemorrhoids; and single cases of strangulated femoral hernia, hydrocoele and varicose veins. In addition, there were 14 examples of venereal disease

Group of disorders	Number of cases
Fractures	47 (12 of femur)
Wounds and bruises	41
Concussion of brain and spine	13
Diseases of bones and joints (other than fracture) but including sprains and bursitis	35
Abscess	18
Ulcers	3
Burns	9
Urinary diseases	7
Haemorrhoids	2

Figure 3.12 Henry Wade. *Wade is shown here as Assistant Surgeon to Leith Hospital and the Royal Infirmary of Edinburgh, 1911. (From The Gambolier, 1911–12)*

Table 3.3 Honorary surgical staff of the Royal Infirmary of Edinburgh 1914

Consulting surgeons	Surgeons-in-Ordinary	Assistant Surgeons
AG Miller	Professor FM Caird	AA Scot Skirving
CW MacGillivray	CW Cathcart	GL Chiene
Emeritus Professor John Chiene	JWB Hodsdon	WJ Stuart
JM Cotterill	David Wallace	JW Struthers
	Professor Alexis Thomson	Henry Wade
	Alex Miles	E Scot Carmichael
	JW Dowden	DPD Wilkie
		Dennis Cotterill

Figure 3.13 6 Manor Place, Edinburgh.
The house was purchased by Henry Wade in 1911; it was sold by his Trustees in 1956

CHAPTER 4

Pioneer of cancer research[A]

1903–07

> We have scotch'd the snake, not killed it;
> She'll close and be herself, whilst our poor malice
> Remains in danger of her former tooth.
>
> (Shakespeare: Macbeth)

The later months of 1903 were among the most important of Henry Wade's life. Success in the examinations for the Fellowship of the Royal College of Surgeons of Edinburgh, the RCSEd; apprenticeship to Mr Francis Caird, Surgeon-in-Ordinary to the Royal Infirmary of Edinburgh (Chapter 3); and election to the Conservatorship of the College Museum (Chapter 6) were signs of promise and indices of potential achievement. It was at this moment that Wade encountered Dr William Ford Robertson[B] (p 88), a meeting that had far-reaching consequences for both men.

Wade had already shown an interest in the nature and origins of cancer,[1] and this concern was to persist throughout his career.[2] The heavy clinical responsibilities that he had assumed through his hospital work did not prevent him from committing long hours to fundamental laboratory research. It is probable that he met Ford Robertson in the rooms of the RCSEd, where Wade had begun his duties as Honorary Conservator while Robertson pursued his sophisticated histological and microscopic investigations. It is equally probable that Wade had been introduced to Robertson by Professor WS Greenfield (p 40), in whose University department Robertson had been working as a Demonstrator, and that Greenfield drew Wade's attention to Robertson's publications. Both Greenfield and Robertson were neuropathologists – experts in diseases of the brain and central nervous system.

The lure of the laboratory

Ford Robertson, the first Pathologist to the Edinburgh Asylums Board (p 88), had been fortunate in securing laboratory accommodation in the rooms of the RCSEd. He worked there before moving to the laboratories of the Board located in the Royal Edinburgh Hospital for Mental Diseases at Jordanburn, Edinburgh. In 1903, Robertson was

---

Chapter Summary

- The lure of the laboratory
- Cancer
- Wade's early views
- Wade's second thoughts
- A new carcinogen?
- Transmissible sarcoma of the dog
- An infective cancer?
- Experimental lymphadenoma (Hodgkin's disease)
- Significance of Wade's cancer research

embarking on an ambitious programme looking into the causes and behaviour of cancer. The stimulus to Robertson's research could be found in the new science of Bacteriology. His principal interest had become the role of infection in organic nervous disease and, in particular, in the causation of that form of neurosyphilis designated General Paralysis of the Insane (GPI).

To investigate GPI on behalf of the Edinburgh Asylums Board, Robertson employed new gold and silver metallic staining techniques in his search for bacteria in tissues. The methods, which had come from Italy and Spain, had already proved of value in defining cellular changes in central nervous system disease. Wade was not to know that Robertson combined originality of thought with a disregard for scientific evidence that did not accord with his own. In spite of the absence of absolute proof, Robertson came to believe that GPI was caused by the indirect action on the cells of the brain of diphtheroid bacilli. He postulated that these organisms parasitized the respiratory and alimentary systems and impaired their defences. It is relevant to note that in 1908, he went so far as to propose that antisera to diphtheroid organisms could arrest the progression of GPI. These later views were at first widely accepted in psychiatric circles. Outside Edinburgh, they were received with scepticism and criticized publicly.[C]

Cancer

Cancer (Latin: crab) is a small constellation of stars in the northern sky and is the fourth sign of the zodiac. Since very early times, the name has also been used to describe a 'creeping ulcer' and, in turn, a malignant new growth – a neoplasm. Neoplasms are an inevitable condition of life on earth and an affliction of all multicellular organisms, both plant and animal.[3]

Nature of cancer

Many cancers extend to form masses that may grow on body surfaces or within the tissues. The designation 'tumour' is therefore often used, although many cancers do not form masses and many masses, such as abscesses and aneurysms, are not cancers.[4–6] The history of cancer is long but scientific views on the nature of the disorder are comparatively recent. Matthew Baillie claimed 'schirrus and cancer of the stomach is not very uncommon towards an advanced period of life and, I think, is more frequently met with in men than in women'.[7] Everard Home made the earliest illustrations of microscopic sections of cancer,[8,9] and Müller showed that tumours are formed of cells.[10] In Edinburgh, Hughes Bennett described cancerous (neoplastic) and cancroid (neoplasm-like) growths.[11] Misled by his humoral theories, Carl von Rokitansky was 'further disposed to believe in cancer formation through a conversion of certain physiological elements into those of cancer'.[12] He believed that tissues and cells came from the humours of the body, not from other cells, and accepted that carcinomata, malignant neoplasms of epithelial tissues 'originate and subsist not rarely as local evils'. As early as 1846, Rokitansky's concept of humoral pathology was challenged and disproved by Rudolf Virchow, the advocate of Cellular Pathology.[13] Virchow subsequently proposed a classification of tumours in which 'homologous' implied the restricted, local growth of benign neoplasms, while 'heterologous' indicated malignancy, a concept well known by the time of Wade's early studies.

Causes of cancer

When Wade began his investigations, the causes, as opposed to the nature, of cancer were understood poorly. In some forms of neoplasm, it was realized that there was an inherited predisposition. Differences in the geographical distribution of cancer were recognized. Cancer increased in frequency as age advanced. In 1903, the average age of the population was very different from today.[14] In Wade's early years, the mean expectation of life in Scotland was no more than 40 years for men, 45 for women. Consequently, the frequency and nature of the cancers diagnosed and treated by Wade were very different from those of the present day. Cancer of the prostate gland (p 242) was uncommon in 1900; it is now the most frequent form of cancer in men. Important social and occupational factors were present. Cancer of the stomach was a price paid for low social class and poverty, and cancer of the scrotal skin was the penalty for having worked as a chimney sweep.[15] The commercial use of plastics had not been conceived, and many dyestuffs were still of vegetable origin. Few women smoked, and lung cancer was not the scourge it is today. No chemical cause of cancer was identified until 1916.[16] Lung cancer in miners working in the Hartz region of Germany had been recorded in 1879 but 16 years passed before the discovery of radioactivity.[17] By 1903, however, the use of X-rays in clinical diagnosis was widespread although the hazards incurred by radiologists had been described only very recently.[18]

Cells and cancer

In the early years of the twentieth century, the changes in cell populations that led to cancer were under vigorous investigation. In terms of the mechanism of action of carcinogens (substances or agents that cause cancer), the direct cancerous transformation of cells was considered possible. As no causes were known, this hypothesis remained unproven. Cohnheim's contentious theory of carcinogenesis attracted much interest:[19] 'In an early stage of embryonic development a number of cells greater than that necessary for the structure of the corresponding part was produced in such a way that some of the cells were not utilised'. There were 'cell rests' – persistent rudiments originating in embryonic life, or in a later condition of postnatal displacement.

By 1900, carcinomas had been transmitted successfully through generations of mice by the introduction of small fragments of tumour from one animal into another. In 1903, Jensen had shown that such tumours were not transplantable in the absence of intact donor tumour cells.[20] There was species specificity and the success or failure of the procedure was related to the degree of relation between the donor and host animals. Through the pioneering work of Ehrlich,[21] the science of immunology was emerging, and the influences of active and of passive immunity were thought to be factors that regulated tumour cell growth.

Micro-organisms and cancer

In 1900, it was considered that cancers might be caused by micro-organisms. Many species of bacteria, protozoa, metazoa and fungi were known and could be viewed with the light microscope. It was becoming clear, however, that not all such infective agents were so large. It was suggested that some agents, not recognizable with the light microscope, could pass through filters with a pore size small enough to retain these micro-organisms.[22]

Robertson and Wade began their collaborative studies by testing evidence from experiments reported in 1901 by Gaylord and others.[23,D] These authors had proposed that carcinomatous tumours were the result of the presence of a protozoon seen as a Russell body. An analogous structure seen in plants was a fungus resembling *Plasmodiaphora brassicae*, a parasite specific to the family *Cruciferae*, which included cabbages and turnips. Infection by *P brassicae* caused 'finger and toe disease' (club root).

In a first report made to the 1904 Oxford Meeting of the British Medical Association, Robertson and Wade began by redefining the microscopic appearances of developing *P brassicae*, a process necessary if the stages of development were to be identified in human tissue.[24] At the Annual Museum Section of the Meeting, they exhibited specimens from their work.[25] Ordinary histological stains they found to be valueless but metallic processes, particularly the ammoniacal silver–gold technique that Robertson knew so well, were valuable although their interpretation was at the limits of resolution of the light microscope.

In the development of *P brassicae*, Robertson and Wade believed they had found four stages: **spore granules**, which resembled micrococci or short bacilli; these granules enlarged to become **spherical bodies** that they assumed, without proof, to be the precursors of the **amoeboid cells** to which **hyperplasia of the root hair cells** of an infected plant was attributed. To their obvious consternation, however, pre-spore nuclear bodies were also detected in healthy turnips. Ford Robertson and Wade confessed to doubts about the significance of their own work and admitted candidly: 'we were misled'.

Wade's early views

Believing, perhaps, that it was best to 'put their cards on the table', Robertson and Wade went boldly into print in 1905.[26] Within human carcinomatous tissue, they described how they had found objects they regarded as identical with the four phases of *P brassicae* development. However, these 'organisms' were **only one tenth to one twentieth of the size of the plant parasite** and were less numerous than in the plant. Using methods of culture that they did not describe fully until the following year, Robertson and Wade succeeded in growing an organism with the characteristics of *P brassicae* from three human carcinomata.

Even during this early period of their work, doubts were beginning to appear. The authors started to retract many of their earlier claims and admitted that 'we have fallen into error in assuming the correctness of the life cycle [of *P brassicae*] described by others'. Moreover, 'at no stage is there the formation of a multinucleated mass of protoplasm…the term is a misnomer'. Indeed, their morphological studies were wholly undercut by the admission that 'the methods used for the study of *Plasmodiaphorae* are not specific. They render the parasite visible but also colour almost everything else in the tissue'. They accepted that 'the search for these parasites in carcinomata is beset with difficulties and, but for the fact that certain special structural characteristics can occasionally be recognised, it would be impossible to derive any conclusive evidence in support of, or against, their presence from the histological part of our investigations'.

Wade's second thoughts

To defend their thesis that human carcinomata were caused by organisms resembling *Plasmodiophora*, Robertson and Wade then fell back upon the results of cultural studies. Their method was to cauterize the surface of tumours removed surgically, excise small pieces and maintain them at 37°C on the surfaces of agar slopes. From these simple preparations, they retrieved organisms that they believed to be *Plasmodiaphorae*. They claimed that they had been 'uniformly successful in preventing contamination of the [culture] medium'. From the tumour tissue, a faint greyish cloud extended into the subjacent agar. However, they could not view any micro-organisms in films made from this nebulous material and were not able to demonstrate organisms by bacteriological stains. They overcame this difficulty by fixing their cultures in formalin, cutting sections (p 80) and staining them with their silver–gold technique. In spite of all their previous reservations, and the fact that only four tumours were studied, they had no hesitation in concluding that within the sections made in this way, there were 'several successive phases of a *Plasmodiaphora*'.

A new carcinogen?

Robertson and Wade concluded that if these organisms were present in carcinomatous tumours, it was 'hardly open to doubt' that they had the same relation to the morbid growth as *P. brassicae* had to club root; that is, they were the 'determining factor'. The authors had little hesitation in extrapolating from these observations to a general hypothesis of the cause of human cancer. *In effect, they believed they had indeed discovered one, if not the only, cause of cancer.*

Not surprisingly, this sensational assertion provoked immediate debate. Their presentations to the 1904 Oxford meeting of the British Medical Association passed without formal comment, but their first definitive paper elicited immediate questions. In an editorial in 1905, the *Lancet* wrote: 'Dr Robertson and Mr Wade have not attempted to meet the objections which have already been raised to the etiological significance which they attribute to the *Plasmodiaphorae*. Until these difficulties are removed…the general significance of these careful observations cannot be properly estimated'.[27]

The following week, Robertson and Wade responded by letter,[28] but the correspondence was annotated by the *Lancet* which said 'We are glad that Dr Ford Robertson and Mr Wade recognise the importance of the omissions to which we drew attention'.[29] Meanwhile, Robertson and Wade had explained their position by demonstrating their sections and cultures privately to a group of friends in Edinburgh.[30] Dr George Thomas Beatson of Glasgow proved to be a less tolerant critic than the Editor of the *Lancet*. On 1st March 1905, in the course of a paper presented to the Edinburgh Medico-Chirurgical Society, he subjected Robertson and Wade's work to scathing comment.[31] The subject of the meeting was 'The etiology of carcinoma.' Robertson and Wade are not recorded as having taken part in the discussion; indeed, it is not known whether they were present. It is not surprising that Beatson was sceptical of the evidence on which Robertson and Wade based their opinion that a mammalian tumour such as human carcinoma was 'undeniably infective'. Beatson stated that, 'so far apparently as they went, they [Robertson and Wade] did not fulfil the postulates laid down by Koch[31,E]. As Beatson said, 'there was yet wanting the crucial test of the reproduction of carcinoma in animals by means of the respective micro-organisms and this was almost an essential for the establishment of the position which these authors took up'.

Robertson was not deterred, but by 1907, when his further long and speculative paper on the histological appearances of carcinomatous tumours appeared,[32] Wade had moved into parallel but less controversial fields of cancer research. Robertson's studies continued independently.[33–35]

Transmissible sarcoma of the dog

Following his earlier interest in *Plasmodiaphorae*, and perhaps because of the adverse opinions expressed by distinguished colleagues, in

December 1904 Wade began his own series of sophisticated investigations of a disease of dogs entitled 'infective sarcoma'. He possessed the originality and independence of the natural research worker, and by the time his studies of cancer ended, he had thrown off the shackles of collaboration and consolidated his own position as an assiduous and responsible investigator. His careful studies tell us much of the state of experimental cancer research at the time. The condition of infective sarcoma, known worldwide among dog fanciers, was transmitted by sexual contact, affected both males and females and resulted in the growth of single or multiple soft, fleshy, vascular masses on the genital tissues. Although there was debate about the identity of these tumours, Wade accepted that the microscopic appearances were those of 'alveolar sarcoma'. Others regarded them as lymphosarcoma, myxosarcoma or carcinoma.

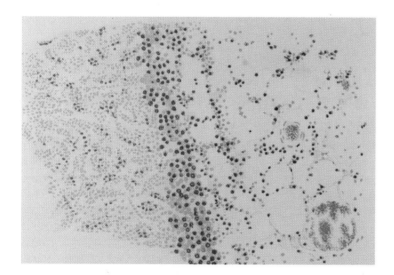

Figure 4.1 Nodule removed after 18 hours *(Wade Plate XLII, Fig.1). Showing portion of tumour introduced and adjacent tissue of host. Intimate union between the two. Necrotic tumour tissue. The tumour formation area. The adjacent areolar tissue of the host in which the formation of additional tumour cells is occurring. (× 100, E.Mb.) (The words are Wade's)*

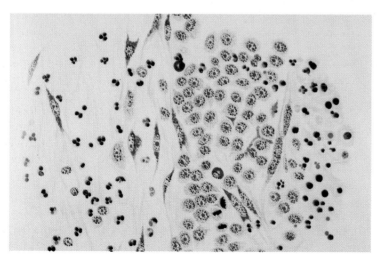

Figure 4.2 Nodule removed after 18 hours. *(Wade Plate XLII, Fig. 2). Showing the line of junction of the portion introduced and the tissue of the host. The tumour formation area, consisting of healthy tumour cells. Two in mitosis. Within, this degenerate tumour invaded by leucocytes. On its outer aspect, the margin of the adjacent areolar tissue with the formation of tumour cells from fibroblasts and epithelial cells. Polymorphonuclear leucocytes. Polyblasts. Fibrin. (× 600, P.R.Mg.)*

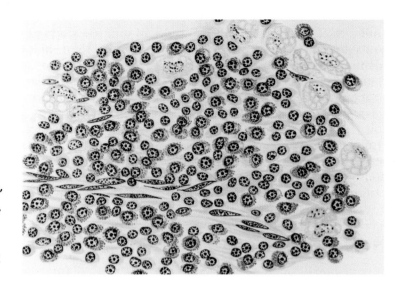

Figure 4.3 Disappearing nodule, 118 days. *(Wade Plate XLIII, Fig.3). Showing the characteristic appearance in the centre of the nodule. Tumour cells swollen, vacuolated, and degenerated. Lymphocytes small dark. Polyblasts and plasma cells, bright red. (× 600, P.R.Mg.)*

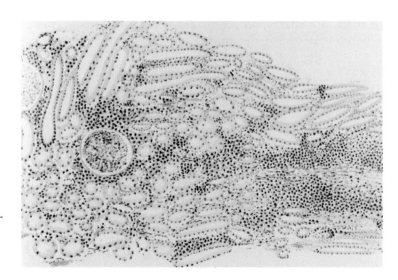

Figure 4.4 Kidney inoculation experiments, three days *(Wade Plate XLIII, Fig.4). Showing accumulation of lymphocyte-like cells radiating through the cortex along the course of the interlobular arteries, and infiltrating the adjacent interstitial tissues. (× 200, E.Mb.)*

Wade obtained material from a bull bitch and a wirehaired fox terrier dog and used the tissues to inoculate not only further canine species but also two foxes and a number of rabbits, rats and guinea pigs. Where this work was conducted is not known. After the transplantation of canine tumour tissue, nodules could be felt in the recipient for three weeks. Thereafter, there was a gradual increase in the size of these 'tumours', followed by their regression and, after two months, their disappearance. His experiments on transmissibility were not the first, as similar inoculations of a dog had been successfully by Wehr.[36] Wade identified metastases in only one animal: the secondary tumour deposits were recognized in the liver, intestine and adrenal gland. In dogs and foxes, the tumour cells survived, and tumours grew that were indistinguishable from those of the original donors; however, cells implanted in the other species did not survive. In transplants that were accepted, the histological structure of the tumour after 47 days was similar to that of the original tumour. Wade also conducted experiments on the serial transmissibility of the tumour, making transplants through eight generations of animals. In this approach, Wade chose the pioneering pattern adopted by Jensen,[20] who followed his transmissible carcinoma through 40 generations of mouse. It should be noted that Wade had obtained samples from Jensen and investigated their properties in some detail.

An infective cancer?

Wade concluded that 'alveolar sarcoma' was indeed an infective cancer conveyed from living donor cells to living host cells by a contagious, intracellular virus. The tumour 'belonged to the borderland between the infective granulomata and the true neoplasms'. Wade was unable to identify the infectious agent in spite, as he said, of using all the common and many of the specialized bacteriological media available at the time. Neither aerobes nor anaerobes could be isolated. Robertson assisted by applying to the tissues the stains he had employed successfully to identify *P. brassicae* but was unable to recognize this agent in the canine alveolar sarcoma. Nor were spirochaetes found. Wade mixed portions of tumours with sterile normal saline, pounded them in a mortar with sterilized sand and attempted to pass them through a Berkefeld filter. The filtrates were introduced subcutaneously into the tissues of 'a number of dogs' with stringent aseptic techniques. Local or systemic tumours grew in none of the tissues. However, inoculated animals developed immunity to the transmissible tumour: repeated administration of tumour extracts to animals that had recovered spontaneously proved abortive. Immunity against one 'strain' of tumour cell was effective against cells derived from a second 'strain'.

On the basis of his histological studies, Wade considered that the natural infection consisted of cells derived entirely from the connective tissues of the host: the contagious agent was conveyed to the host cells *in situ* by the transplanted cells. The continued growth of the tumour ceased, he believed, because of host resistance. A capsule formed around the neoplasm, and the tumour cells were lost by gradual cytolysis, mediated by lymphocytes and polyblasts, a term used to describe 'free' inflammatory macrophages, the scavenging cells of the loose connective tissues. This cellular response, in turn, was reflected in an increase in the number of mononuclear cells in the circulating blood. A state of immunity following spontaneous recovery was attributed to the development of a 'toxin' that could be isolated by filtration and was capable of inducing glomerulonephritis.

Henry Wade incorporated his studies in a thesis submitted in 1907 to the University of Edinburgh for the degree of MD.[37] He was awarded a Gold Medal.

The substance of Henry Wade's thesis was contained in a paper that was beautifully illustrated with colour drawings made by Mr Richard Muir (p 82) and published in 1908 in the *Journal of Pathology and Bacteriology*.[38]

Experimental lymphadenoma (Hodgkin's disease)

Wade maintained an active interest in the investigation of the bacterial, spirochaetal and protozoal causes of human cancer. Beatson's influential criticism was perhaps one reason why Wade was persuaded to begin further experiments. Consequently, it is not surprising to find among his papers a notebook entitled 'Lymphadenoma. Experimental research. Commenced Wednesday Nov 27th 1907'. The opportunity to investigate the infective nature of lymphadenoma was offered by Dr GL Gulland, who had a patient under his care in the Chalmers Hospital, Edinburgh. On 27th November 1907, Wade excised a lymph node from the left axilla of this patient, cut it into pieces and placed six of them under the axillary panniculus carnosus – the subcutaneous muscle – of a dog-faced monkey and a small *Callithrix* monkey. The injected material was examined histologically and the blocks taken to the Asylums Laboratory. A black guinea pig was also injected with a tissue emulsion. The wounds healed well. By 13th December, only a small nodule remained in the first animal, and eventually all signs of the nodules vanished. Thirteen months later, one animal was alive and healthy; the other had died. Examination *post-mortem* revealed no special enlargement of the lymph glands and no sign of the original nodules. The experiments continued until 16th February 1909, after Wade had become Assistant Surgeon to Leith Hospital (p 186).

Significance of Wade's cancer research

To undertake significant biological laboratory research has always called for meticulous planning, persistence, patience and considerable physical stamina. To pursue such experiments while acting as a Surgical Assistant and, simultaneously, as a Pathologist to the RIE, is a mark of single-minded endurance and an index of ambition. Whether Wade's experiments were uniformly successful or not – nine of every 10 comparable studies are unsuccessful in the best of hands – the fact that he undertook them is a remarkable tribute to his intelligence, far-sightedness and strength of character. A particularly interesting aspect of Wade's studies of 1904–09 is that they came close to those of Peyton Rous who discovered in 1910 that a malignant tumour of chickens, a sarcoma, was transmissible by a filterable virus.[39] In 1966, at the age of 87 years, Rous was awarded the Nobel Prize.

In the meantime, Wade had become an early member of the Pathological Society of Great Britain and Ireland. The Society was established in 1906. In 1920, the *Journal of Pathology and Bacteriology*, founded in 1893 by Kanthack, was adopted as the organ of this prestigious Society. Kanthack's successor in the Chair of Pathology of the University of Cambridge was Sims Woodhead (p 343), so the association between the Society and the Journal is easy to understand.

Figures 4.1–4.4 are from Wade.[37] The words of the captions are reproduced as he wrote them. The plates are not identical with those in his MD thesis.[38]

The drawings were made by Mr Richard Muir, Technician to the University of Edinburgh Department of Pathology. They are now reproduced by permission of the University of Edinburgh.

Key to Wade's abbreviations: E.Mb.= eosin and methylene blue; P.R.Mg.= pyronin, resorcin and methyl green.

CHAPTER 5

Pathologist and laboratory scientist

1906–08

A man must make his opportunity, as oft as find it.

(Francis Bacon, *The Advancement of Learning*, 1605)

L earning surgery, completing a programme of research in cancer and committed to caring for one of Europe's most important medical museums, Wade now joined a band of young surgeons and physicians serving as Assistant Pathologists to the Royal Infirmary of Edinburgh, the RIE.[A] He was appointed on 5th March 1906 and started this, his fourth simultaneous task, on 2nd April.

In the early years of the twentieth century, it was common practice for aspiring surgeons and physicians to contribute to the pathology laboratory service of the RIE, an effective way in which to master the knowledge of pathology that was the key to surgical diagnosis. Several of his friends and contemporaries followed the same path. With the exception of a Pathologist and an Assistant Pathologist to the RIE, the professional laboratory staff of the hospital was small. The University Professor of Pathology, WS Greenfield,[B] was still nominally a clinician with patients to look after in the wards of the hospital. Charged with teaching and with few assistants, he had little time for clinical laboratory diagnosis. Wade thrived in the environment of the pathology laboratories and was reappointed on 11th February 1907 and again on 3rd February 1908. He retained his position until 26th May, not long before his appointment as Assistant Surgeon to the Leith Hospital (p 56).

Hospital laboratories in 1906

That Wade profited from his experience in Pathological Anatomy is evident from the great emphasis he placed on the subject in his position as Conservator of the Museum of the Royal College of Surgeons of Edinburgh, the RCSEd (Chapter 6). His time as Assistant Pathologist to the RIE exposed him to the .challenges encountered in a great variety of diseases prevalent at the time. Among these conditions,

Chapter Summary
- Hospital laboratories in 1906
- The new sciences
- Learning the anatomy of disease
- Learning the microscopy of disease
- Understanding bacteriology
- The Laboratory of the Royal College of Physicians of Edinburgh
- The Research Laboratory of the Royal College of Surgeons of Edinburgh
- The Laboratory of the Asylums' Board

tuberculosis was very frequent but cancer relatively less common than it is now. Very many of those patients Wade examined *post-mortem* suffered from urinary disorders, Wade's growing field of interest. It was the speciality to which he devoted much of his later professional life and in which, as Chapter 12 shows, he became an internationally recognized authority.

Hospital laboratories were proliferating. To achieve precise surgical diagnosis by depending simply on the interpretation of clinical signs and symptoms was no longer acceptable. It was as essential to use the microscope to examine tissues as it was to identify the bacteria that caused common infections such as enteric fever (typhoid), tuberculosis and osteomyelitis (bone infection). In both respects, Britain was at risk of lagging behind Austro-Hungary, France and Germany. Indeed, Joseph Lister's house surgeon, Watson Cheyne (p 273), complained in 1876 that he had been obliged to investigate the nature of the bacteria, the agents of infected surgical wounds, 'in a little passage behind the operating theatre in the old (1741) Infirmary'.

The new sciences

Anatomy and Pathology had undergone a century of revolution. Microscopes had confirmed the existence of cells, revealing the intimate details not only of normal but also of diseased tissues. A new science, tissue pathology, Histopathology, had been born.[1–3] The organization and disorganization of the brain, endocrine organs, muscles and kidneys were understood increasingly. Physiology was changing: inspired experiments offered understanding of the internal environment (*le milieu intérieur*) of Claude Bernard.[4] Chemical methods were being applied to the analysis of the blood, urine and secretions, giving a foretaste of another new subject: Clinical Chemistry. As Chapter 3 shows, diseases of the blood[5] and of the immune system were emerging as subjects for new medical specialities.

During these two years, Wade realized that it was desirable to master two particular groups of laboratory procedure in addition to, but distinct from, those he was learning as a surgeon.[6] The first group were those of Pathological Anatomy: the gross or 'macroscopic' examination and analysis of the organs and tissues of the body, generally after death. The second comprised those of Surgical Biopsy:[7] the examination and microscopy of tissue samples removed before or during an operation. Coincidentally, Wade was also acquiring a practical understanding of bacteriology.

Learning the anatomy of disease

Throughout the first half of the twentieth century, more than 1,000 deaths occurred each year in the RIE. A substantial proportion of these fatalities was of surgical patients. It was highly desirable to judge the precision of diagnosis and treatment by examining their tissues and

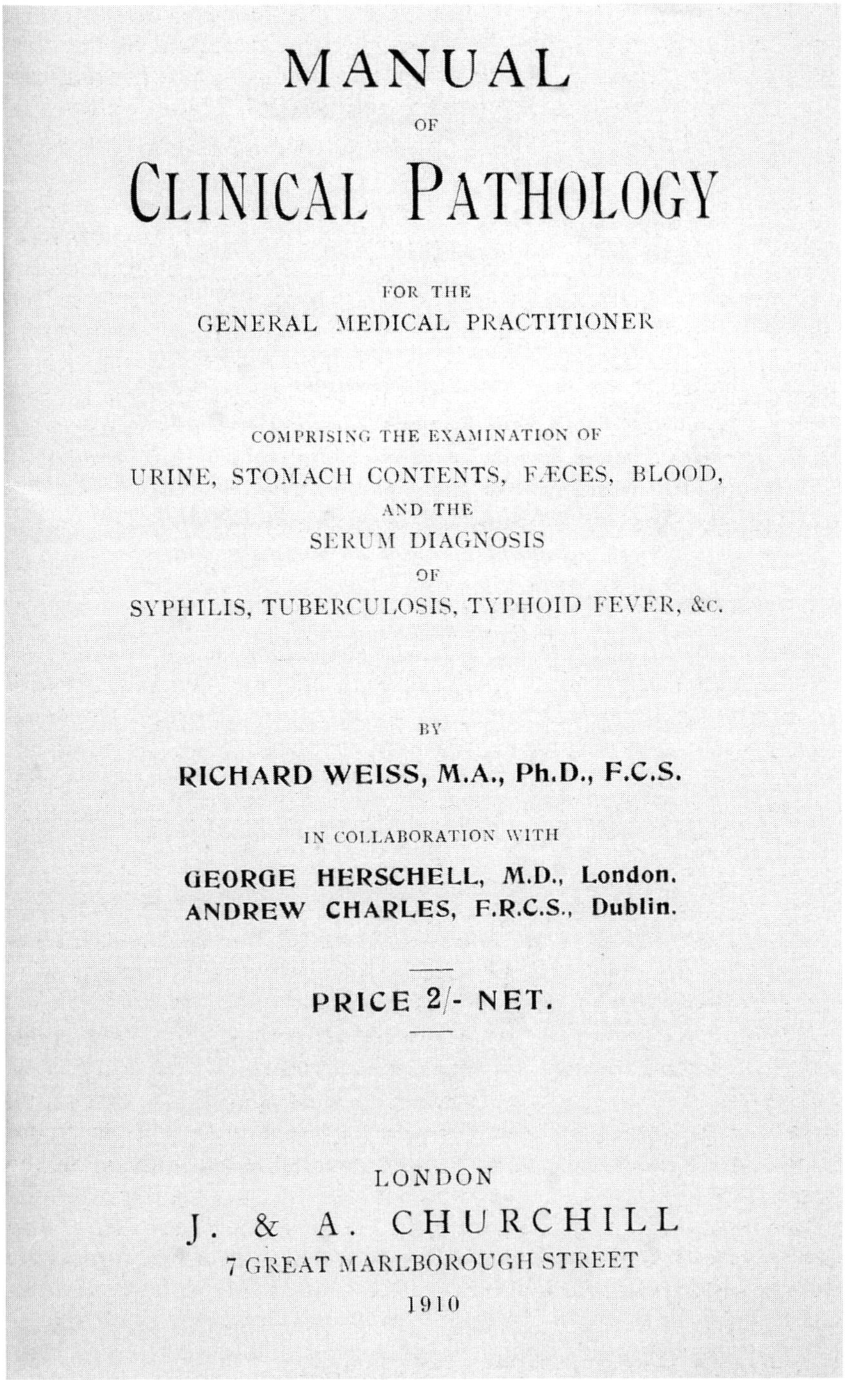

MANUAL

OF

CLINICAL PATHOLOGY

FOR THE
GENERAL MEDICAL PRACTITIONER

COMPRISING THE EXAMINATION OF
URINE, STOMACH CONTENTS, FÆCES, BLOOD,
AND THE
SERUM DIAGNOSIS
OF
SYPHILIS, TUBERCULOSIS, TYPHOID FEVER, &c.

BY

RICHARD WEISS, M.A., Ph.D., F.C.S.

IN COLLABORATION WITH

GEORGE HERSCHELL, M.D., London.
ANDREW CHARLES, F.R.C.S., Dublin.

PRICE 2/- NET.

LONDON
J. & A. CHURCHILL
7 GREAT MARLBOROUGH STREET
1910

Figure 5.1 Clinical chemistry. *In the early years of the twentieth century, Clinical chemistry and serology were established as essential aids in surgical diagnosis. Their importance is exemplified by Weiss's 1910* **Manual of clinical pathology,** *which accompanied the diagnostic set shown in Figure 5.2*

Figure 5.2 Chemical diagnosis. *A chemical and serological diagnostic set for the general medical practitioner*

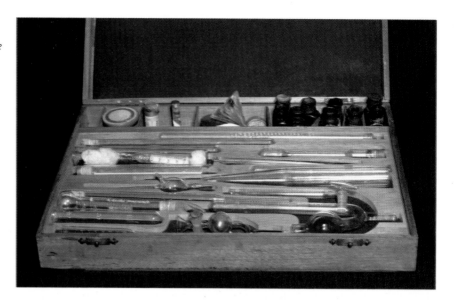

Figure 5.3 Ureameter. *Glass apparatus from the diagnostic set shown in Figure 5.2 illustrating the kind of apparatus used for the measurement of glucose, urea and albumin before the First World War*

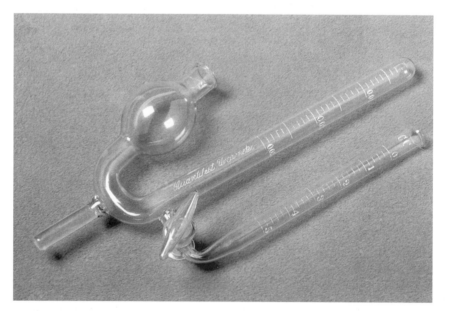

organs *post-mortem*. Such an examination was a means of correlating the signs and symptoms that had been recorded in life with the anatomical findings after death, an approach of great value in assessing the effectiveness of surgical practice and of inestimable worth in medical education. The autopsies were frequently performed by those surgeons or physicians who, like Wade, had chosen to spend time as Assistant Pathologists. This practice was regarded as an extremely valuable part of their training, and continued at least until 1950. It was a tradition dating back to 1839, when John Reid was appointed to serve the original 1741 hospital. Later in the nineteenth century pathological anatomy was placed on a sure footing by Karl von Rokitansky and his erudite critic, Rudolph Virchow.[8,9] In Wade's time, early in the twentieth century, there were few better guides than George Adami.[10]

In Edinburgh, the practice of pathological anatomy was accommodated in a distinctive, stone-built building, completed in 1879, near the hospital chapel and boiler house but separate from the hospital wards. In time, the building came also to accommodate the bacteriology laboratory. Bodies were conveyed discreetly from the hospital wards through the lower basement. When an autopsy was to be performed, students were alerted and passers-by warned by a notice on the outer door that read: *Sectio cadaveris hodie*. The use of Latin was presumably based on the assumption that new patients and their relatives entering the RIE via the West Gate of the hospital would not understand the significance of this admission of therapeutic failure.

The working conditions differed little from those tolerated by anatomists in previous centuries. The autopsy room was an amphitheatre with a tier of wooden benches for students. The room contained several wooden tables. The tiled walls bore blackboards. There was no mechanical ventilation. A central cement floor supported the tables. The mortuary was heated by a coal-fired furnace.[C] The preparation rooms were above the mortuary. Lighting had been by gas but, by 1898, the first Edinburgh electricity company was able to provide a supply. There was a room where the coats and shoes of a prosector were placed. It was a simple wooden-floored changing room.[D] No provision was made for female staff: there was none. Before starting a dissection, a prosector removed his coat and jacket and donned an apron and rubber boots. In the conduct of dissections, gloves were not considered necessary. However, there was a price to be paid and, at a later date, an ominous notice placed near the door reminded prosectors that a pathologist had died from streptococcal infection because he had not worn gloves. It did not help that the sponges used in a dissection were not disinfected. The viscera were either removed *en bloc* or the parts were dissected individually. Organs were weighed; the tissues examined; their appearance, shape, colour and texture observed; and their dimensions measured and recorded. Notes were written by hand. A drawing might be made. An experienced pathologist often devoted as many as two, three or more hours to the investigation of a single 'subject'. There were frequently three or four cases in one morning.

In the preparation rooms of the RIE, daylight flooded through plate-glass windows held within wooden frames. Oppressively hot in summer, the rooms were uncomfortably cold in winter. The working surfaces were polished teak benches that could be cleaned but not disinfected. Where microtomy (the cutting of tissue sections) and microscopy (the examination of tissue sections with a microscope, p 80), were practised, the benches were designed for sitting. Those at which dissection or staining were conducted, were constructed for standing. A common plan combined island benches with others placed along walls. Technicians, among whom tuberculosis was an occupational hazard, sat on wooden stools and faced each other through a tall central array of shelves that bore slide trays, glass bottles, chemicals, stains and reagents.

The collected Wade papers include the records of 15 fatal cases of prostatic disease from the RIE compiled during 1909–1912.[E] The reports are typed on foolscap paper, some with purple carbon copies. The style adopted during the period 1903 to 1914 is indicated by two records found within the Wade archives. It is often brief, the standard of typing low. Dr Theodor Shennan's reports are particularly short and unrewarding. Four brief summaries at the end of the file are written long-hand. They may be the first drafts of cases analyzed by Wade himself (Appendix 5.1).[F]

Learning the microscopy of disease

By 1906, it had become increasingly difficult for a surgeon to form an accurate diagnosis without knowledge of the microscopic structure of a diseased part.[11] Biopsy was now becoming an integral part of responsible surgical practice. The new approach to surgical diagnosis can be illustrated by three examples.

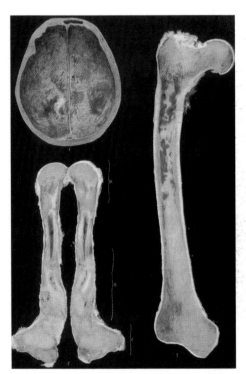

Figure 5.4 Pathological anatomy. *In this case of osteitis fibrosa cystica, the skull, femur and humerus are displayed*

In the first, a case of tibial osteomyelitis (bone infection), the disease resulted from an unhealed compound fracture, a fracture in which fragments of the broken bone had penetrated the skin surface. Pus was draining from a sinus (a small opening) at the site of the infection. The margins of the sinus seemed to be formed of granulation tissue, red, swollen, tender but innocuous. Nevertheless, a small piece of tissue taken from this site, examined microscopically, revealed not only infection but a cancer: a squamous cell carcinoma of the skin epithelium. Under these circumstances, amputation was unavoidable.

In the second case, the patient had noticed that a small wart on the skin of the leg had become irritated and the surrounding skin inflamed. The behaviour was characteristic of malignant melanoma. When the tissue had been examined microscopically, however, the lesion turned out to be benign, the condition of seborrhoeic keratosis. The patient could be reassured that her life was not threatened.

In the third example, an industrial worker complained of abdominal pain related to meals. He was an inveterate cigarette smoker and preferred an irregular and poor diet. It seemed certain that he had a peptic ulcer. The new operation of partial gastrectomy was performed. To the consternation of both surgeon and patient, microscopic examination of tissue taken from the edge of the ulcer showed the presence of a gastric cancer, a malignant tumour of epithelial tissue or carcinoma. It was doubtful whether the patient would survive more than a year.

Figure 5.5 Pathology building of the Royal Infirmary of Edinburgh. *Built as part of the 1879 Royal Infirmary of Edinburgh, the laboratories were extended and reconstructed in 1934*

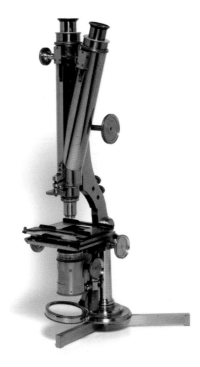

Figure 5.6 Microscopy.
Binocular Beck compound microscope of superior quality used in tissue diagnosis in the RCSEd during the first quarter of the twentieth century. It is salutary to recall that, by 1905, Carl Zeiss manufactured microscope objective lenses with a Numerical Aperture as high as 1.5

Some older surgeons were unwilling to accept the value of this approach, remaining confident that the inspection of a diseased organ or tissue was sufficient to determine its identity if not its prognosis. A large soft tumour was a 'sarcoma', an ulcerating colonic mass a 'cancer' and a black skin lesion a 'melanoma'. By the time Wade entered the field of surgery, these simplistic attitudes were beginning to disappear.

Porters collected surgical specimens daily from each operating theatre. The number of specimens received by the laboratory was in proportion to the number of surgical operations performed (p 195). Pieces of tissue were cut from the specimens by hand. A technician wrote a dictated report. Nearby, at the other end of the same bench, it was not uncommon for staff to drink their tea and eat their sandwiches.[G] There were no staff rooms. The hazards of contagious infection and occupational tuberculosis passed unrecognized.

Most of the specimens arrived in fluid, within glass containers. It was essential to protect specimens against putrefaction. For this purpose, ethanol had long been tested.[H] However, formalin, a solution of formaldehyde in water, was employed increasingly. The fluid, a 'fixative', hardened the sample, facilitating cutting. The use of formalin with added mercuric chloride ('corrosive formol') or potassium bichromate ('Helly's solution') came later: all, it transpired, were hazardous. For display, colours were preserved by Kayserling's solution. Each specimen was accompanied by a form, generally written by a House Surgeon. The form specified the suspected diagnosis and gave the patient's details. Among the common specimens received in this way were appendices, gallbladders, kidneys and parts of the colon, stomach, thyroid gland and female breast.

To prepare samples for the microscope, a series of procedures was essential. They were those that Wade learned to use when he first turned to cancer research (Chapter 4).

Specimens were made ready by taking small samples, or 'blocks'. The search of individual cells or groups of cells from a suspect lesion (the technique of diagnostic cytology) came many years later. Blocks were immersed in increasing concentrations of ethanol to remove water, 'cleared' in chloroform to replace the alcohol and immersed in molten paraffin wax. The wax later solidified and supported the tissue during the cutting of thin sections (see below). Blocks were then impregnated with molten wax in the process of 'embedding'. Early attempts had been made to automate these time-consuming procedures. An automatic, mechanical tissue processor was first described in 1909.[12] The purpose of this complex sequence was to allow the detailed examination of parts of a specimen by microscopy.[13,I]

As visible light could pass only short distances through solid materials, very thin slices of the embedded block had to be cut. For this purpose, heavy metal instruments, microtomes, had been devised in the middle years of the nineteenth century. The microtomes incorporated sharp metal blades held vertically or horizontally. Particularly massive microtomes were used for cutting bone. Microtomy was labour intensive and demanded great skill. Very large tissue sections could be useful (Appendix 5.2).[14–17] The methods developed for this purpose had been used in Edinburgh as early as 1880.[J]

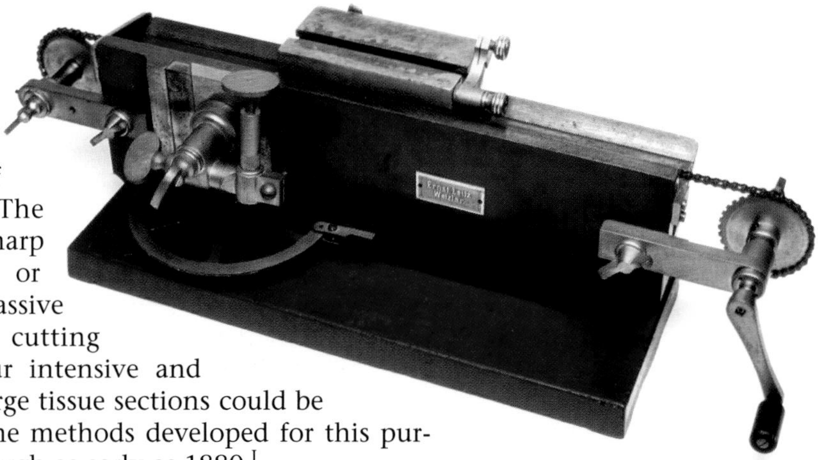

William Rutherford (p 14) was among those who developed the new methods and described them. When an immediate diagnosis was required during an operation, sections of modest quality could be cut from frozen tissue,[12] using a so-called freezing microtome and avoiding the need for fixation and processing. Freezing was by ethyl chloride vapour or carbon dioxide gas jet. Rutherford (1873) and Cathcart (1883) (p 91) both designed excellent instruments of this kind.[12]

Figure 5.7 Leitz sledge microtome. *This heavy duty sledge microtome was manufactured in 1912. The massive steel body ensured rigidity and strength during the cutting of bone sections*

Large or small, the sections could not be seen properly when light was transmitted through them. For microscopic study and diagnosis, it was necessary to give them contrast by introducing colour. A time-honoured procedure was to immerse the section in the natural blue dye haematoxylin to colour cell nuclei, followed by exposure to the synthetic red dye eosin to colour cytoplasm.[K] Fuchsin in picric acid, resorcin, crystal violet with neutral red, and Congo red enabled the demonstration of collagen, elastic, bacteria and amyloid, respectively. After a section had been stained, it was dried, covered with a mountant such as Canada balsam and protected with a very thin glass cover slip.

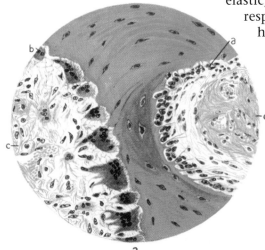

Figure 5.8 Section of bone from a case of osteitis fibrosa cystica. *Before sections of bone were cut, the calcium was removed chemically. The sections were then stained with two commonly used dyes: haematoxylin (to demonstrate cell nuclei) and eosin (to show the remaining structures)*

To record the changes of disease, seen with the naked eye or viewed by microscopy, freehand drawing was customary. However, few surgeons possessed the time or the skills to prepare their own artwork. Henry Wade had the advantage of the skilled assistance of Mr Richard Muir who illustrated Wade's MD thesis and his subsequent paper in the *Journal of Pathology and Bacteriology* (p 70).[18,19] However, the use of photography[L] was increasingly frequent and most of Wade's scientific papers are illustrated with photomicrographs, at least in part. Until the introduction of 35-mm film and compact cameras, these records were made by means of an optical bench, a very heavy and rigid structure that bore a plate camera and a microscope. The arrangement of the microscope might be horizontal or at an angle. The image created by the microscope was projected onto a glass photographic plate. Much later, small cameras were fitted to the vertical microscope tube.

Effective laboratory practice rested on the rapid passage to the surgeon of precise and reliable reports. It is likely that the forms adopted for this convention led Wade to introduce his Scroll Book to the Museum of the RCSEd after he became Conservator in 1903 (p 91). Reports were written by hand and signed, a hallmark of their authenticity. Typewriters were coming into use: they might cost as much as £20, a figure comparable with the annual wage for a manual worker. However, surgeons would not readily accept a biopsy report that was not holographic and, indeed, preferred reports written in the hand of a professional, laboratory colleague whom they knew and trusted. Tape recorders did not become available until shortly before the First World War: Wade used one in 1913. The written reports were dispatched by hand, post or, in rare and particularly urgent cases, by telephone. Copies of all reports were kept in perpetuity as bound collections. No central hospital filing system yet existed. Each laboratory and each surgical unit in the hospital preserved their own copies of patients' records.

Understanding bacteriology

Wade was becoming familiar with the advances taking place in the new science of bacteriology. Monti summarized contemporary views.[20] He wrote of 'the doctrine of pathogenic microbes' and 'the doctrine of cellular proliferation and therapy', detailing 'nephrites', 'cystites' and 'arthrites' [*sic*]. Not surprisingly, malaria, typhoid fever, bubonic plague and cholera were recorded. For the surgeon, the new concepts of 'perityphlitis' (appendicitis) and 'peritonites' were compelling. The discovery of *Spirochaeta pallida* (*Treponema pallidum*) in 1905, the Wasserman reaction in 1906 and the introduction of salvarsan in 1909 revolutionized the surgeon's approach to the common problems of syphilis.[21]

Like his contemporaries, Wade learned the principles of bacteriology from the books that brought understanding of the new subject to Britain from European sources.[22–26] The pace of discovery was dramatic. As Mortimer explains,[22] *Mycobacterium tuberculosis* (the cause of tuberculosis, the 'white plague') had been discovered in 1882, *Vibrio cholerae* (the agent of the dreaded epidemic disease cholera) in 1883,

Salmonella typhi (the source of enteric fever, a frequent cause of death in Victorian times) in 1880 and *Corynebacterium diphtheriae* (the source of the common childhood disease diphtheria) in 1884. One explanation for feared outbreaks of meningitis in schools and barracks had been recognized when *Neisseria meningitidis* was identified in 1887 and the possibility of protection against lockjaw and tetanic paralysis came after *Clostridium tetani* was isolated in 1889.

Anxious to introduce his surgical audience to this new knowledge, Wade initiated a display of 100 bacterial cultures in the Museum of the Royal College of Surgeons of Edinburgh in 1909.

The Laboratory of the Royal College of Physicians of Edinburgh

Wade's career was greatly influenced by far-reaching changes taking place in surgical and medical science. The Edinburgh Royal Colleges were drawn into this revolution. They realized that they must follow the University's example and exploit laboratory medicine. The Royal College of Physicians of Edinburgh, the RCPEd, therefore took the momentous decision to create a research laboratory of its own. On 15th February 1887, they agreed a charter to establish such a laboratory 'for the prosecution of original research'.[14] A house at 7 Lauriston Lane, Edinburgh, was selected. In June 1896, not long

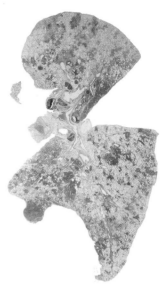

Figure 5.9 Large section of whole lung in a case of miliary tuberculosis. *Later it was found that the sections could be adhered to sheets of paper and inserted into case notes for reference*

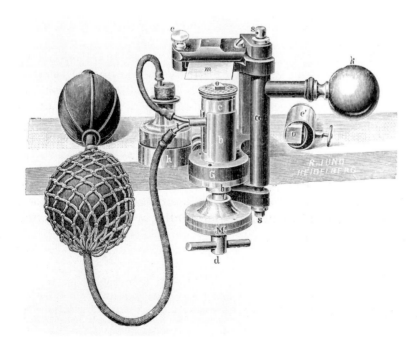

Figure 5.10 Jung (Heidelberg) Student freezing microtome used to cut sections of fresh tissue. *In the later years of the nineteenth century and the early years of the twentieth, surgeons came to use this machine to facilitate rapid tissue diagnosis in the course of an operation. The procedure helped the optimum choice of operation: for example in the case of a breast cancer (Figure 1, page 19 from Aschoff and Gaylord[42])*

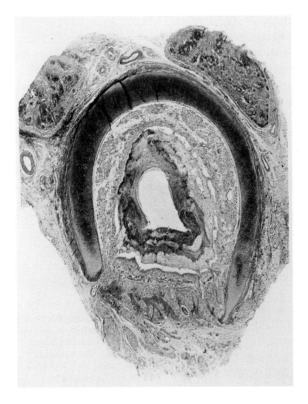

Figure 5.11 Section of larynx in a case of pseudomembranous tracheitis. *The reaction is closely similar to the response that might follow the difficult technique of laryngeal intubation often adopted by Wade in cases of oropharyngeal and oesophageal surgery. (Plate 34 from Aschoff and Gaylord[42])*

before Lauriston Lane disappeared in a spate of new hospital building, the laboratory moved to larger rooms in Forrest Road. Then, in 1901, the philanthropist, Andrew Carnegie, gave £2 million to the Scottish Universities. The RCPEd was successful in obtaining part of this money.

The benefits of this imaginative gesture persisted for the first half of the twentieth century, and the laboratory exerted a great influence on surgical diagnosis and research. Rooms were devoted to chemistry, histology, bacteriology and experimental physiology. The laboratory was a focus for original investigation; it was not a teaching centre. Those who used the facilities were principally part-time workers in clinical disciplines. They were supported by a small full-time staff. The value of the laboratory was appreciated quickly. By 1889, 11 Fellows of the RCPEd, two Members and 18 other practitioners were busily at work. Contrary to the original purpose, the early studies published from the RCPEd laboratory centred on the description of rare or unusual cases rather than on planned research.[14] By 1894, more than 1,000 reports were being made annually. By 1925, the number of items submitted for diagnosis each year had reached 10,995. The first superintendent of the RCPEd laboratory was Dr G Sims Woodhead.[M] He was followed by Dr James Ritchie.[N] Outstanding among the staff of the RCPEd Laboratory, particularly in the provision of a diagnostic surgical service, were James and Edith Dawson.[O,P]

The RCPEd laboratory became a focus for much of the most far-sighted and influential medical and surgical investigation in southeast Scotland.

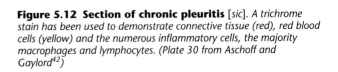

Figure 5.12 Section of chronic pleuritis [*sic*]. *A trichrome stain has been used to demonstrate connective tissue (red), red blood cells (yellow) and the numerous inflammatory cells, the majority macrophages and lymphocytes. (Plate 30 from Aschoff and Gaylord[42])*

Among the many surgeons who took advantage of the RCP Laboratory was Alexis Thomson, a man of wide interests.[Q] At a time when the construction of the City Hospital for Infectious Diseases was about to begin (1902), it was not surprising that the Town Council should exploit the laboratory for help with the diagnosis of the many prevalent communicable diseases. Tests for the recognition of diphtheria and typhoid fever were undertaken. During the South African war (p 32), there was a proposal that an anti-typhoid vaccine should be made. When a request for the study of plague arose (1900), the room recently vacated by the Scottish Asylums Pathologist (p 88) was equipped for this purpose.

The Research Laboratory of the Royal College of Surgeons of Edinburgh

The history of the RCPEd Laboratory now merged with the rival ambitions of the RCSEd and provides an explanatory background to Wade's studies of cancer described in Chapter 4.

In 1897, the RCSEd decided to establish a Research Laboratory of its own. The move was instigated by the President, Sir John Struthers. At the end of the nineteenth century, the role of bacteria in disease was attracting intense interest. New species were being discovered almost daily. Equally, the part played by microscopy in surgical diagnosis was being recognized more and more widely. It was of no surprise therefore that the functions of the Surgeons' Research Laboratory, like those of the Physicians',[27] came to be centred on the examination of surgical specimens, pathological histology, bacteriology and microphotography [*sic*].

The Council of the RCSEd chose rooms on the second floor of the flat at number 7, Hill Square, Edinburgh, to be their Research Laboratory.[28] The rooms were fitted with gas stoves, avoiding coal dust, and with electric light and hot and cold water. A sum of £300 was allocated for scientific apparatus. On the advice of the Museum Committee, a 'spirit' store was constructed at a cost of £28.[29] Quarterly instalments of £10 were paid to George Reid, the Conservator's Assistant, for the care of the new laboratory. His position was of great importance, and, in 1898, as Chapter 6 explains, he was granted the house on the first floor of the building, adjoining the Museum, free of rent and with coal and gas in addition to his salary of £80 per annum.

All was not well, however. In spite of support by Fellows who sent specimens for

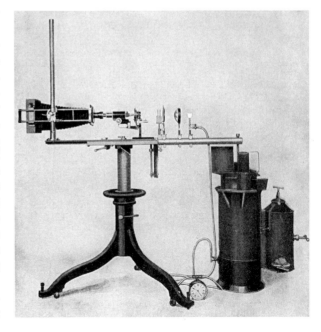

Figure 5.13 Optical, photographic bench. In the early years of the twentieth century, *heavy optical benches were used to support a plate camera and microscope. Illumination was provided by an acetylene gas flame, an 'auerbrenner' (coal gas mantle), kalklicht (limelight) or electricity. The wavelength of the light selected to match the colour of a dye chosen to stain particular features of a microscopic section was selected by the use of matching filters. (Figure 26, p315 from Aschoff and Gaylord[42])*

REPORT BY THE PATHOLOGIST

Received 24 – 4 – 1922

Vol. XXV No. 570

Physician or Surgeon MrWade.

Ward 10

Patient's Name Mrs Agnes Purves. Age 24

Nature of Specimen Synovial Membrane.

Source. Knee Joint.

Report issued 3 – 5 – 1922

This tissue shows well marked connective tissue proliferation with formation of large epithelioid groups & very definite caseation.

Tb. Synovitis.

Pathologist.

microscopic diagnosis and others who promoted bacteriological work, the laboratory did not prosper. On 15th December 1898, Mr David Wallace proposed, and the Convener of the newly constituted Research Laboratory Committee agreed, that an independent body should report on the whole of the institution (the Research Laboratory) and its continuation.[30] The new Committee comprised John Duncan, Charles Cathcart (p 91), A McKenzie Johnston, Harold J Stiles, A Logan Turner and David Wallace. They reported on 20th July 1899 that the College had three options: to retain the laboratory in its present form with the minimum of expenditure; to increase expense and make the laboratory more useful; or to do away with it and negotiate with the RCPEd for a 'conjoined institution'.[31]

Figure 5.15 Typewriter from 1905. *The use of typewriters to prepare laboratory reports was rare in the early years of the twentieth century. In 1905, a typewriter cost £20, equivalent to one quarter of an average year's salary for a technician or museum attendant*

With respect to the first option, the laboratory was claimed to be capable of very limited work. The advantage of better equipment was obvious from the experience of the RCPEd laboratory, from the number of surgical Fellows preferring to work there and from the number of specimens reported to them from Forrest Road. With regard to the second option, Mr Cathcart and Dr Hunter agreed that an additional £300 per annum would benefit the laboratory, promoting better work, allowing technical assistance and enabling original research. The third choice drew most support, however: the Committee's opinion was that it would be better to amalgamate with the RCPEd, the cost of whose laboratory was £1,200 per annum. In reaching this decision, the committee members were aware that the financial state of the RCSEd was precarious. Their choice had a further advantage. Access to the north portion of the RCSEd laboratory would give the Museum Conservator and his assistants the increased accommodation they greatly needed. The south room could accommodate the Asylums' Laboratory (see below), which was to leave the RCPEd.

Figure 5.14 Page from a Museum Report book. *The pages of these handwritten 'scroll books' served a double purpose in the Museum of the RCSEd. They were used to send reports to surgeons of the microscopic structure of a tissue sample and to record the sample for the Museum archives. Until the 1960s, older pathologists might be suspicious of the authenticity of reports prepared by typewriter and insisted that the description be holographic*

The Laboratory of the Asylums Board

To explain the situation that had arisen with regard to a laboratory for the Asylums, it is necessary to recall another development taking place in Edinburgh at this time.

Many recent advances had been made in the care provided for the mentally incapacitated. The plans included the construction of a new hospital at Bangour, West Lothian (Chapter 14). In 1896, the Committee of Superintendents of the Scottish Asylums therefore proposed a new laboratory service. They believed it would be an advantage if the laboratory could be associated with that of the RCPEd. The Superintendents approached the RCPEd Laboratory Committee, which was supportive of the idea. However, the Committee was apprehensive that the duties of an Asylums' Pathologist might extend more widely than was the Physicians' policy and could include reporting on morbid (pathological) specimens from the various asylums; the instruction of staff of the asylums on microscopic techniques applicable to the nervous system; and the promotion of original studies on neurological topics. These proposals were not all in accordance with the Physicians' aims: it was not the Physicians' intention to train technicians. Moreover, the work planned by the Asylums Board demanded the reporting of pathological material rather than original research, while space in the Forrest Road building was at a premium and only an unoccupied 'hall' was available.

Nevertheless, an Asylums Laboratory within the RCPEd laboratory was approved in January 1897. The Asylums Board agreed to create a supervisory Committee that would bear the cost of all expendable apparatus and supplies. No more than £200 was to be spent fitting out the 'hall', and the use of any other part of the College's laboratory was in competition with other prospective users. The first Pathologist to the Asylums Board was William Ford Robertson (p 61). Ford Robertson had left his post as Pathologist to the Royal Edinburgh Asylum to become the Director of the first Scottish Asylums Laboratory. As Chapter 4 explains, Wade came to work closely with him. The arrangement between the RCPEd and the Asylums Board endured until June 1900, the year in which the Physicians decided that economies were necessary.

It was at this time that Ford Robertson moved to the Laboratory of the RCSEd. With the south room now vacant, the RCSEd realized they could benefit by offering accommodation to the Asylums Laboratory. A recommendation was passed to Council for negotiations with the RCPEd on 18th October 1897. The Surgeons were under severe financial pressure. The allowances for the rent of their Library, Museum and Museum laboratory were being cut by £50 each, a sum equivalent to at least £5,000 today. Under these harsh conditions, it was clear that the £440 available to allow negotiations for a proportional sharing of laboratory costs with the RCPEd was inadequate. The Surgeons therefore decided that £200 should be offered to the RCPEd provided

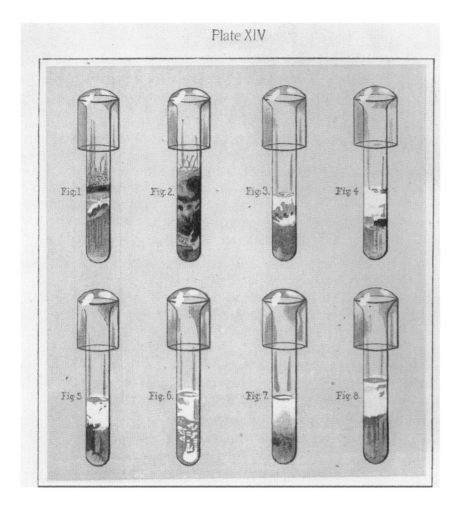

Plate XIV

Fig. 1. Fig. 2. Fig. 3. Fig 4

Fig 5 Fig. 6. Fig. 7 Fig. 8.

Figure 5.16 Illustration from the work of Joseph Lister. *Lister was the first to obtain a pure culture of a bacterium. In this drawing, he demonstrated 'glasses' of unboiled milk. They show the alterations in appearance produced by various organisms other than* Bacterium lactis. *(From: Lister J. Trans Path Soc Lond 1877–8; **29**:425–67)*

they agreed to pay £200 per annum as rent for an Asylums Laboratory within the RCSEd.[32] Immediately after a meeting on 14th November 1899, Ford Robertson, Dr Clouston's representative, expressed his satisfaction with the Surgeons' south laboratory room.[33] In a shrewd financial move, the room was then leased to the Asylums Board for a rent of £35 per annum for five years.[34] The final step in this saga took place when the Laboratory Committee of the RCSEd was disbanded on 8th July 1902,[35] although the south room of the College's laboratory continued to be rented by the Asylums Board until May 1904.[36]

Within a few months of his appointment as Conservator of the RCSEd Museum, Wade met Ford Robertson and joined his research programme. Their collaboration is described in Chapter 4. It endured until 1907.

CHAPTER 6

Museum Conservator

1903–20

Where there is much desire to learn, there of necessity will
be much arguing, much writing, many opinions.

(John Milton, *Areopagitica*, 1644)

To have perceived an overall organisation, relating all the
elements, had a quality of the miraculous. The next day I
could hardly wait for the museum to open.

(Oliver Sacks, writing of the British Museum in *Uncle Tungsten. Memories of
a chemical boyhood*, 2001)

Within three days of his 27th birthday, Henry Wade's life changed again. Gratified by his success in the examinations for the Fellowship of the Royal College of Surgeons of Edinburgh, the RCSEd, he was elected Conservator of the world famous College Museum.

The Conservatorship of the RCSEd, fell vacant on 15th October 1902 when Theodor Shennan (p 246) was appointed as Pathologist to the Royal Infirmary of Edinburgh, the RIE. Shennan continued as 'Interim Conservator' but it was essential to find a successor. The challenge was assumed by a young David Waterston (p 344), However, he left on 21st October 1903 to return to the University of Edinburgh Department of Anatomy.[A]

Age had never been an important criterion in the choice of a Conservator: Robert Knox had been 32, John Goodsir 26 and Charles Walker Cathcart[B] 34 years old when they were appointed (p 345). It was not surprising therefore that those selected as candidates to succeed Waterston should have been four young College Fellows.[C] Wade was the successful applicant. His election took place at the College meeting of 15th December 1903.[D] He was supported by a majority of eight votes, enjoying the influential backing of Joseph Bell, Charles Walker Cathcart, Francis Caird and Theodor Shennan. Two days previously, Wade had been elected to the Edinburgh Medico-Chirurgical Society. He was already a member of the elite Galenian Society. Wade assumed his new position on 15th December

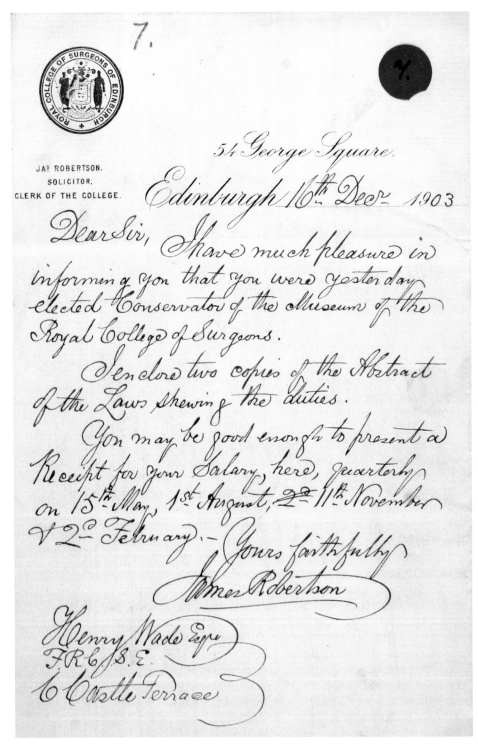

Figure 6.1 Henry Wade's appointment as Museum Conservator. *Letter written in 1903 appointing Henry Wade to the position of Conservator of the Museum of the Royal College of Surgeons of Edinburgh*

1903, acutely aware of the extensive contributions made by his predecessor, Cathcart who was by now a Surgeon-in-Ordinary to the RIE. Cathcart remained an influential figure in the affairs of the Museum and a member of the College Museum Committee until the time of his death in 1933.

The position of Conservator was one of responsibility and prominence. Wade rose to the challenge. For 25 years, he was intimately associated with the Museum; for nearly 12 of those years, he was responsible not only for the collections, their cataloguing and use but for many of the teaching programmes central to the life of the College. There was another reason for Wade's pleasure. In succession to Joseph Bell, the President of the College in October 1903 was Patrick Heron Watson (p 340). He had been chosen for a second term of office in preparation for the commemoration in 1905 of the 400th Anniversary of the Incorporation of Barber Surgeons. The Museum would play a prominent part in these celebrations,[E] and the choice of a new Conservator was crucial to their success.

Nature of the museum

At the time of Wade's election, the College was at the height of its fame as an internationally recognized centre of surgical education and training, one of only four such institutions in Great Britain and Ireland.[1,2] The College Museum was a central instrument of undergraduate and postgraduate education (Chapter 13), hospital diagnosis and research.[3,4] It had grown and matured as eighteenth century anatomists amassed organs and tissues to teach the structure of the human body. In the nineteenth century, the biological and clinical sciences prospered as the impact of the microscope took hold. The concept of the cell as the fundamental unit of health and disease dominated biological thinking[5-7] while bacteriology began to dictate clinical laboratory diagnosis and research (Chapter 5).[8] The significance of the Museum advanced as surgeons took advantage of the subsequent revolutionary discoveries.

For more than 200 years, anatomical parts necessary for teaching had been collected in Edinburgh. The systematic, prolonged preservation of such specimens was realistic, however, only when it became possible to prevent putrefaction by chemical means. The incidental consequence of adopting this new approach was the accumulation of a steadily growing collection of preserved anatomical and pathological specimens. Wax casts, surgical instruments, artwork, photographs, books and papers were added, often by donation. A first demand placed on the young Conservator was to modernize, conserve and enlarge the number and scope of this treasure trove, so that surgical teaching and examination might prosper. A second requirement was the need to maintain and update a precise catalogue of the Museum contents. A third and further purpose was to display the contents of the Museum to students attending the courses of instruction of the

Extramural School of Medicine of the Edinburgh Royal Colleges, the SMRC, and to those of the University who might wish to take advantage of the unique material. There was also the incidental need to open the doors of the Museum to historians and to members of the public interested in anatomical structure, surgical disease and advances in surgical science.

Behind the practical needs of teaching surgery and display, the College realised it should provide laboratory facilities for those of its Fellows who wished to pursue original scientific research. The steps taken to create such a Laboratory are described in Chapter 5. Surgery had advanced generally on the basis of original investigation, the design of new instruments and apparatus, trials of new operative techniques and the publications that stemmed from such work. Through the skills of outstanding scientists such as Goodsir (1842) and Pettigrew (1873),[9,10] the College enhanced its reputation in the nineteenth century as a focus for original anatomical, biological and surgical inquiry. The achievements of these pioneers were sustained in the early twentieth century by the work of David Middleton Greig,[F] by pathologists who numbered among them James and Edith Dawson (p 84) and by far-sighted surgeons including Harold Stiles (p 340), Norman Dott (p 214), John Fraser (p 188) and Walter Mercer.[G]

Museum Committee

The work of the Museum was supervised by a College Museum Committee[H] to which Wade, as Conservator, reported quarterly. The minutes of the Committee were placed before the meetings of the College Fellows. In this way, they came to the President's Council. The minutes suggest that the relationship between the Conservators and the Committee was not particularly close. It was the practice of a Conservator to tell the Committee how much had been accomplished in the Museum during the preceding three months. However, the minutes record no formal discussions on the aims and purpose of the Museum and no debates on possible changes in policy or style. The development and use of the Museum depended heavily, therefore, on the individual character and enthusiasm of the Conservator.

The Conveners (Chairmen) of the Museum Committee holding office during Wade's long association with the College were JM Cotterill, CW Cathcart, A Logan Turner and W Quarry Wood.[I] In a subtle manner, membership of the Committee, like that of the College Library Committee, came to be regarded as a necessary preliminary to election to more prestigious College positions.[11] For this reason, many distinguished Fellows served an apprenticeship on the Museum Committee before promotion to the Council. They included JWB Hodsdon (p 270), Francis Caird (p 41), JW Struthers (p 270) and Walter Mercer (p 346). The work of the Museum Committee was not onerous.

Museum buildings

The buildings in which Wade found himself had a long history which has been described fully by others.[1,2] Old Surgeons' Hall was superseded in 1832 by Playfair's new building.[J] In 1825, a magnanimous offer had been received from Dr John Barclay, College Lecturer in Anatomy. He offered to bequeath his great collection of comparative anatomy, the anatomy of creatures other than man, to the College 'provided that the College build a Hall to receive it and that it shall retain my name and the necessary degree of care to preserve it from hastening fast into decay' (p 347). Barclay also stipulated that if his offer was not accepted within two years, it would be annulled. The offer was accepted. Barclay died in 1826. His bequest was one of the main reasons why the Playfair building of 1832 was constructed.

Until the latter part of the nineteenth century, New Surgeons' Hall with its Museum, Library and offices was separated physically from the adjoining College properties of 6 and 7 Hill Square.[K] Later, they were connected by a 'bridge'. The basement of the Playfair building contained a macerating room where skeletal structures were prepared for display by the removal of the soft tissues. Near the macerating room were a fume chamber and a sink. In the northwest corner of the gallery of the Playfair Museum hung a pulley. A rope led downwards through the main floor to the basement. The pulley was used to raise heavy specimens from the macerating room.

During the later years of the nineteenth century, additional properties in Hill Square were acquired and small modifications made to Playfair's architecture. New windows were installed in the 'Old' Museum, the Playfair Hall, in 1894. A spirit store was added in 1897 at a cost of £28,[12] the amount required to make a safe concrete floor and ceiling. The original electrical supplies had been judged to be in an unsafe state, and the Museum was rewired in 1902 with 'every wire in a metal pipe'.[L] The Playfair Hall was then repainted at a cost of £500: it had last been redecorated in 1883. Before the repainting, it was necessary to move 8,000 heavy anatomical specimens. In the light of contemporary financial values, it is revealing to note that the Laboratory Assistant, George Reid, was voted an additional £5 for this entire work. In 1904, a telephone linking the College Officer to the Museum cost £3. In 1906, sanitary defects were discovered in numbers 7–10 Hill Square, faults demanding the expenditure of a further £300.

New Cathcart Museum

One of the most important developments for the College during Wade's time as Conservator was the construction of a further 'New' Museum. The challenge came in 1907, when, as a result of the painful lessons learned from celebrating the 400th anniversary of the Charter of the College in 1905, the Council minuted: [13]

Figure 6.2 Barclay Hall of 1908. *The controversy that surrounded the Barclay collection of comparative anatomy is described on p 97. The Barclay Hall, constructed in 1908 and opened in 1909, took the place of the much larger Museum Hall (the 'Old Hall') in which Barclay's collection was displayed from 1832 until 1908. On the wall of the 1908 Barclay Hall the Figure shows one of the artefacts, an elephant skull that remained there until the Hall was divided in 1992, the first floor replaced and a Dental Museum constructed. The elephant skull is now in the Sir Jules Thorn Hall (Figure 6.3), formerly the 'New' Cathcart Museum*

'No Institute of comparable size is so poorly housed. There are over 100 resident Fellows [Fellows resident in Edinburgh]. There is no Hall, insufficient light, no cloakroom and very inferior lavatories. The Library needs more space. The basement is wasted, unused space. It is therefore proposed to 'get rid of' the Barclay collection and use the first floor Barclay Museum. The Barclay Collection has ceased to be of any value to the Fellows or to anyone visiting the Museum.'

But this was not a simple matter. Legal opinion defined two alternative courses of action: the change could be effected either by removing the Barclay Collection to another part of the College, for example to the Hill Square rooms that had been occupied by the Asylums Board (p 88), or by obtaining a provisional order that would allow the complete disposal of the collection but might cost £250 in legal costs. The first option was chosen. The Fellows stipulated that the space freed in the Barclay Hall should be reserved for the Museum,[13] a view opposed by the President's Council.

After careful consideration, a final decision to build was taken by the Council on 10th March 1908.[13] CM Cathcart played a large and critical part in the debate. The architect was to be Balfour Paul. The final cost, it was thought, would be in the region of £4,000. The purpose of the building plan was to design and construct a New Museum from the first and second floors of 7 Hill Square, adjacent to the College's laboratory, and a smaller Barclay Museum from rooms at 9 Hill Square, where the two remaining houses on the north side had been acquired. The new Barclay Museum would accommodate the residue of the Barclay Collection. Simultaneously, the original Barclay Museum, now to be the College Hall, would be extended northwards and southwards by 10 feet (3.05 m) in each direction and the balcony removed. In the basement, the Museum store and working space, together with other unused space, would become a Library store. Provision for a Museum store would be made from the basements of other College buildings in Hill Square. An additional staircase would be added to the north aspect of the Playfair building to allow easy access to the refurbished hall.

The building work was completed by the autumn of 1909. It proved convenient to delay the opening of the 'New' Museum until the end of the year. It was designated the Cathcart Museum. With suitable ceremony and at a cost of £200, the buildings were declared open by Lord Rosebery on 14th December. He brought with him the mortar used by his ancestor, Gilbert Primrose [Prymrose], at the time that Primrose had been Deacon (President) of the Incorporation of Barber Surgeons in 1581.[1,2] To mark the occasion, the President (Mr JM Cotterill) donated an ornate 'presidential chair' and each Vice President a 'supporting chair'. Subsequently, Lord Rosebery had a replica made of the Primrose mortar and presented it to the College. The architect's report of 16th December 1910 put the final cost of the

Figure 6.3 New or Cathcart Museum of 1908. *The Museum offices and laboratories of 7 Hill Square, together with the adjoining spaces, were also reconstructed in 1908. The Hall that emerged was dedicated to teaching and display, and was at first designated the Cathcart Museum after the Conservator, Charles Cathcart, who played such a large part in its design. In the 1950s and 1960s, the Cathcart Museum was again redeveloped. It came to contain the fine array of postgraduate teaching displays designed by Professor Eric Mekie and his colleagues. The ground floor of the Hall is now the Jules Thorn Hall of the History of Surgery*

reconstruction at £16,554/16/7d: more than four times the original estimate and almost exactly three times the College's annual revenue.[14] This was not the end of the story, because it was at once realized that the old Museum required repainting. Barely three years later, the woodwork of the New Museum was found to have shrunk and demanded repair, while specimens could not be well seen because of the inadequate lighting.[M]

Further alterations to the Museum buildings took place later in Wade's lifetime. On 20th May 1953, John Bruce, by then Convener of the Museum Committee, reported to the Council that the College had recently acquired a 'dwelling house', (a flat or apartment) at 4 Hill Square. The flat was adjacent to the 'cadaver room' [of the Museum] and on the same level as the New Museum. He recommended that, at a cost of £710, the new space be adapted as an extension to the Museum by an opening up of the 'cadaver room' to form a bay in the New Museum. The space of the new flat could be fitted up for demonstration purposes as a *Perspex* workshop and a photographic department. Two years later, Mr James Hartley reported that a 'dwelling house' was for sale at 12 Hill Square;[N] however, the apartment was 'in a deplorable condition and the College should not buy it'. This was the year when the College considered spending £11,500 on an additional room for the Library, a new Council room and the construction of an office for the recently created College Journal. It was also the moment when Smith, the College Officer, refused to move into the basement at 8 Hill Square.[15]

Museum Laboratories

It is essential to make a distinction between the College Museum Laboratory and the College Research Laboratory (p 85) set up in 1897[16] and closed in 1899 when its work was amalgamated with that of the Laboratory of the RCPEd (Chapter 5).

The Museum laboratory provided the essential technical support for the collections and for teaching. From the 1890's onwards, with the increased use of microscopy in diagnosis, it was planned that a function of the laboratory would be the provision of histological reports (p 85) on surgical biopsy specimens from the RIE and associated hospitals. In effect, this was to be a service for Fellows, assisting them in their daily surgical practice. CW Cathcart promoted this service strongly and, on 17th October 1900, he reported that, in addition to the microscopy of those items entered into the new catalogue, 238 specimens had been examined and described on behalf of practising Fellows. Subsequently, the College was helped greatly by Dr James Dawson (p 84) who was Assistant Pathologist to the RIE from 1916 to 1919 but on sick leave in 1920. Later Conservators who had not been trained in pathological histology were obliged to call for outside help with microscopic diagnosis.

Figure 6.4 One of 15 oil paintings by Charles Bell.
The paintings were made from sketches prepared by Bell after he had cared for the wounded brought to the south of England in 1809 after the retreat from Corunna

When the College decided to open the Research Laboratory described in Chapter 5, the hope was that serious scientific investigations of the kind practised by John Barclay, Robert Knox, William McGillivray and John Goodsir might be promoted. Wade pursued this ideal in his studies of the pathogenesis of cancer (Chapter 4), and the erudition of David Middeleton Greig during the 14 years following his appointment in 1921 added to the College's record of scientific achievement. With these exceptions, the position of the Museum as a busy twentieth century teaching 'collection' militated against the conduct of serious research. Occasional publications such as those of Joseph Bell and John Chiene had drawn heavily on the College's records but the possibilities for research offered by one of the world's greatest surgical archives were exploited infrequently. Although the College began to publish its own *Journal* in 1960, the Museum produced no comparable publication. This was not surprising. For the most part, twentieth century Conservators were busy active surgeons. Wade wrote many papers in his surgical speciality (Chapter 12) but the majority had a strong clinical, rather than academic, flavour.

Museum finances

A minute of the College Special Finance Committee of 1908 epitomizes the harsh realities confronted by the College.[17]

> 'The Committee cannot too strongly emphasise the importance of the strictest economy being exercised by those who are responsible for the disbursement of the Corporation [the College] and it trusts that the Fellows will realise the necessity for refraining from putting forward any new schemes involving serious outlay until the undertaking above referred to [the reconstruction of the Barclay Hall and the creation of the New Museum] have been satisfactorily carried through.'

The College cherished its independence but the price paid for freedom from governmental, Town and University interference was financial constraint (Appendix 6.1). The old College buildings were of immense value for the teaching programmes of the School of Medicine (Chapter 13). In addition, they were almost irreplaceable as sites for examinations and for numerous political and social occasions. However, they remained a liability; the cost of cleaning, maintaining, repairing and insuring the Playfair Hall and the associated workrooms and offices increased steadily. To these costs were added those of the New Museum and the smaller 1909 Barclay Hall. The principal burdens were those incurred by the expense of maintaining these old buildings, and the necessary provision of staff salaries and wages.[O]

Conservators

The story of the Conservatorship started in 1804, when the College formed a Committee of five Curators with the responsibility of using the wealth of anatomical and pathological teaching material for the development of a Museum. In 1825, the formal position of Conservator was created, and Robert Knox was appointed.[18–20] The brilliant and capricious Knox was succeeded by William MacGillivray;[21] John, Harry and Archibald Goodsir; Hamlin Lee; Rutherford Sanders; James Bell Pettigrew; Charles Walker Cathcart; Theodor Shennan; and David Waterston.[A]

Most of these scientists were men of unusual talent and distinction. John Goodsir, for example, was a pioneer of Cell Theory.[5–7] MacGillivray moved to the Chair of Anthropology in Aberdeen.[21] Sanders was Professor of Pathology in the University of Edinburgh from 1853 to 1869, while Pettigrew became Chandos Professor of Medicine and Anatomy in the University of St Andrews.[P]

The early Assistants, Keepers and Conservators were College employees. Later, the position was filled by surgeons or pathologists, some of whom were still engaged in the practice of their profession,

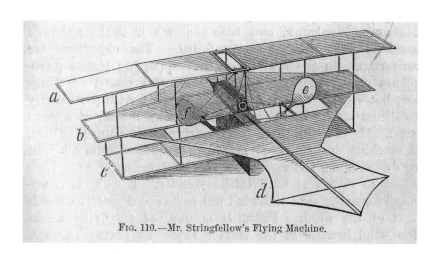

Fɪɢ. 110.—Mr. Stringfellow's Flying Machine.

Figure 6.5 A 'Flying machine from Pettigrew's 1873 book.[10] *Although Tansey and Mekie's history of the Museum of the RCSEd [4] dismisses the years between 1860 and 1885 as a period of neglect, the Conservators during this time were men of academic distinction. Pettigrew, for example, was a scientist, physiologist and aeronaut who became a Fellow of the Royal Society of London before moving to the Chair of Medicine and Anatomy of the University of St Andrews while Sanders was Professor of Pathology in the University of Edinburgh*

Figure 6.6 A Lister carbolic acid spray.
Although Lord Lister's medals and decorations remain in the possession of the University of Edinburgh, the Royal College of Surgeons of Edinburgh possesses three examples of the carbolic acid sprays designed by Lister during the early days of his exploitation of the theory of antisepsis

while others had retired from practice. All gave their services voluntarily, content to be rewarded with a modest honorarium. In 1914, for example, Wade received £50 per annum,[22] a sum that increased to £100 on his re-election in 1919.[23] To attract a candidate of the highest calibre and to ensure that he gave sufficient time to the Museum, however, the Council agreed to offer Greig £300 in 1921.[24] In 1930, his honorarium became £450.[25]

The challenge faced by those surgeons who were honorary Conservators and had not retired, was to find time for the work of the College while caring for patients and fulfilling hospital responsibilities. Charles Cathcart and Wade were in this category: each resigned from the Conservatorship when the demands of their positions as consultant surgeons became overwhelming, as did a young Charles Illingworth in 1946. By contrast, Wade's successors, David Middleton Greig (pp 30, 112), JNJ Hartley (1948)[3] and Eric Mekie had retired from surgical practice when they assumed the role of Conservator and were consequently able to devote their entire time to the Museum. A further distinction could be made on the basis of interest and commitment. During 'periods of relative quiescence',[4] some individuals contributed little because of conflicting interests, inadequate time or lack of incentive.

Wade as Conservator

Within a few weeks of his election, Wade made an early impact by suggesting to the Museum Committee that an exhibition illustrating modern developments in surgery be prepared for the 400th anniversary of the College. Thereafter, his strategy was not only to collect examples of classical surgical diseases but to add specimens that illustrated the 'new' diseases of the time and advances in their understanding. In 1907, for example, he made it known that he wanted more specimens illustrative of modern surgery.[26] Appendicitis was 'in the news', and he actively collected examples of diseased vermiform appendices with the intention of creating a display devoted to this important and recently much publicized topic.[27] He placed strong emphasis on conservation, realizing that the anatomical and pathological specimens required for effective undergraduate and postgraduate teaching could be effective only if the material was in a perfect state. The relationship between the Museum and teaching was very close (Chapter 13). Wade's ultimate intention was to make use of the Museum collections not only for educational purposes but also for research. Tutorial instruction in the Museum was of obvious importance while the admission of the general public remained a well-intentioned but secondary College objective.

Collections

Early in the nineteenth century the number of artefacts in the collection was more than 1,000. Towards the end of 1824, Charles Bell wrote to the College from London, offering virtually the whole of his anatomical collection of 3,000 specimens for £3,000. In the long period from 1836 to 1888, only 1,056 items were obtained.[28] By contrast, between 1888 and 1897, as Listerian asepsis catalysed the growth of operative surgery, 810 further items were added (Table 6.1). Over the years, many other smaller collections were offered to the College. The Mackintosh collection of obstetrical instruments had been purchased in 1837. When the Royal Society of Edinburgh accepted Douglas MacLagan's recommendation to limit their collection to geology and mineralogy, specimens from the Society were donated to the College. The Struthers collection followed. Some individual collections were exotic. In October 1901, Shennan stipulated that: 'Fellows present items [specimens] on condition that after suitable preparation, one half should be returned to the donor'.[29]

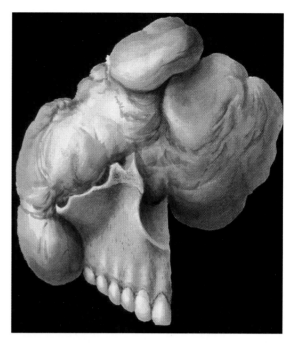

Figure 6.7 Watercolour drawing of a nasopharyngeal tumour. *This is one of 111 such works of art in the collection held by the Museum of the RCSEd of Edinburgh. In almost all instances, the artist is unknown. The relationship of the tumour to the dentition of the upper jaw is close. The drawing serves to emphasize the importance placed by the College on dental anatomy and surgery*

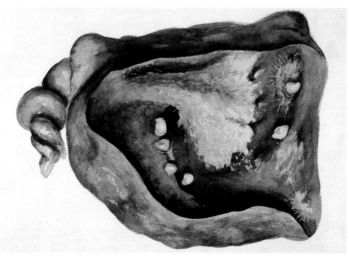

Figure 6.8 An ovarian dermoid cyst, showing the array of teeth characteristic of this form of teratoma. *The illustration is another of the watercolour drawings from the collection of the Museum of the Royal College of Surgeons of Edinburgh*

Table 6.1 Volume of internal work and number of visitors to the Museum of the Royal College of Surgeons of Edinburgh before and during Wade's tenure of office as Conservator 1903–14 and 1919–20

Year	Visitors (total)	Public	Students	Specimens mounted or remounted	New specimens	Specimens reported	Conservator
1898	4,367	2,483	1,884	338	51	Not known	
1899	5,067	3,042	2,025	819	48	"	Cathcart
1900	5,935	3,542	2,453	607	39	"	Waterston
1901	4,961	2,765	2,196	306	74	"	
1902	6,785	2,848	3,947	499	203	"	Shennan
1903	5,098	2,047	3,051	777	59	"	
1904	8,898	4,672	4,226	807	89	132	
1905	10,103	4,872	4,038	577	85	120	
1906	6,642	3,446	2,976	289	135	113	
1907	9,662	4,380	5,282	524	201	250	
1908	9,907	2,287	7,620	486	205	118	
1909*	3,160	0	3,160	370	26	59	Wade
1910	5,850	0	5,850	860	69	91	
1911	6,688	1,043	5,592	621	57	63	
1912	6,833	1,086	5,773	694	40	36	
1913†	2,352	1,468	1,738	474	35	93	
1914‡	2,194	0	2,194	375	26	60	
1915	Not known	0	Not known	101	12	8	
1916	"	0	"	172	16	8	
1917	"	0	"	134	12	2	Jardine
1918	"	0	"	126	9	2	
1919	"	0	"	595	44	3	
1920	"	Not known	"	Not known	Not known	Not known	Wade

*Museum closed to the public for building works.
†Museum closed to the public because of the suffragettes.
‡Museum closed by the war.

The items Wade continued to gather were for the most part harvested at random. Some represented the personal collections of individuals, while others were donated by well-intentioned Fellows or Licentiates concerned that their personal or family possessions should not be lost or discarded. Occasionally, as in the case of Mr Wynstone-Waters, the offer of a personal collection was at first refused because of conditions not acceptable to Council. A letter from Wade to Cathcart early in 1920 reported a meeting with Sir Montague Cotterill (p 270) who 'purposed donating his private collection' to the College. Wade wrote:

'In certain directions, for example in the surgical pathology of cerebral tumours, they will be a valuable supplement. I went over the specimens with him and have arranged for their transport to the Museum.'[30]

Although the Cotterill collection was small, it included seven examples of neurological disease. This was a period before surgical neurology had become established as a recognized speciality and the specimens of acoustic neurinoma, cerebral glioma and spinal myxofibroma were of considerable rarity. Shortly afterwards, Dr FW Collinson of 32 Winckley Street, Preston, wrote to Wade to offer the largest loose body from a knee joint that he had ever seen. It had come from Mrs Marsden, aged 39 and a 'winder'.[31] Wade acknowledged the letter on 1st December 1919:

> 'We have nothing like it.'[32]

As the war of 1914–18 ended, College Fellows donated a number of specimens collected from the battlefield. They included a case of instruments left by the Germans at Mons and one half of an aeroplane propeller. Those anatomical and pathological specimens, casts, drawings, paintings, photographs, instruments and microscopic preparations that were not on display were kept in a store in the basement of 12 Hill Square – an area beneath a pawnbroker's shop.

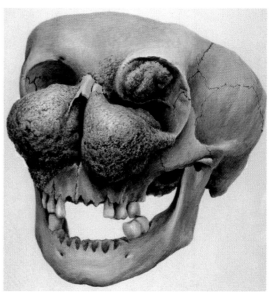

Figure 6.9 Watercolour drawing of a skull. *A full explanation for the bilateral deformities illustrated in this watercolour drawing has not been obtained. The anatomical changes have been described either as those of leprosy or as leontiasis ossea. It is not known whether the defects had a familial or hereditary basis*

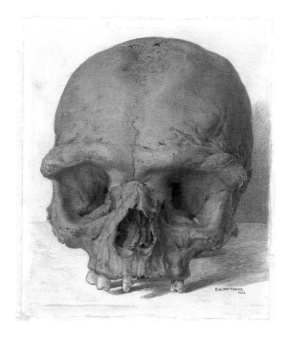

Figure 6.10 Neanderthaloid skull. *The drawing is reproduced from DM Greig's paper.[54] The artist was Robert Wilson Matthews. Greig was the first to describe hypertelorism and published extensively on disorders of the skeleton*

Wade the collector

Although the College had no planned policy for collecting, this did not prevent membership of the Museums Association, which was confirmed on 2nd February 1911.

During his years as Conservator, Wade contributed 336 anatomical and pathological specimens (Appendix 6.2). A substantial number were acquired during the period when he was an Assistant Pathologist to the RIE; of these, 311 remain. Another of Wade's objectives was the formation of an odontological collection. Among this material was a collection of maxillary and mandibular bones in which teeth were shown prominently. During the years between 1903 and 1914, when Wade left Edinburgh for the army, it was still common practice to illustrate scientific papers, books and museum displays with drawings and watercolour paintings. Of these works of art, 111 survive (Appendix 6.3). The identity of the artists is uncertain: only two surnames have been identified, Campbell and Sewell. The watercolour drawings that illustrate Greig's later paper on *A neanderthaloid skull* (p 346) are signed by Robert Wilson Matthews and it is possible that Matthews executed some of the drawings in the collection that came under Wade's care.

Wade's anatomical preparations

In view of Wade's early interest in disorders of the urinary system (Chapter 12), it comes as no surprise to find that 140 of the specimens he added to the Museum were renal in nature (Appendix 6.2). With

Figure 6.11 Duck-billed platypus. *The photograph is of a live animal. The single example retained from Wade's time is preserved in a glass jar. It had been dissected and the image is unrewarding*

the exception of organs from six cases of bilharziasis (schistosomiasis) that he brought back from Egypt in 1919 (p 160) and demonstrated to the Edinburgh meeting of the Pathological Society of Great Britain and Ireland,[33] Wade did not collect many exotic curiosities as he travelled the world (Appendix 6.4). However, he valued an improvised surgical instrument made for him during his service in Egypt and a number of Turkish photographs, kept after the Armistice had been agreed in Damascus in October 1918 (Chapter 8).

Prior to his visit to Australia in 1935 (p 268), Wade was sent three specimens of duck-billed platypus, *Ornithorhynchus anatinus*, and two of spiny anteater, *Echidna*. It is not recorded whether the anteaters were of the short- or long-nosed variety. The specimens came with a letter dated 26th April 1932 from Pitt and Scott, General Shipping, Forwarding and Passenger Agents, informing Wade that 'a written statement signed by a responsible official of the Medical School, University of Edinburgh [was required] before the specimen could be delivered under tape and seal for examination and clearance at the University'. There is no note of the identity of the donor although Wade's brother-in-law, Dr Eric Sinclair, was Superintendent of a mental hospital in New South Wales (p 7) and his brother George had moved from Tasmania to be in the same State.

Much of Wade's histological work centred on the acquisition of microscopic sections of whole organs or of substantial parts of organs (p 81). It seems probable that these slides were made not in the College but in the Laboratory of the RCPEd. After the First World War, this work continued, with the amassing of a very large collection of sections of kidneys and other organs. Of the 101 large sections of diseased kidneys, nearly two thirds were from people with tuberculosis. In addition, there were 14 cases of hydronephrosis, 12 of carcinoma, three of 'nephritis', two each of Wilms' tumour and unexplained haematuria and one each of papilloma, pyelonephritis, interstitial fibrosis and lymphoma.

Figure 6.12 Microscope slide from one of the Royal College of Surgeons of Edinburgh's collections. *The oldest collection dates back to 1848. Another collection, of commercial origin, was donated or purchased in the 1880s, possibly at the instigation of Charles Cathcart. A third collection comprises the many very large slides studied by Wade and by Edith Dawson, whose interests were urinary disease and breast cancer, respectively*

Conservation

Throughout the first half of the twentieth century, continuing an old tradition, an important and even predominant part of the work of the

For their optimum conservation, Wade believed correctly that surgical specimens should be sent to the Museum in a fresh staten. Traditionally, specimens had been mounted and remounted either in alcohol ('spirit') or dry. By 1900, however, it was no longer satisfactory to immerse specimens in this preservative. Instead, the 'Jones method' was adopted. In this procedure, fixation in formalin was followed by immersion in methylated spirit and preservation in glycerine and water. The cost of the technique was relatively high, but colours were preserved well and the results enhanced. Later, a number of items were mounted by 'Waldie's method', a technique mentioned in the preparation of 24 examples of lymphatic gland disease. Other technical advances included the adoption of photography. Repairs to the Museum's microscope were sometimes needed, and the purchase of a new stand from Zeiss aided this work. Early in 1904, as we have seen, Wade proposed an exhibition of developments in surgery as part of the celebrations for the 400th Anniversary of the College (p 93), which was to be marked on 27th and 28th July 1905.[34,E]

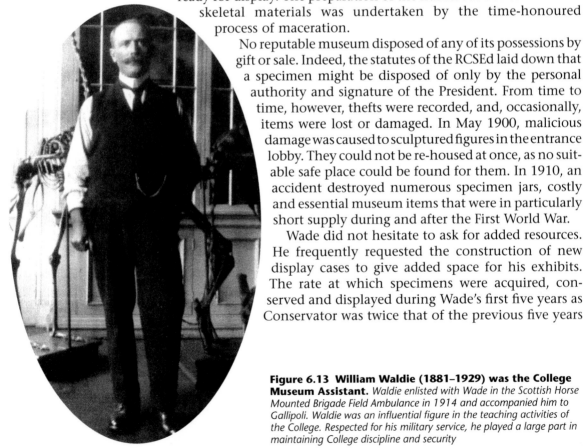

Museum consisted of the remounting of old anatomical and pathological specimens and the preservation and mounting of new material. For the work of conservation, two rooms were used to make items ready for display. The preparation of the numerous bones and other skeletal materials was undertaken by the time-honoured process of maceration.

No reputable museum disposed of any of its possessions by gift or sale. Indeed, the statutes of the RCSEd laid down that a specimen might be disposed of only by the personal authority and signature of the President. From time to time, however, thefts were recorded, and, occasionally, items were lost or damaged. In May 1900, malicious damage was caused to sculptured figures in the entrance lobby. They could not be re-housed at once, as no suitable safe place could be found for them. In 1910, an accident destroyed numerous specimen jars, costly and essential museum items that were in particularly short supply during and after the First World War.

Wade did not hesitate to ask for added resources. He frequently requested the construction of new display cases to give added space for his exhibits. The rate at which specimens were acquired, conserved and displayed during Wade's first five years as Conservator was twice that of the previous five years

Figure 6.13 William Waldie (1881–1929) was the College Museum Assistant. *Waldie enlisted with Wade in the Scottish Horse Mounted Brigade Field Ambulance in 1914 and accompanied him to Gallipoli. Waldie was an influential figure in the teaching activities of the College. Respected for his military service, he played a large part in maintaining College discipline and security*

(Table 6.1). Nevertheless, he strongly supported the painstaking work accomplished by his predecessors and maintained their records with the greatest care. He was closely aware that Cathcart and Shennan had completed a New Catalogue[Q] and punctiliously pursued the systematic cataloguing of additions to the Museum.

Wade placed much stress on diseases of the tropics, about which the Museum Committee wrote to Fellows in 1904.[35] Brought up in the post-Listerian tradition of asepsis,[36] Wade also instinctively emphasised the new science of Bacteriology. Through his collaboration with William Ford Robertson (p 88), Wade was acutely aware of the phenomenally rapid growth of this new biological speciality. It comes as no surprise to learn that he chose to 'put bacteria on the surgical map' by preparing demonstrations of organisms in culture for the main Museum hall.[37]

Museum staff

Much of the work of Wade's loyal staff was of a routine character, although the volume varied greatly. At the time of Wade's election as Conservator, the Museum Assistant was Mr George Reid. A Junior Museum Assistant, William Gill, was responsible for the preparation of histological sections. In May 1910, George Reid, who had served the College for many years, stated that he wished to give up both the College 'house' he occupied at 7 Hill Square and some of his duties.[38] Almost certainly because of the war, he was still in the College's employment in 1915 but was not in good health. He was succeeded as Museum Assistant by William Waldie on 13th May 1913 but Waldie was soon called to the army.

Waldie (1881–1929) had come from the laboratories of the RIE. He left the College on the outbreak of war, in 1914, at exactly the same time as Wade, to join the Scottish Horse Mounted Brigade Field Ambulance.[39] He survived the war and returned in May 1919 to resume his duties at the Museum. A deeply respected and popular College servant, he retired in 1929 through ill health and within a few weeks had died.[40] The College paid his funeral expenses, which amounted to £7, and made sure his widow received a modest pension.

The Museum Committee soon agreed that an additional assistant was required whose duties 'would be mainly in the Museum but [he] will perform any College duties needed'.[R]

Visitors

Strict College by-laws regulated the use of the Museum. The laws were revised in 1910, and a record kept of the number of visitors (Table 6.1). Fellows of the College had the right to enter the Museum without notice and to introduce distinguished colleagues. Among them

Figure 6.14 Numbers of visitors to the College Museum 1898–1919. *The total numbers of visitors is shown in black and the numbers of students in red. The distance between the two lines indicates the numbers of members of the public who visited the museum during each year. A surge in the number of the public is shown during the period of the 400th Anniversary celebrations of 1904–05. A large but temporary increase is seen in the number of students who visited the Museum after the start of the postgraduate teaching programme of the School of Medicine of the Royal Colleges in 1906 (Chapter 10)*

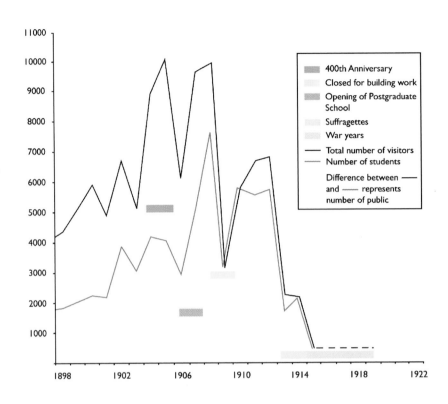

was Dr John D Comrie, who was allowed to take photographs of the College portraits.[41] Beyond this, there were two categories of visitor: students and public. The numbers of members of the public visiting the Museum varied significantly according to the time of year but was always greatest in the late summer and autumn. In 1908, the Museum was closed to the public for two years to allow the completion of the building works described on p 95.

From the summer of 1913, great changes in Museum visiting took place. In May 1913, the threatening activities of the suffragettes led to the public being excluded entirely. This state of affairs continued until hostilities ended in 1919 and the contents of the Museum were restored to their normal places. The number of students dropped significantly in 1913 but from August 1914 onwards the records do not indicate whether the small numbers attending the classes of the School of Medicine (p 246) were allowed to use the Museum in any way. In the years subsequent to 1919, the numbers attending SMRC classes were noted carefully but the minutes contain no record of the numbers of visiting members of the public.

War

It has been claimed that Wade held the position of Conservator from 1903 until 1920[4] but this is not correct. His responsibilities were disrupted by the outbreak of war in 1914 (Chapter 7). On 21st October, he wrote to the Museum Committee:

> 'I apologise for my sudden departure from Edinburgh without notice as the summons to take up duty as a Medical Officer with the Scottish Horse was urgent. I place my resignation in the hands of the Committee.'

The Committee reported to the Council,[39] who responded generously.[42] They had no choice but to accept his resignation. He was at once elected to the Museum Committee. During Wade's absence on military service, Frank Evelyn Jardine,[5] a younger Fellow, acted as Interim Conservator and received the same honorarium as Wade: £50 per annum.[43] Wade remained on the Committee *in absentia* until his release from military duties on 2nd September 1919.

The war of 1914–19 quickly exerted damaging effects on College activities. Many members of the College staff were called to the forces. They included William Waldie. However the Council agreed to keep his position open,[39] and were generous to him when he returned to the College in 1919. Throughout the war, he continued on a salary of 32/6d weekly but received a 5/– weekly war bonus.[44] While he was away, Professor Ritchie's 'man' Hamilton received 14/6d per week to work in the Museum.[43]

Property deteriorated and decreased in value, investments declined and the College income fell. Staff numbers declined, and those who remained were the unfit and the elderly. The quality of the College records decreased. Not only were the minutes shorter and less complete, but the ink with which they were written decreased in quality. The Council considered whether the Museum should be kept open,[39] leaving the decision to Cathcart, Convener of the Museum Committee. At first, the decision was in the affirmative,[45] although the most valuable items in the collections were removed to safety in the basement.

The SMRC continued its teaching programme but no Museum demonstrations were recorded. However, the building remained unheated and, by 1916, it proved impossible for the Committee to inspect the Museum because all lighting had been turned off.[46]

The diagnostic service provided to Fellows was in abeyance. The activities of the Interim Conservator and his beleaguered staff were minimal, and no new displays proved possible. Neither glycerine nor methylated spirit were available, so the conservation of specimens was halted – an experience in striking contrast to that of the embryonic Armed Forces Institute of Pathology in Washington DC during the American Civil War. In the background, political debate smouldered.[47,48]

Impact of peace

Within days of ending his contract with the army, Wade was again taking part in College meetings and was re-elected Conservator.[49] On

15th October 1919, Jardine – the Interim Conservator – joined the Museum Committee. On 23rd February 1920, Wade wrote again to say that he had been trying to obtain three months' study leave to visit the USA (p 186). He suggested that, in his absence, Mr David Wilkie 'could attend to the duties of the office of Conservator'. The Museum Report of May 1920 confirms that David Wilkie did indeed fulfil this responsibility. On his return from America, Wade was once more offered the position of Conservator. However, the demands of surgical consultancy were overwhelming. On 5th February 1920, Wade wrote to Cathcart to say that he could not present the Museum report to the College meeting. The Council recognized the conflicting demands on Wade's time. He resigned once more,[50] and the RCSEd was obliged to seek a successor. On 20th October, the President speculated that 'an increased honorarium might attract candidates who would be in a position to devote more time to the Museum'. Meanwhile, Wade was elected for a brief third term.

Fortune favoured the College, and, on 11th November 1920, it was reported that 'the name of David Middleton Greig had been brought to their notice'.[F] The President, Secretary and Conservator had by then been to Dundee and seen the rich collection of material that Greig had amassed. The President promptly proposed the appointment of Greig as Conservator. He was to receive an honorarium of £300 per annum, together with 'removing' costs of £100. Greig's first report was in January 1921. He asked that the College publish his book and for electric power to be provided in his workroom.[51]

Wade's days as Conservator were at an end. He returned to the Museum Committee and remained a member until 1928, when he was succeeded by Mr K Paterson Brown.

Figure 6.11 is reproduced by courtesy of Diane Logg, Communication Manager, Heasleville Sanctuary, Australia. The Sanctuary is 'the home of the platypus'.

CHAPTER 7

Field ambulance to Gallipoli

1914–15

If you could hear, at every jolt, the blood
Come gargling from the froth-corrupted lungs,
Obscene as cancer, bitter as the cud
Of vile, incurable sores on innocent tongues
My friend, you would not tell with such high zest
To children ardent for some desperate glory,
The old lie: *Dulce et decorum est pro patria mori.*

(Wilfred Owen, *Dulce et decorum est*, 1917)

By 1914, Henry Wade had become an experienced surgeon of considerable seniority. He was Assistant Surgeon to both the Leith Hospital and to the Royal Infirmary of Edinburgh, the RIE, and could have expected soon to reach a pinnacle of surgical success by becoming one of the seven Surgeons-in-Ordinary to the Infirmary, This would have been a position granting responsibility for an entire surgical unit. It was not to be. In a sense, he now paid the price for taking part in the Great South African War in 1900: his name was on the list of army reservists, and, since 2nd February 1904, he had been an officer in the volunteer forces of the Royal Army Medical Corps, the RAMC. In October 1909, he was drawn into the unattached list of the Territorial Army. Then, with little overt warning, a European war broke out.

When Gavrilo Princip, a Serbian grammar-school boy, shot Archduke Franz Ferdinand on 28th June 1914, a fuse was lit that ignited the greatest conflict of all time. Franz Ferdinand was heir to the Hapsburg throne. The succeeding political intricacies, military intrigues and nationalistic ambitions culminated in confusion and misunderstanding. They provided an ideal setting for opportunists to fulfil their purposes. The final pretext for open warfare was, nonetheless, trivial.

On 2nd August 1914, Germany demanded of Belgium the use of her territory for military operations against France.[1-3] The ultimatum to Belgium was to expire within 24 hours. Claiming that her lands had been violated, Germany presented France that day with a declaration of war. Britain had already decided that the expiry of

Chapter Summary

- Mounted Brigade Field Ambulances
- Wade the photographer: military training
- Mobile operating car
- The Dardanelles
- Final offensive
- Field ambulance at Suvla Bay
- End of campaign
- Disaster and evacuation

the ultimatum to Belgium would be a sufficient cause for action. On 4th August, therefore, a British ultimatum was dispatched to Germany demanding the cessation of those operations against Belgium that had already started. No sufficient reply was received, and Britain was at war with Germany from midnight. The military leaders of both nations were dangerously confident.[4,A] Austria declared war on Russia on 5th August and was embroiled with Britain and France seven days later.

Turkey, the centre of the Muslim Caliphate, formed an alliance with Germany against Russia on 2nd August 1914 and became a belligerent ally of Germany and Austro-Hungary on 31st October. War against Russia, and therefore against her allies France and Britain, broke out on 5th November. The Turks campaigned on three land fronts: against Russia in the Caucasus and against Britain and her allies in Egypt and in Mesopotamia (Chapter 8).[5] The Turkish naval enterprise was confined to the Black Sea.[B]

The British medical services responded as best they could.[6,7] The organization of the RAMC was based on the bitter experiences of the South African War (p 21). The Corps centred on casualty clearing stations (CCSs), field ambulances and mounted brigade field ambulances. There were, of course, general hospitals.[8]

Mounted Brigade Field Ambulances

Wade was now 38 years old and a consultant surgeon. He was called to the territorial RAMC on 10th September 1914 and became a Captain in the Scottish Horse Mounted Brigade (SHMB) Field Ambulance.[9]

Box 7.1 Mounted Brigade Field Ambulances of 1915

Highland

Lowland

Welsh Border

South Wales

Yorkshire

Notts and Derby

North Midlands

1st South Midlands

2nd South Midlands

1st South Western

2nd South Western

Eastern

South Eastern

London

Scottish Horse

Figure 7.1 Wade as an officer of the Royal Army Medical Corps. *His uniform is described as that of a Captain in the Scottish Horse Mounted Brigade Field Ambulance. Alternatively, it has been claimed that the uniform is that of a Lieutenant Colonel, a position to which he was promoted after his arrival in Egypt, in 1916 (Chapter 8). However, the uniform is of a style worn in Europe, not in the Dardanelles or in the Mediterranean*

Each of the 15 Mounted Brigades had a Field Ambulance.[10,C] The experiences of the Highland Mounted Brigade Field Ambulance were similar to those of the SHMB Field Ambulance. They were recorded in detail and throw much light on the composition and activities of these units.[11] Although the Mounted Brigades were cavalry, their Field Ambulances were equipped with motor ambulances, lorries, cars and motorcycles.

The SHMB was raised in Dunkeld, and, until recently, a regimental museum bore testimony to its achievements.[D] Fifty-six of Wade's contemporaries, many of them Edinburgh medical students, others colleagues and associates, volunteered with him. Among them was his close friend William Ritchie.[E] In 1920, Wade described the early course of his war in a student magazine.[9] The younger volunteers served in the SHMB Field Ambulance until the early months of 1915 when most joined the combatant services. Wade made a poignant record of their fate in a memoir he entitled *Flowers of the Forest* (Table 7.1). Six of the group were killed in action, two died on service, one was posted missing and one taken prisoner. It is possible to speculate that recollections of his own time in South Africa (Chapter 2) and tales of the American Civil-[12] and Franco-Prussian wars were in his mind as he wrote.

Early in 1915, the SHMBFA was posted to the north of England. They were stationed at Bedlington, a small town seven miles southeast of Morpeth and 16 miles north of the port of Newcastle. It was an

Table 7.1 Flowers of the Forrest (April 1918). The fate of those who volunteered with Wade in 1914

Fate	Volunteer and military status	
Killed in action	Ainslie A (2Lt KOSB)	Harte JF (2Lt R Scots)
	Charlton WF (2nd Lieut DLI)	Ritchie RJW (Capt HLI)
	Dunlop WJ (2nd Lieut RFA)	Whitelaw RHL (Lieut HLI)
Died on Service	Hunter GA (2nd Lieut SH & ICC)	Campbell EJ (2nd Lieut A & SH)
Missing	Charlton DF (Lieut DLI, twice wounded)	
Prisoner of War	Macgowan JC (SH, attached RFC)	
Qualified and serving as Lieutenants RAMC	Anderson AG	Middleton CJ
	Foster M	Morgan EMT
	Haynes HCA	Morris JC
	McIlwaine AL	Smith JHR
Returned to Medicine	Barlow P (SP; ⅔)	McPhail IR (Surg Prob; Final)
	Brodie PM (2nd Lieut SFH; Final)	Mackay GS (Lieut SH & RH; ½)
	Burn HW (Trooper SH; Final)	Mill JD (Lieut SH & RH; ½)
	Candlish EE (Lieut RFA; ½)	Miller DA (Lieut RH, wounded; ¼)
	Carmichael EA (Private RH; Final)	Rogers JS (2nd Lieut NF)
	Cuthbert AH (Sergeant RAMC)	Spence TRC (Lieut RSF, wounded; ½)
	Dick HH, MC; (Capt RSF; ⅔)	Tattersall WR (Lieut DLI, wounded; Triple
	Gammie AE (2nd Lieut GH)	Qualification)
	Lawson WT (Lieut DLI; ⅔)	Thomson HB (Dresser, Pt LH; ⅔)
	McLachlan A L (Corporal RAMC; ½)	Todd, TRR (Lieut SH; ⅔)
	McLeman J (Lieut DLI, eye wound; ⅔)	
Still serving at the end of the War	Brown WH (Lieut ASC)	McIver E (Lieut NF)
	Conder AC (Lieut RH)	McIver DP MC (Lieut A&SH, wounded)
	Davies JR (Lieut NF)	Mallet HH (DC)
	Dick KS (Lieut RSF, wounded)	Morison DJ (SP)
	Eadie JA (2nd Lieut SH)	Rae AMW (Lieut SH & ICC)
	Ebsworth K (TC, wounded)	Rae R (Lieut SH & ICC)
	Gorrie RM (Lieut RFA)	Stewart FM (Lieut A & SH)
	Gray EPT (Capt RH)	Sturrock EWB (Lieut SH, invalided, home service)
	Hogg AW (Lieut RFC, wounded)	Sweeney WJ (2nd Lieut SWB)
	McAinsh DT (Lieut A & SH)	Tait TS (2nd Lieut BW)
	McArthur AM (Lieut TC)	Thomas LG MC (Capt NF, Staff)
		Walker AR (2nd Lieut SH, RFC, ICC)

The abbreviations used are:
A & SH = Argyle and Sutherland Highlanders; ASC = Army Service Corps; BW = Black Watch; DC=Dental Commission; DLI = Durham Light Infantry; GH = Gordon Highlanders; HLI = Highland Light Infantry; ICC = Indian Army; ; KOSB = King's Own Scottish Borderers; LH = London Regiment; NF = Northumberland Fusiliers; RAMC = Royal Army Medical Corps; RFA = Royal Field Artillery; RFC = Royal Flying Corps; ; RH = Royal Horse; RSF = Royal Scots Fusiliers; SFH = Seaforth Highlanders; SH = Scottish Horse; SP = Surgeon Probationer; SWB = South Wales Borderers; TC = Tank Corps

The fractions shown after some names indicate the stage reached by a student in his medical course.

area much used by the military for training: the country was part-wooded, part arable farmland. There were many small rivers and streams and a sufficient road network. Not far away were the artillery ranges of Otterburn and the port of Blyth.

Wade the photographer: military training

Henry Wade carried a camera to all his wartime destinations.[F] His photographs and the short notes that accompany many of them,

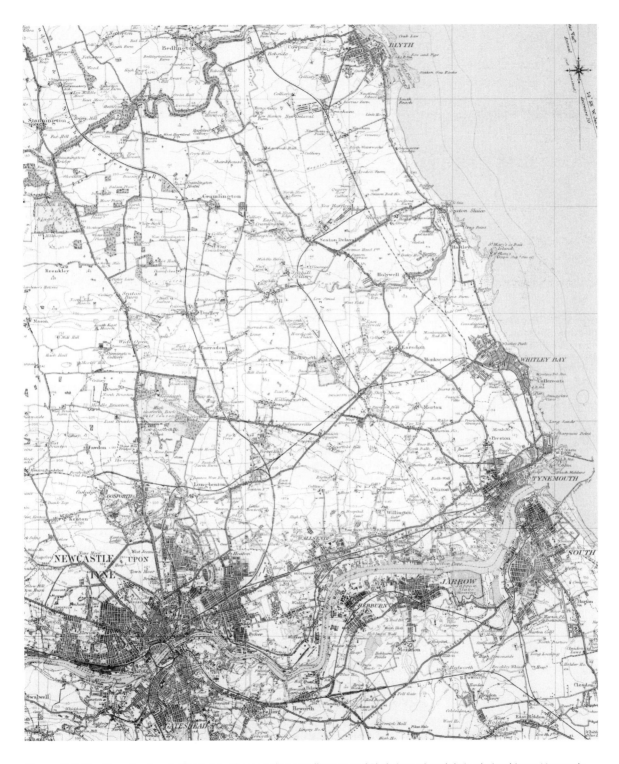

Figure 7.2 Northumberland, 1914–15. *The map shows Bedlington and Blyth (at top) and their relationships to Newcastle and the surrounding countryside. (Copyright, see p 3)*

Figure 7.3 Bedlington, Northumberland, 1914–15. *The Scottish Horse Mounted Brigade Field Ambulance spent the winter of 1914–15 training in Northumberland. Here, troopers practise stretcher drill*

serve as a vivid record of his travels in the years 1914–1919 and document his experiences fully. No doubt due to the exigencies of active, wartime, military service, he was not always able to assemble his negatives and prints until he returned to Scotland when peace was concluded in 1919. The photographs are now contained in 39 numbered and labelled print albums.

During the long periods of inactivity between military operations, Wade used his camera freely. By the spring of 1919, he had accumulated nearly 1,000 photographs (p 410). The first 221 were of the SHMBFA training in Northumberland. It was much more difficult to use a camera on the field of battle and only 19 prints were of the military actions at Suvla Bay, Gallipoli (p 129). The later photographs of Egypt, Palestine and Syria (Chapter 8) display a similar selectivity. From the best of his negatives, Wade made whole-plate sized prints. They are stored in large coloured albums. It is probable that smaller versions of these prints were chosen to construct the beautiful panoramic montages that comprised the exhibition he prepared for the Edinburgh meeting of the British Medical Association of 1927. To illustrate the many lectures and talks Wade gave after the war ended, he selected 383 negatives for preparation as 3¼ × 3¼ inch glass lantern slides. These slides are listed in a 'small brown notebook' (Appendix 7.1) and stored in wooden boxes lettered A to H. The slides are introduced by an explanatory note that reads:

'Series of lantern slides made from photographs taken when a Captain in the Scottish Horse Mounted Brigade Field Ambulance August 1914 to July 1916 and Colonel, Army Medical Service, Consulting Surgeon to the Egyptian Expeditionary Force July 1916 to May 1919.'

In this and the subsequent chapter, the captions of the original photographs are fused to make a descriptive diary in which Wade's own spelling is retained. Wade was brought up in a deeply religious family (p 4). It is not surprising to find, therefore, that in some of his photographs he used a biblical name for a location rather than a contemporary designation.

War has often been described as consisting of long periods of extreme boredom punctuated by brief episodes of violence and terror. As a corollary, the soldier–photographer tends to accumulate great numbers of pictures of troops in training, soldiers on the march, huts being built, latrines dug and stretchers carried but few records of combat. Wade's photographs are no exception. Wade's early 1915 photographs reveal the stark contrast between 'make-believe' practice and the 'real' war soon to be experienced in Gallipoli. From the brief notes that accompany his prints, it is possible to reconstruct the early scenes in Northumberland during field training.

Bedlington

In the later months of 1914, a stern Captain Henry Wade in breeches and cavalry boots stands with his left arm across his body. A Brigade Staff car, marked with a Red Cross, carries Captain WT Ritchie, Lieutenant Paul and Staff Sergeant Cunningham. It is an open tourer with a hood, a folding windscreen and a 'running board'. Major Richardson, Captain Buchanan, Captain Verel, and Privates McLauchlin and Martin appear in full uniform. Privates Waldie (p 109), Upfold and Thomson are officers' grooms. Ten troopers of the Horse Transport stand to attention. The cook house is a canvas extension to a wooden hut. Private Beggs presides over a steaming cauldron. Corporal Thomas splits wood for the fire. Latrines are dug. Privates Imrie, Eadie and Millar join in. A motor convoy is seen. With three conventional, motor ambulances is the Rolls Royce motor car presented by Mrs. McKinnon[G]. There is a day of field training in Blagdon Woods. Practice in bridge building requires a tiny structure of two logs and earth-covered planks. A Dressing Station is put together. Troopers sit beside a camouflaged stretcher. Captains Brown and Buchanan survey a rural scene: a marquee is in the background. The men assemble for the march home.

Figure 7.4 Captain Wade (right) and a fellow officer. *Many officers and men are shown in Wade's numerous photographs but not all are identified individually*

A field day

Lorries and ambulances gather for a field day. The Wade Operating Car is seen, the rear doors open, an awning slung from the roof and supported on slender poles. Corporal Clarke is nearby. Captain Lascelles talks to small boys in Bedlington. Six hungry troopers collect their dinner rations from Corporal Stewart while Corporal McGregor issues potatoes from a cauldron. A pay parade takes place. The Paymaster sits with three others at a table. Eight men line up in anticipation. In early morning 'physical jerks', 22 men stand near a marquee directed by a fully uniformed officer. Captain Verel poses while Corporal Thomson takes a photograph, the camera mounted on a tripod. The horses reappear with Corporal Waldie on Wade's horse, Bugler Barlow on another. The

Figure 7.5 Corporal William Waldie mounted on Wade's horse. *Each officer of the Field Ambulance had his own horse, although the transport of the Brigade was motorized*

Field Ambulance has a mascot, 'Cuckles', a wire-haired terrier. A moustachioed Captain Buchanan and a clean shaven Captain Verel are seen 'close-up'. Captain Brown smiles as he eats his dinner in the Mess. A sleeping Captain Wade is 'snapped', a bottle of Guinness placed, mischievously, near his head. A line of men carry folded tents. Troopers bear stretchers across a football field.

Trench warfare in Cramlington

A Staff car carries Lieutenant Colonel Sloan, Commanding Officer of the Field Ambulance. It is still winter. The car bears a Red Cross, has four 12-spoke wheels with solid tyres and a folding roof. Training for trench warfare continues in the open countryside at Cramlington. A trench, dug to a depth of several feet, is lined with timber. Planks serve as duckboards. A 'patient' hangs from the stretcher poles, while a groundsheet is used to lift a 'casualty'. The Troopers make an improvised dressing station, and ambulance personnel with bandages bend over three 'wounded'.

Blyth

The men manufacture a crossing of a tributary of the river Blyth. Three soldiers crouch across the stones. Eight others, fully dressed, risk the crossing. Captain Verel rests on a gate. There has been a route march and the ambulance personnel are at Blyth. They have crossed the river Tyne on a small 'roll-on, roll-off' ferry. The troopers bathe in the sea. It is the spring of 1915.

Figure 7.6 Motor vehicles of the Field Ambulance assembled for a training exercise. *The training programme began in and around Bedlington but extended to the port of Blyth and then to Newcastle*

Newcastle

The ground is snow-covered. The officers are accommodated in the small Imperial Hotel, Jesmond Road. The Biscuit Works of T. Squire and Son are used as a billet for the 'other ranks'. This disused building is enclosed by a wooden hoarding that carries advertisements for Ingersoll 'War Watches', Nestlé's milk, and for the Hippodrome and Palace Theatres. Armstrong College has been converted into the *First Northern General Hospital*. It is a fine, red-brick building 50 yards from the grounds of the *Royal Victoria Infirmary*. The entrance to the College is guarded by a sentry. Patients stand nearby with two Nursing Sisters. Inside, the Great Hall accommodates 40 or 50 beds. A practical classroom serves as a ward. More Sisters, elegant and authoritative, care for the

Figure 7.7 A two-seater officers' car *of 1914–15. Among the makes used by the army were Humber and Rolls Royce*

patients. The commanding officer of the Hospital is Lieutenant Colonel Gowans. He rides in an open, 2-seater car. Major Paterson, the Hospital Registrar, holds a long folded paper. In his office, a biblical scene hangs on the wall. Major Grey-Turner is one of the Consultant Surgeons.

The first real casualties

The Hospital now receives casualties from the battle of Neuve Chapelle, which took place on March 10th. The offensive petered out. There were 11,652 British killed, wounded, missing and imprisoned. The injuries depicted by Wade include a granulating gunshot wound of the shoulder, a head wound, a brain lesion, a chest injury and a diagonal, 6-inch laceration below the left knee. A nursing sister is seen in her 'surgery'. In the Dispensary, a table is covered with medicine bottles. Four aides are in white gowns. A classroom has become a pack store, a lecture theatre a linen store. Outside, Alnwick Castle offers views of the river. On Sunday, many townspeople walk in the countryside and stand beside the river or on an old stone bridge. From the College, the docks are seen. A Norwegian steamer, camouflaged in 'war paint', lies at anchor, preparing for the Mediterranean.

Mobile operating car

During the period of training at Morpeth in late 1914, Wade made one of his several important contributions to the practice of war surgery. With few exceptions, surgical dressing stations and operating theatres had been tented or sited in huts. From his experience in the South African War (p 21), Wade realized that the results of military surgery might be improved if operating theatres with modern facilities for the conduct of procedures under antiseptic conditions, could be placed as close as possible to the battle front. Recalling Napoleon's General Dominique Larrey (Appendix 2.1),[13] Wade wrote 'The surgeon must go to the wounded man and not the wounded man to the surgeon'. Wade's ingenuity now led to the design of a new form of mobile surgical operation car. The design was completed in December 1914, the first car made in Newcastle. He found the Wolsley car chassis to be ideal for his purpose. The vehicle was equipped with an operating table and carried sterilizers, instruments and dressings so that emergency procedures could be undertaken quickly. The car was drawn up beside the tent that formed the operating theatre itself. Electric cables from storage batteries provided lighting.

Figure 7.8 Wade's operating car. *Constructed on a Wolsley chassis, Wade's original idea was 'to take the surgeon to the wounded, not the wounded to the surgeon' by constructing a mobile, surgical operating unit*

Figure 7.9 Wade's operating car. *In the field, the car carried instruments and sterilizers necessary for safe surgery. The rear of the car was linked to tented accommodation*

Wade's ideas were copied and, by the end of the 1914–18 European War, Abadie had built a mobile operating theatre on a 20 HP Renault car chassis for use in France.[14] These were the first occasions when the petrol-driven motor car had been adapted to provide mobile battle-field operating theatres. It was a concept on which Second World War surgical theatres were devised for use in the North African desert warfare of 1942–43.

Prolonged military training was boring and repetitive. This frustration was felt keenly when the Ambulance learned that the German military campaign of 1914–15, the progeny of the Schlieffen plan, had brought the enemy to within a few miles of the English Channel. They were almost within sight of the white cliffs of Dover. It was with a certain sense of relief that Wade and his companions heard that they were to be part of a new and ambitious plan to thrust the Turks from Constantinople. The British Cabinet, under the leadership of Asquith, had taken a fateful decision to launch an attack on the Dardanelles. For several weeks, how-ever, the news of the campaign that had changed from naval onslaught to invasion was grave and disquieting.

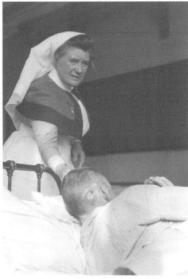

Figure 7.10 Improvised hospital beds at Bedlington. *Anticipating the great numbers of casualties arriving from Flanders in 1915, temporary hospital accommodation was constructed wherever the army medical services were stationed*

Figure 7.11 A nursing sister caring for a soldier with a head wound. *The SHMB Field Ambulance was now stationed in Newcastle. The scene is of Armstrong College, then acting as a temporary hospital. The casualties were from the battle of Neuve Chapelle, 1915*

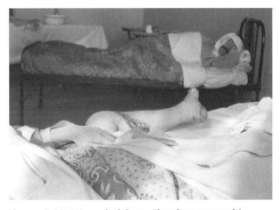

Figure 7.12 Practising the use of the Thomas splint after the war, in 1930. *In Palestine and Syria (Chapter 8), Wade became an enthusiast for the use of the Thomas splint, which saved the life of many with gunshot wounds of the legs*

Figure 7.13 Wounded from Flanders treated in Newcastle. *During this period, Wade cemented his friendship with Grey-Turner, a surgical colleague (Chapter 16).*

Figure 7.14 A casualty among the troops of the SHMB Field Ambulance. *The motorcycle bears the Field Ambulance number plate. The fate of its driver is not recorded*

The Dardanelles

The name 'Gallipoli' has passed into history to designate one of the most costly military campaigns ever fought. For those who have visited the Dardanelles, climbed the steep scrub-covered hills leading up from the beaches, walked across the battlefields and viewed the Allied and Turkish memorials, the scene is one of ghostly beauty.[15] Today, the battle can be in part recalled by viewing the BBC's *The Great War*, in which many original cine films are shown. A vivid impression of conditions at Anzac beach can also be gained through the medium of the Australian film *Gallipoli*.

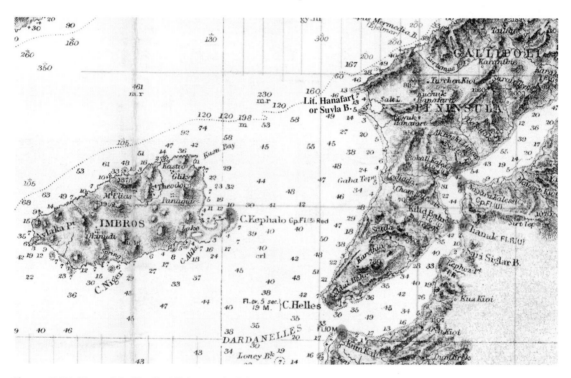

Figure 7.15 Map of Gallipoli. *Off the mouth of the Dardanelles are the islands of Imbros (now Gökçe) and Lemnos (now Limnos). The former was the site of General Hamilton's headquarters, the latter the military and naval base for the attacks of 1915. The 'Narrows' are at centre (far right). Nearly 20 miles north of Cape Helles, Suvla Bay was the focus of the assaults of 6th August 1915. The SHMB provided support for the attack. (Copyright, see p 3)*

From beginning to end, the outcome of the Dardanelles campaign was balanced on a knife-edge. The bravery of the troops has never been disputed, and the outstanding contributions made by the Australians and New Zealanders are still commemorated in their national Anzac Day. In many ways, the strategic planning was farsighted; however, the tactics were hasty and ill-planned, with parts of the British leadership weak and indecisive. Recalled from Egypt, General Sir Ian Hamilton was appointed Commander-in-Chief on 12th March 1915.[16] He had been instructed by the War Office to cooperate with the Royal Navy, to effect a landing on the Gallipoli Peninsula and, thereafter, to proceed to occupy Constantinople.[15] His headquarters were on the island of Imbros (now Gökçe), less than 20 km from the tip of the Gallipoli peninsula.

The naval onslaught

Warning of an onslaught had been given on 3rd November 1914 with an unwise, preliminary bombardment that merely served to alert the Turks to the possibility of an attack. It was followed by a further, massive naval assault on the outer forts defending the Narrows in the spring of 1915. On 18th March 1915, a fleet of 18 warships under the command of Admiral de Robeck sailed into the Dardanelles Straits. Within a few hours, the French battleship *Bouvet* blew up. Soon afterwards, two British ships, the *Inflexible* and the *Irresistible*, struck undetected mines. Another, the *Ocean*, suffered the same fate. A third of the attacking force had been put out of action. On 22nd March, de Robeck informed General Hamilton that his ships could not penetrate the Turkish defences without the help of the army. Hamilton had available some 75,000 men. They included the experienced 29th Division released by Kitchener from India, the Australian and New Zealand Army Corps, the Anzacs, together with a French force. The offer by Greece of three divisions of troops was vetoed by the Russians.

The first military assault

Dismayed by the costly failure of their seaborne attack, the Navy, supported by the views of the majority of the Cabinet in London, decided that a way through the Dardanelles Narrows could not be forced by ships unless there was a simultaneous attack by the Army. A military onslaught against the Germans and Turks in the Dardanelles was agreed reluctantly by the War Council. The operation did not begin until April 1915. One reason for this delay was the time taken to concentrate the necessarily large numbers of troops. Another lay with the faulty packing of the stores brought in transport ships from England. The supplies, armaments, munitions, animals and seaplanes, taken first to Egypt, had to be repacked, an operation that occupied 40 days. By the time they reached Limnos, Turkish agents in Alexandria had been thoroughly alerted to the Allied plans.

An attack was planned for 23rd April but was delayed for two days because of storms. British, Australian and New Zealand troops therefore landed on the Gallipoli peninsula on 25th April 1915.[1] The offensive, one of the most dangerous forms of assault, concentrated on five beaches at the southwest tip of the Gallipoli peninsula and no more than one to three miles apart. A simultaneous assault by the Anzacs, aimed at Gaba Tepe, was diverted inadvertently to a beach some distance to the north, a site later remembered as Anzac Cove. A diversionary attack by the French was made on the opposite side of the Straits at Kum Kale, while a naval feint was directed at the crucial northern objective of Bulair where the possibility of an overwhelming military attack had already been discounted.

The provision of medical support essential in any offensive was no better than the defective overall planning. At first, only two hospital ships were available. An estimate was made that the beach attacks would result in no more than 3,000 wounded, yet the ships could deal with barely 700 casualties and would be compelled to evacuate the wounded to Malta or Egypt in voyages of three or four days, respectively. The Director General of the Army Medical Services (DGAMS), Surgeon-General WE Birrell, reached Mudros only one week before the date of the landing. No contingency plan had been made in case an advance from the beaches, where hospitals could be established, was not successful. Birrell called for eight more hospital ships. This was agreed[17] although the additional ships would not be available until two days after the offensive had begun. Birrell calculated there would be three times more wounded than had been anticipated, yet small craft dedicated to landing troops were not to be diverted to the rescue of casualties.

The battle 'ebbed and flowed in an historic setting amidst all the sombre magnificence which a fleet lends to modern war'.[1] The story of the battle evoked some of the finest of the writings of modern military historians. After bitter fighting and heavy losses on both sides, a stalemate was reached, a situation that could not be sustained militarily or politically. However, no safe evacuation from the peninsula was practicable during the short summer nights. Moreover, an early withdrawal from Gallipoli, exposing Serbia to the defection of Bulgaria and a direct attack by Germany, was too hazardous to contemplate.

Final offensive

The Cabinet Dardanelles Committee sought now to end the Gallipoli campaign by a final decisive onslaught into which new divisions and additional medical personnel were drawn. As Winston Churchill wrote,[4] the aims of the campaign were three-fold: to break out 'with a rush' from Anzac Beach, cutting off the Turkish army from contact with Constantinople; to establish artillery positions that denied the Turks sea traffic to and from Constantinople; and to secure Suvla Bay as a winter base for the troops remaining on the peninsula.

There were to be three simultaneous attacks on 6th August 1915, involving a total of 120,000 men supported by large naval forces. The Turks were now known to have a force of nearly 100,000 men and 270 guns on the peninsula and possessed substantial reserves some 50 km to the northeast at Bulair. The plan was for a powerful Allied force to make a largely diversionary attack at Helles. Simultaneously, a great offensive was to be initiated by Australian forces from Anzac Cove. The principal aim of this onslaught was to capture and hold the dominant Sari Bair Ridge. The key to the ridge was a feature called Chunuk Bair. There was to be a surprise attack at Suvla Bay, whence a rapid advance would permit domination of the Anafarta Hills. There was an early prospect of success but hope was quickly dashed. Bitter fighting at Helles achieved the objective of preventing all but a single Turkish Division from being withdrawn to support their forces to the north. By the evening of 6th August, Anzac forces had stormed Lone Pine trench from the southeast. However, the main attack, by 16,000 men up the ridges leading to Sari Bair, had not been decisive. By dawn the troops were exhausted, the action delayed.

Contrary to all the precepts of successful war, the War Office together with the Secretary of State for War, Lord Kitchener, had created a fatal combination of 'old generals and new troops'.[15] The commander of the crucial Suvla Bay expedition was General Stopford. He was aged 61 years and was selected in preference to the talented commander of the 10th Division, Sir Bryan Mahon, his junior. Stopford was in indifferent health and had never led troops in battle nor commanded even a battalion in an engagement. He was conservative in approach and had decided prematurely that additional artillery support was needed before any attack. He had sprained his ankle and remained on board the destroyer *Jonquil* for two days after the first troops landed early on the morning of 6th August. Communication between the ship and the shore, by rowing boat, was dangerously slow.

Far from being the immediate, overwhelming and conclusive attack that had been intended, the battle of Suvla Bay became uncoordinated and indecisive. A desultory and delayed onslaught was mounted from the direction of Lala Baba, the Salt Lake, Chocolate Hill and Hill 60. It failed to surmount the 'succession of razor-edged spurs and peaks, the deep gorges covered with dense scrub' that led to the Sari Bair ridge. There were 'no carts for supplies, the guides became lost, food and water were insufficient and the heat enervating'. The three brigades of the 11th Division that reached the shore by 10 o'clock that night were confronted by no more than 1,800 Turks with 20 guns. Nevertheless, the offensive was not pressed home and it was broad daylight before Hill 10 finally was taken.

Once again, the medical plans proved defective. As Carlyon records graphically, a telegram reached the DGAMS, General Birrell, barely three hours after the first landing at 'B' beach.[17] The message said:

'When does the next hospital ship arrive? This one is full.'

These challenges did not, of course, affect the work of the Field Ambulances directly, but General Birrell must be held responsible for some of the shambles. Carlyon writes: 'The wounded suffered outrageously throughout the campaign and this was partly Birrell's fault. He had helped reinvent the medical nightmare of the Crimea'.

The 10th Division then disembarked at 10 a.m. on the morning of 7th August, so that, as the day passed, 20,000 troops confronted the remnants of a small Turkish force. But nothing happened. The troops remained idle. Many bathed, lay on the shore, smoked and lazed. Time passed. Soon it was too late. Meanwhile, Turkish reinforcements marched from Bulair and the entire Turkish force was withdrawn from the Asiatic shore. At dawn on 8th August, the assault on Chunuk Bair was renewed. It failed, although the strong Turkish force that had arrived to defend this key feature was decimated by artillery fire and by the guns of the fleet. Twelve thousand Allied casualties were sustained. A further attack at Suvla Bay was resumed at dawn on 9th August. By now, however, the enemy was three times as strong as he had been on 6th August. Their 7th and 12th Divisions had reached the line, and the Allied assaults were driven back.

When night fell over the battlefield, lurid with the fiercely burning scrub, the Allied IXth Corps occupied positions only a little more advanced than those it had gained on the first day of the landing. Ample Turkish forces stood entrenched and victorious on all the decisive positions. At Suvla Bay, nearly 8,000 officers and men had been killed or wounded in the course of 9th and 10th August.

Field Ambulance at Suvla Bay

The SHMB Field Ambulance sailed for the Mediterranean in July 1915 on the *Aquitania*, a hospital ship.[H] At the very moment the Brigade was posted to Gallipoli, Wade had second thoughts about his future. He was clearly unhappy with his position and expressed an interest in an appointment at the 2nd Scottish Military Hospital, Craigleith, the hospital now known as the Western General Hospital, Edinburgh. However, the post was filled before he could apply. A telegram and a War Office letter told him bluntly that he was too late.

The Scottish Yeomanry landed on the Greek island of Lemnos (now Limnos), where there was a large base at Mudros from which the Gallipoli campaign had been initiated. A number of Wade's surgical motor cars had been shipped to Gallipoli where they were employed to the limited extent that the difficult conditions allowed. Many other ambulances were horse-drawn.

Wade's battlefield photographs record his view of the surgical support for the Suvla Bay offensive (Appendix 7.1).

Suvla Bay, W and C beach

Here are the tented quarters of the Field Ambulance, an operating hut with adjoining surgical operating car and some motor ambulances. Soldiers watch the shelling of the Turkish lines. Part of a Casualty Clearing Station and members of the army nursing staff and of the nursing Voluntary Aid Detachment (VAD) are seen. On a wide expanse of sandy beach, the Ambulance is dispersed around a pole flying the Red Cross flag. The Union Jack is not hoisted alongside the Red Cross flag. This flag, with its connotation of religious strife, annoys the Turks and provokes the shelling of the Ambulance. The flags of the SHMBFA and the South Midland Field Ambulance are seen in the distance.

Suvla Bay beaches

Not far from the flagpole, twenty men stand with packs and bags. The ground is sand. Beyond, the gently sloping hills of Lala Baba, which are quite unlike the steep beachside of Anzac Cove, are held by the Turks.

In another view, the panorama is of the battlefields of X and Y beaches and in one perspective, the Welsh ambulance is recognised. No horses are seen. Both the Operating Car and a hut built of shell cases are used as operating theatres. The windscreen of the Ambulance Car is protected against the sun by a tarpaulin. Captains Buchanan and Brown, and Lieutenants McDonald, Woodman Smith and Kennedy are pictured, as are Corporal Jackson and Private Macara. It is intensely hot [an indication that the photographs were taken early in the autumn campaign but after the initial attacks had lapsed into stagnation].

Suvla Bay: evacuation approaches

The uniforms are quite different from those adopted in training. There is little formality. Shirt sleeves and pith helmets are the order of the day and trousers replace breeches and riding boots. Four officers wear helmets, one a Balmoral. Two officers have towels around their necks. One is in shorts, another has a white armband. Major Richardson looks out from his dug-out where a wall of sandbags is partly covered by a tarpaulin. He wears braces but no hat or helmet. The Mess table has been re-laid after the explosion of a shell at the base of the Flag Staff. In spite of their difficulties, the troops are in good spirits. They prepare an ablution bench and make coffee. Others stand, watching the shelling of Turkish positions on Salt Lake Plain. A small steam launch of a naval party is beached beside five rowing boats, each carrying several men.

Figure 7.16 A sand-bagged surgical position at Suvla Bay. *The only protection against shell bursts was by means of sand bags or ammunition boxes*

Figure 7.17 View from the SHMB Field Ambulance's position at Suvla Bay

Figure 7.18 In August 1915, the flag flies over the encampment of the SHMB Field Ambulance at Suvla Bay. *When the Red Cross flag was displayed, it was shelled by the enemy, who believed it to be political in character*

Figure 7.19 Officers of the SHMB Field Ambulance await the advance. *When the landing was effected on 6th August 1915, and for some days afterwards, the attack was not relentless. There was time to sit and think!*

Figure 7.20 The beach at Suvla Bay. *Wade's photograph illustrates the conditions under which the offensive of 6th August 1915 and the disembarkation of December took place*

Figure 7.21 An operating car at Suvla Bay. *During the autumn of 1915, weather conditions were favourable and the operating car could deal with the wounded in the open air. As winter approached, dysentery and malaria became scourges and the priorities for both armies were food and warmth*

Figure 7.22 Tented encampment of the Field Ambulance. *It is an axiom of war that photography during action is difficult or impossible, whereas, between fighting, long periods of boredom often encourage the use of the camera. In training, Wade took more than 200 photographs. At Suvla Bay, only 19 could be recorded*

Ross[18]quoted a letter by JP Upfold published in the *Scotsman* on 22nd February 1955, the day following Wade's death. The letter explained:

'I had the great good fortune to be one of his [Wade's] assistants in his 'shell-case' operating theatre on Suvla Bay, Gallipoli. To give some idea of the high esteem in which Sir Henry was held on the field of battle, patients brought in to the theatre would say, 'Is this Henry Wade's place?' and when assured that it was the remark would be, 'Well, if anything can be done to save my life, he is the man to do it'. After a serious operation, [Wade] had lighted a cigarette, and I had asked him what were the chances of that lad's recovery, he would reply, 'While there is life, there is hope; I have done all I can – I have cleaned up the wound and the rest is in the hands of nature'. Such humility was an inspiration to all who had the good fortune to be associated with him during those days at Suvla Bay. We had strict instructions from him that if a patient was brought down the line who required his attention, he had to be informed immediately, no matter what time of night or day it was.'

End of campaign

The closing phase of the campaign approached. On 10th August, two British battalions of 1,000 men were driven back from Chunuk Bair. On 15th and 16th August, the 54th Territorial Division supported two brigades of the Irish Division in an attack along Kiretch Tepe Sirt ridge, in a bold move that would have outflanked the whole Turkish 5th Army. The Allies were compelled to yield any ground they had taken. On 21st August, the experienced 29th Division, brought from Helles and supported by the dismounted Yeomanry Division in order to reinforce the 10th, 11th, 53rd and 54th Divisions, attacked across the low hills and scrub land without result. It was the end.

The military offensive was a failure. The idyllic picture of resourceful, disciplined medical teams calmly viewing the Suvla Bay battles from a position on the beach, distant from the firing line, was wholly misleading. The military situation quickly became critical. Lone Pine trench was captured after fierce fighting but the peak at Chunuk Bair had been lost and the heights of Sari Bair not taken. Overall, there was stalemate. The battles at and near Suvla Bay were the largest of the Dardanelles campaign and, in effect, the last. The golden moment had passed at the end of June. There had been undue delay in deciding what to do after the abortive first landings. When General Hamilton reported on 17th May, his appreciation was not considered until three weeks later. Meanwhile, the British Government had been reconstructed with all the turmoil that this entailed. The disastrous consequence of these delays had been that the reinforcements requested by General Hamilton had been postponed for six weeks. Moreover, throughout this period, there were very large, reserve forces in Egypt, which were needed urgently for success at Gallipoli but remained unused.

Events now conspired to make evacuation inevitable. The weather had deteriorated. Winter was approaching and sickness, particularly dysentery, was rife. The campaigns in Flanders required every available soldier. The French demanded support for a new offensive in Salonika. With extreme reluctance, the War Office accepted this view. General Hamilton disagreed.[16] He was recalled to Britain on 16th October. His successor as Commander-in-Chief, General Sir Charles Monro, arrived at Gallipoli two weeks later. He found the defences confused, disorderly and congested. Within 24 hours, he telegraphed a highly critical report to London. He recommended evacuation but warned that up to 30–40% of the troops could be lost. At first, his view was opposed bitterly by Kitchener, who was dispatched to Gallipoli to see for himself. He arrived at Mudros on 9th November. Realizing the gravity of the situation, and in a weakened position in relation to the War Cabinet in London, he issued a peremptory order for the evacuation to proceed. On 26th November 1915, a hurricane struck the peninsula. Many died in the resulting floods, and the severe conditions that followed led to hundreds of deaths from exposure and frostbite.

The final decision to abandon the peninsula was taken on 14th December. For once, fate played into the hands of the disconsolate Allies. The weather improved and effective cooperation between the army and navy achieved a miracle. Suvla and Anzac were evacuated on 20th December 1915. Helles was abandoned on 8th January 1916. The retreat was a tactical success, and almost every surviving man and intact gun was taken safely from the Suvla beachhead and from Anzac Cove. There were many sick – more than 50 hospital ships had been pressed into service – but few battlefield casualties.[19]

Disaster and evacuation

The scale of the losses incurred at Gallipoli proved almost beyond belief. Eleven naval vessels, including several battleships, had been damaged irreparably or sunk. From among the 163,466 troops who had taken part, there were 114,743 casualties. At least 21,882 men had been killed: many were from Australia and New Zealand. The casualties suffered by the Turks were at least as heavy. Thousands of horses had been lost. Throughout the 100 years' history of the Royal Army Medical Corps, the inherent and understandable differences between the combatant and non-combatant units of the military have generally remained hidden beneath a fine veil of respect and courtesy. At the end of the dispatch that General Hamilton sent to the War Office recounting the events in Gallipoli from 5th May 1915 to 30th June, he described the Royal Army Medical Service [*sic*] in the following terms:

'The Royal Army Medical Service[20,21] has had to face unusual and very trying conditions. There are no roads, and those wounded who are unable to walk must be carried from the firing line to the shore. They and their attendants may be shelled on their way to the beaches, at the beaches, on the jetties, and again, though I believe by inadvertence, on their way out in lighters to the hospital ships. Under shell fire it is not as easy as some of the critically disposed seem to imagine to keep all arrangements in apple-pie order. Here I can only express my opinion that efficiency, method, and even a certain quiet heroism have characterized the evacuation of the many thousands of our wounded.'

Following the evacuation of Gallipoli, a photograph shows Wade in a tented hospital bed, where, it is reasonable to assume, he was recovering from the prevalent bacillary dysentery. The hospital is at Giza, Cairo, so the infection seems to have developed before or during the four-day voyage from Suvla Bay to Egypt.

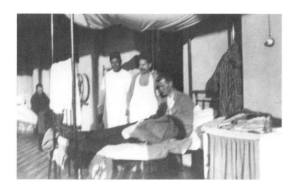

Figure 7.23 Wade in hospital. *Taken ill towards the end of the Gallipoli campaign, Wade became part of the Egyptian Expeditionary Force (EEF). It is not certain whether at that time he was suffering from dysentery or malaria, but in correspondence after the war, there is reference to attempts made to diagnose his malaria. He was treated in the military hospital at Giza (El Giza) on the outskirts of Cairo. From there, he was sent home on sick leave*

Figure 7.24 Hospital ship. *The identity of the ship is uncertain: ships' names were not displayed. Wade's notes do not state this explicitly but the ship is probably the Neuralia, bound for Naples, where she transferred her passengers to the Aquitania, whose destination was Southampton*

Arriving in Egypt in 1916, Wade is ill. He may have bacillary dysentery although, at some unspecified time, he also contracts malaria. He is a patient in the Red Cross Hospital at Giza, Cairo. Wade sits up in bed, two medical attendants in white aprons beside him. An awning above his head, supported by poles, he looks down at the bedclothes, ill at ease. Lieutenant Munro of the Scottish Horse is also a patient, his face distorted with pain, a quietly smiling Nursing Sister without badges or mark of rank nearby. A less senior aide, a volunteer, wears a simple cap and leans against a table or trolley. A smiling teenage boy, Mahomet, is the Officers' batman. He has a fez with a tassel and holds a menu in his left hand.

Recovering, Wade is granted sick leave. He boards the hospital ship *Neuralia* as she sails to Naples, transferring her patients to the *Aquitania,* which is bound for Southampton. He is accompanied by AAH Sinclair and another Medical Officer. They lean against the ship's rail. Wade photographs the harbours at Alexandria and Malta as he passes through them. Home again, he travels first to Aberdeen to visit his sister Margaret, then to see his mother in Larbert. Some days later, he pictures her standing sombrely in her garden. It is the moment for her youngest son to bid goodbye as he leaves again for the war. Joining *HMS Shropshire*, Wade sails for the Mediterranean. He boards the hospital ship *Oxfordshire* which carries him safely to Alexandria where he disembarks, rejoining that part of the Field Ambulance which had not been sent to Salonika.

Figure 7.25 Convalescent officers sailing for home. *Wade stands against the ship's rail with two of his fellow officers*

Figure 7.26 Conversations on a hospital ship. *Serious, even grim in later life, Wade enjoyed social exchanges as much as his fellow officers*

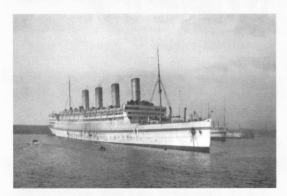

Figure 7.27 Hospital ship Aquitania. *Aquitania and the ill-fated* Britannic *were among the large liners used to transport wounded from the Mediterranean and convalescent soldiers from Britain*

Figure 7.28 A view from a hospital ship. *The exact place and time of the photograph are not certain. However, other photographs in the same group illustrate Malta and Gibraltar, so the view may be assumed to be of the Mediterranean*

The convalescent Wade was fortunate. His voyage was not many weeks after the sinking of the *Britannic*, the sister ship of the ill-fated *Titanic*. Special steps had been taken to strengthen the bulkheads of the *Britannic*, but on 21st November 1915, while serving as a hospital ship, she was sunk by mine or torpedo on the approach to the Greek islands. An explosion shook the bow of the ship near Kea as she sailed on her first voyage to collect the wounded and sick who had been taken to Lesbos. The ship sank within 57 minutes and still lies in 400 feet of water. There were 1,100 people on board. The 28 who lost their lives were naval and military personnel, crewmen, nurses and medical staff.

Confronting a new theatre of war, Wade could not have anticipated nearly three more years of battle or foreseen the dreadful and bitter challenge of treating many hundreds of wounded. But fate was on his side. Recovering from the fearful experiences of Gallipoli, restored to health and promoted to new responsibilities with the army in Egypt, he was awarded the Order of the White Eagle of Serbia for his distinguished contribution to the campaign in the Dardanelles.

His years in Egypt, Palestine and Syria are described in Chapter 8.

CHAPTER 8

From Egypt to Syria

1916–18

Think, Soldiers! From the top of these pyramids,
forty centuries are looking down upon you.

(Napoleon I, before the Battle of the Pyramids, 1798)

T he Scottish Horse Mounted Brigade (SHMB) left Suvla Bay with its Field Ambulance in December 1915. In Cairo, Henry Wade became part of the Egyptian Expeditionary Force (EEF). Recovering from dysentery, he was granted sick leave and travelled home briefly. As Chapter 7 explains, Wade returned to Egypt, sailing on *HMS Shropshire*, touching Gibraltar and Malta and retracing parts of the voyage made in 1798 by Dominique Larrey when he left Toulon with the Grande Armée that Napoleon Bonaparte had assembled for the invasion of Egypt.[1,A] Wade found the Ambulance near Cairo.[2–4]

A world at war

On 5th November 1914, Turkey, already at war with Russia, joined Germany and Austro-Hungary in campaigns against France and Britain. Dominated by the 'Young Turks', Sultan Mehmed Reshad called for a 'holy' war, attempting to rouse Muslims from around the world to his cause. With few exceptions, he was unsuccessful. Nevertheless, equipped with German guns and rifles, the Turkish Army began operations on three fronts simultaneously.[5,6]

The first Turkish aim was an incursion into the Caucasus. It proved a catastrophic failure.[7–9]

A second Turkish objective was to wrest control of the Persian Gulf from the British. The new 'dreadnoughts' of the British Navy were gigantic oil-burning warships. The British Government had secured a controlling interest in the Anglo–Persian Oil Company but their ships depended for fuel on access to terminals at Shatt-al-Arab, where the Tigris and Euphrates merged. The Indian Government dispatched 3,000 troops to secure Basra. There followed one of the most disastrous campaigns of the First World War. Half a million men were eventually committed to a failed advance on Baghdad. Faulty planning,

Chapter Summary
• A world at war
• The defence of Egypt
• Wade in Egypt
• The battles of Gaza
• Jerusalem falls
• Advance on Damascus
• Weapons
• Transport of wounded
• Wounds
• Surgical treatment
• Non-battle casualties
• An armistice is declared

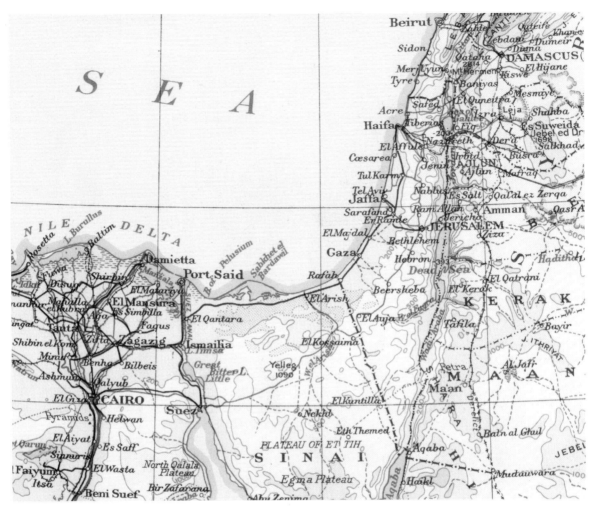

Figure 8.1 Egypt, Palestine and Syria: *from Cairo to Damascus. Roads and pipelines followed the coastal plain (centre) and led from the military base at El Qantara (El Kantara) to El Arish, Rafah and Gaza. The capture of Beersheba opened the way to Jerusalem and hence to Damascus (top right). The railway, the key to much strategic planning, followed a line from the Gulf through Mudauwara (bottom right) to Damascus, where Deraa proved to be of critical military importance. (Copyright, see p 3)*

Figure 8.2 Hospital ships in harbour. *Wade's photographs are a clear indication of the great number of ships required to support the medical services*

Figure 8.3 Encampment at El Qantara (El Kantara).
In 1915 and the early days of 1916, a vast and growing army assembled at El Kantara

inadequate supplies, the spread of tropical and infectious disease and hopelessly poor medical support culminated in failure. The survivors surrendered unconditionally at Kut on 29th April 1915. It was the very moment chosen for the invasion of the Gallipoli Peninsula (Chapter 7).

The third Turkish purpose was the recovery of Egypt from Britain and Libya from Italy. When Turkey declared war, Egypt became a British protectorate. The Egyptians favoured a German victory that might bring independence but were not responsive to the call for a 'holy' war. The British responsibility was to secure the Suez Canal,[7,8] the vital international route that conveyed Indian, Australian and New Zealand troops to Europe. One hundred miles long, not less than 190 feet wide and 34 feet deep, the Canal was a formidable obstacle, defended by patrolling warships as well as by a growing army. Contrary to earlier agreements, Britain now protected the Canal by closing it to foreign vessels.

The defence of Egypt

Alerted to the Turkish plans, a British and Allied Egyptian Expeditionary Force, the EEF, was concentrated near the Canal. Believing that they were confronted by Turkish forces much larger than was the case, reinforcements were demanded. In January 1915, the army mustered 70,000 men. By the end of 1915, there were nearly five times as many (Table 8.1). They included divisions that had left Gallipoli. The SHMB Field Ambulance reached Kantara (now El Qantara) early in 1916. Kantara had become the base for the EEF. Sited on the Suez Canal, 90 miles north-east of Cairo, the township was of immense strategic importance. It lay only 28 miles south of Port Said, 32 miles north of the point at which the Canal enters the Great Bitter Lake.

With the outbreak of hostilities, the Turks at first moved cautiously, provoking diversions with intrusive patrols and raids. In January 1915, Djemal Pasha led 20,000 of his troops across the Sinai Desert and attempted to cross the Canal. In spite of the barges made in Germany for such a purpose, the Turks did not persevere. They lost 2,000 men. No attempt was made to intercept the retreating forces, as Kitchener, in London, believed that any reverse might threaten Britain's prestige in the Muslim world.

Table 8.1 Ration strength of the army assembled for the defence of Egypt and the invasion of Palestine and Syria, 1915–18

Year	British and Dominion troops, officers and other ranks	Indian and other nationalities	Total
1915	74,133	–	89,371
1916	187,926	7,455	225,922
1917	186,549	63,329	268,768
1918	231,090	94,871	385,327

Interrupted only by sporadic mining of the Canal and explosions on the railway, the EEF used the remainder of 1915 and much of 1916 to create a fortified zone to the east of the waterway. General Murray, the Commander-in-Chief, employed forced Egyptian labour to construct a railway and to lay a water pipe line northwards, along the coast. In August 1916, Kress von Kressenstein, the German commander of the Turkish forces, attempted to force the issue. He unwisely attacked the EEF at Romani, 22 miles to the northeast of Kantara. His modest force of 16,000 men was repulsed with heavy losses inflicted, particularly, by the Australian cavalry of the Anzac division.

Wade's photographs continue to record the course of the campaign: The battle of Romani follows. Advancing across the Sinai desert, the army quickly takes Rafah. It is March 1917. Generals Miarr [*sic*] and Keble confer in the desert. Horses have given way to camels, and the SHMB Field Ambulance has become the Camel Corps Ambulance. They establish their position. The SHMB Field Ambulance is at 'Oasis Junction', bivouacked near the Australian Light Horse Brigade, who are lined up with the SHMB. Wade records the nursing sisters, the medical officers and the ambulance personnel. Aeroplanes, observation balloons, camels, mules, traction engines and railways are subjects for his many images. Photographs of the ambulance personnel include Private Porter and Sergeant Cuthbert. The Australian Light Horse Brigade is converted to an infantry unit. Turkish wounded from the battle start to arrive. Although the military actions have been small, awards for gallantry demonstrate that there have been opportunities for initiative and bravery.

Figure 8.4 Troops in camp in Egypt. *In the early days of the campaign, the troops were allowed to bathe in the waters of the Suez Canal and in makeshift pools and baths*

Figure 8.5 Water – the key to survival and hygiene. *The photograph emphasizes the enjoyment offered by access to bathing and swimming*

Figure 8.6 Wade and fellow officers in Egypt. *Wade's photographs include many portraits of himself and his fellow officers and men. Here he is seen in the front row, right*

Figure 8.7 Influence of air on military medical tactics. *In the early stages of the Egyptian and Palestinian campaigns, German planes dominated the air, dropping darts as well as hand grenades. However, British aircraft, such as the Sopwith Camel, arrived in increasing numbers*

Figure 8.8 Conflict in the air. *Not surprisingly, many planes were damaged or destroyed during the ensuing aerial warfare until the Egyptian Expeditionary Force achieved dominance*

Figure 8.9 Balloons and observation. *As in South Africa in 1899–1902, observation balloons played a part in detecting concentrations of enemy troops*

Figure 8.10 Aerial observation influenced medical care. *Orders were given that Casualty Clearing Stations, such as that illustrated here, should not be assembled until immediately before an attack lest the enemy be forewarned*

Moving almost imperceptibly from prolonged defence to attack, Murray followed the path of his supply lines and established a defensive base at El Arish, 70 miles beyond Romani.

The army is compelled to spend many months in Kantara, close to the Suez Canal and the Sweet Water Canal, waiting first, for a Turkish attack and then, when the Turks withdraw, for an Allied offensive. It proves possible to discern the Turkish positions. The weather alternates between intense, dry heat and torrential rain with flooding. The SHMB Field Ambulance is seen in a dust storm. Wade photographs an officers' breakfast, the entire table covered by a mound of flies. Sanitary conditions are primitive in spite of organized efforts to construct decent latrines. Washing is less difficult because the troops have recourse to the waters of the Suez Canal, where, it is assumed, the RAMC have satisfied themselves that cercariae,[B] released from *Bulinus* snails, are not ready to pounce on the bare legs of the bathers, transmitting the worm disease biharziasis (schistosomiasis) (p 107). There is intense activity constructing defence works at Kantara and, later, at El Arish.

The Service Corps build a pontoon bridge. The conscripted Egyptian Labour Corps (ELC) is employed heavily. They construct a road and move a hut. During these times, the troops spend many hours building fortifications. The Army Service Corps Depot is shown. In desert warfare, water is the key to action and the construction of a pipeline occupies a large part of the engineers' time. But the army 'marches on its stomach', and troops are seen drawing rations. A field kitchen is on the move. In the early days of the campaigns, British, Australian and Indian forces depend heavily on their horses. Large numbers are seen being watered. Later, camels come into their own, and a convoy of camels is photographed in the Sinai desert. In the times when there is neither military action nor the building of defensive works, the troops enjoy athletics and games. The SHMB organize a swimming gala and a race meeting. At Hill 40, there is an improvised racetrack, where hundreds of soldiers urge on their favourites. Life in the intensely hot climate explains the many revealing photographs of bathing and swimming, often in the canal. In view of the early dominance of German aviators, it is surprising to see that such large gatherings are allowed. Wade has time to visit the 5th RFS, Ismalia and Katia Ogridena before returning to Kantara.

Motor ambulances and Wade's surgical cars arrive. A surgical car is shown beside an operating hut. Nearby are the tents of the Field Ambulance hospital. The solid rubber tyres of the ambulances are not ideal for desert sands and some become trapped. Here, and in the Sinai desert, Wade depicts stretcher bearers; patients on a stretcher bed; New Zealand, British and Turkish wounded; and horse, mule and camel hospital transport. The staff of the Field Ambulance, including Private Campbell, inspect two sand sledges. A sledge crosses the railway that runs beside the Suez Canal. Camels transport the wounded in the identical style adopted in Napoleonic times. A 'lying-down' cacholet is used, but sitting wounded are also depicted. Some are brought from Katia. Two of the Turks, Ali and Achmed, are named. In some instances, both staff (Brown, Buchanan, McLauchlin, Clark and Ferguson) and patients are identified: Private McLauchlin is cheered by a parcel from home.

Wade in Egypt

On his arrival in Egypt, Wade retained the definitive rank of Captain in the SHMB Field Ambulance. He still held this substantive rank in August 1917 but had been promoted to Temporary Lieutenant Colonel in July 1916, an appointment confirmed on 23rd August. One reason for promotion was that Colonel Warren Low was returning home. On the instigation of the Surgeon General, Wade was ordered by his Director of Medical Services, the DMS, to act as Consulting Surgeon. He was transferred from General Headquarters and made responsible to the Deputy Director of Medical Services, the DDMS, in the field. Wade advised and assisted the staff of Numbers 53 and 54 Casualty Clearing Stations (CCSs).[10,11]

In Cairo, Wade sees the funeral of the Khedive, who has died suddenly. The procession passes the Abdin Palace and moves along Mohamed Ali Street. Excavations are taking place at Forstat, and there are hieroglyphics on a wall. There is an opportunity to watch feluccas on the Nile and to record a boy on the bridge. The delta is fertile but reaching the desert, Wade notices amateurish attempts at the irrigation of land. A cloudburst has occurred at Abdazza and a train is seen, buried in the earth displaced by the waters. There is an opportunity to visit the western Oasis of Kharga. The Temple of Hibis and a Roman fort catch Wade's eye. A train transports the sick. A party of men from the Field Ambulance wait at the station. One of the interests at Kharga is that part of the buildings is underground. At the public well, blind water carriers fill their bags. There is a fine mosque. Although the village gardens are attractive, the presence of a patient with smallpox is a reminder of the hazards faced by the local people. In pictures entitled *Journey by water from Giza to Sakara, during Nile floods*, Wade records several aspect of the Giza pyramids. He is accompanied by Fraser.

A funeral party passes along a dyke, donkeys transport goods and women are busy making dung cakes. In the background are groups of 'irregular' troops. In Sakara, Wade sees the entrance to the tomb near the steps of a pyramid and makes a reference to the philanthropy of the American, Pierpoint Morgan.

Life in the Sinai desert as a consulting surgeon forms the next group of images. Wade photographs a Bedouin camp and, once again, emphasizes the crucial role of water in desert life. Water is drawn from a well. The pipeline, water tanks at the railhead, water being transported from the railway and the watering of horses, both at the railhead and near the hospital, are illustrated. There is an ambulance convoy in the desert, and, for the first time, an ambulance train is shown, an indication of the scale of casualties anticipated from the forthcoming offensives. Although stretchers carry the sick, they are helped by American tractors. Wade wishes to portray his fellow officers, the padre, ambulance personnel and troops: 42 are photographed. The army moves forward to the gates of El Arish, where bridges are being built.

The battles of Gaza

On 9th December 1916, a new War Cabinet was formed in London and the Prime Minister, Lloyd George, demanded a positive strategy. The capture of the Holy City of Jerusalem would be of immense psychological as well as military significance. Responding to this call, and aware that a seaborne assault was not possible, Murray's forces crossed the frontier into Palestine. Rafah was taken on 9th January 1917, but the capture of Jerusalem was beyond their immediate reach. An attack on the Holy City presupposed the capture of Gaza, as the EEF was tied to its coastal lines of communication. To make matters more difficult, a division of Murray's troops had been recalled to France.

The first Battle of Gaza.

Careful planning by General Dobell and a fine force of cavalry now enabled a first attack on Gaza. It was 26th March 1917.[7,8] The small Turkish forces were strongly entrenched, and a frontal assault by the 53rd Division was successful only after bitter fighting. However, an encircling cavalry movement from the east and north reached the coast, and the net was ready to close. Unhappily, information was painfully slow in arriving at headquarters. As a result, the achievement of the assaulting forces was not appreciated until it was too late.

The troops were withdrawn to a great ravine, the Wadi-Ghazze. For his part in the inconclusive first battle of Gaza, Wade was cited for the Distinguished Service Order. The award was ratified on 3rd April 1918.

The second Battle of Gaza

In London, the Chief of the Imperial General Staff, General Robertson, mistakenly believed success had been achieved. He pressed for an advance on Jerusalem. Unable and unwilling to admit paralysis, Murray misguidedly launched an unjustifiable further attack on Gaza in April 1917. The three assaulting divisions were repulsed with heavy losses. Haunted by failure, General Murray was mercifully recalled to Britain in June. He was replaced by the lively and forceful General Allenby, a masterly commander of cavalry whose overt ambition was to capture Constantinople. Meanwhile, Lloyd George had asked for Jerusalem 'as a Christmas present'.

The third Battle of Gaza

After the fiasco of the second Battle of Gaza, a period of trench warfare followed. Months passed, during which time Allenby undertook an extensive reorganization of his forces. His understanding of strategy, careful tactical planning and skilled concentration of forces now paid rich dividends. The Turkish defensive positions stretched from Gaza in the west through Sheria to Beersheba in the east. Decoying the Turks by a misleading show of strength against Gaza, on 31st October 1917, Allenby deployed an overwhelming concentration of infantry and cavalry against Beersheba. The offensive was in five phases. The attacking forces included the Australian Mounted Division, to which the SHMB was now attached as a machine gun squadron. Led by Australians wielding bayonets, the town was captured on the day of the assault. As Cruttwell says wryly: 'they had not yet been supplied with swords'.[7]

Wade's photographic record continues.

It is the lull before the storm that becomes the first battle of Gaza. As if to emphasize this paradox, Mozart is performed at the Temple of Hibis. Preparations are made for the first attack. With the preparations, Wade travels to Tel-el-Fara, Wadi-el-Esusin, the continuation of Wadi Ghuzze, and a flooded area in Shellal. He sees the construction of a railway bridge at Um-Urgan in the Wadi Ghuzze before moving to Tel-al-Fara. A railway engine is derailed. At Khan Unis, the wounded arrive at the CCS and motor ambulances come by train. The CCS moves forward and camps. The 52nd Division advances, accompanied by the Camel Corps Ambulance. The 4th Light Horse Hospital Field Ambulance crosses Wadi Ghuzze at Abu Ghallyon Chalk Cliff and the Brigade bivouac, constructing ablution areas at Wadi Ghuzze, near Tel-el-Fara. Wade identifies a delousing train and observes railway construction between Wadi-Sheik-Nuran and Shellal.

The first battle over, Wade returns to Cairo shortly before the second battle of Gaza.

After the second battle, Wade watches horses being watered in Wadi Ghuzze, with the chalk cliffs of Esani in the background. Tanks lie abandoned. Wade photographs Colonel Cahill's Stationary Hospital. The forces advance to Khan Unis, where the SHMB Field Ambulance hospital is in action. Shortly afterwards, General Murray's successor, General Allenby, arrives and the army's General Headquarters move swiftly to Kelab. Many photographs record the military advance into Philistia, the coastal region north of Gaza.

The third battle of Gaza looms, and Wade finds himself at Amara. The artillery advances towards Quelfa. Evacuation of the wounded is in part by four-wheel drive tractors that had towed the guns. Amara proves to be a busy railhead. From here, Turkish, as well as Allied wounded, are evacuated, some by train. A wire road has been laid, and surgeons are shown being conducted across its surface. An aeroplane circles overhead. It is not clear whether it is German or British. There are British walking wounded.

Wade is with the Field Ambulance as Beersheba is taken. The station is seen in the distance and the town hall shown. A photograph records Allied ambulances, the unit's flag and a nearby mosque, together with a street scene milling with bewildered local people. A well is conspicuous. Fruit sellers are active. The fighting ended, Wade returns to Cairo via Ludd, El Arish, Kantara and Port Said.

Jerusalem falls

Prior to the advance on Beersheba, the Field Ambulance hospital took over a rest camp at El Arish, which was to be used as a centre for attending to slight wounds and medical disorders. In September 1916, the Ambulance became part of the Australian Mounted Division Advanced Operating Unit. Later, the Brigade converted to camels and the wounded were carried by 'camel ambulance', in much the same way that Larrey had adopted in 1798.[12,A]

Perceptive and imaginative, Allenby fully realized the importance of the Army Medical Services. He took into careful account the views of senior medical officers. A large hospital, a medical supplies depot and a reception station were assembled in Cairo to serve the needs of an army that eventually grew to nearly 500,000 men. Strategically alert, Allenby was also aware of the tactical significance of ambulances and tents: they could give information to the enemy's aeroplanes about forthcoming offensives. For this reason, CCS's were instructed not to unpack their equipment until the last possible moment before an attack was launched.

The outstanding success of the third offensive enabled the overrunning of Gaza and, north-east of Hebron, the capture of the rail junction that led to Jerusalem. Half the Turkish army now retired northwards along the coastal plain and half into the Judean hills overlooking Jerusalem. Allenby's forces survived precarious roads, poor weather and formidable Turkish counterattacks to enter the city on 17th December 1917.[7,8]

Wade's photographs resume.

The Judean Hills overlook the city. The road is being repaired and used by donkey water carriers. Wade is outside the Italian Hospice. He photographs the Jaffa Gate, the temple area and the Mosque of Omar. He walks along the Via Dolorosa and sees Solomon's Well while noting Bedouin encampments and local people collecting firewood. In Jerusalem, he observes the Jericho Road to the east of the city, a view of the city from the Mount of Olives and another of the Mount itself. He views Ramleh from the Norman Tower, recording the Norman ruins and the Jerusalem road four miles east of Enab. Subsequently, he sees the sea front at Jaffa and Defran. The 4th Light Horse Field Ambulance bivouacs near Enab, on the Ramleh-to-Jerusalem Road. Wade enters Bethlehem and Nazareth with the advancing army and, at Baalbeck, takes advantage of an opportunity to visit the magnificent ruins of Karnak.

Advance on Damascus

The way was now open for an assault on Damascus, the key to Aleppo and the Turkish frontier. Wade's increasing influence and responsibilities were confirmed when he was gazetted Temporary Colonel (TF) on 8th September 1918 at precisely the same time as his distinguished contemporaries Frederick Treves (p 53) and Alfred Webb-Johnson (p 320), each in command of one of the Surgical Divisions of the EEF.

A combination of geography and expediency determined Allenby's strategy. There were two avenues for a drive northwards: the sea and the railway. The rocky coast and the commitment of naval forces to British home waters and to the Atlantic determined that the maritime approach was impracticable. However, the single line railway that ran southwards from Constantinople to Damascus divided. An easterly component, the Hejaz railway, passed through Amman on its long route to the Gulf, while the westerly section headed for Cairo, with an important connection with Haifa.

To his chagrin, Allenby was now handicapped by a further withdrawal of troops for the Flanders campaigns. Although reinforcements reached Allenby from India, he was compelled to send 60,000 of his best troops to Europe. The Turks also suffered, and the German command changed. Falkenhayn was replaced by Liman von Sanders, but the expertise and confidence of his Asia Corps could not compensate for the typhus and malaria that scourged the Turks and led to ever-increasing numbers of deserters.

The period of relative inactivity that followed the capture of Jerusalem allowed Allenby a respite to plan for a 'Final Advance', an offensive that would carry the EEF to Turkey itself. The EEF had at last achieved air superiority, and the purpose was to capture Deraa where the single railway line from Damascus divided. The task of destroying this rail link was given to the Arabs.

Wade took photographs of the final advance.

It is March 1918. The army approaches Jericho. The Field Ambulance rests near the Good Samaritan Inn. The troops enter Jericho and encounter an Australian Field Ambulance. One of Wade's surgical cars is evident. There are wounded from a cavalry charge. Wade records the Wadi Kelt and views Talat-ed-Dum, the Jericho Road near Bethany, the Desert Corps headquarters looking towards the Dead Sea and the Mount of Temptation in the Jordan Valley. 'Jericho Jane' is recorded in Wadi Nimrin and the First Lothian Hospital Field Ambulance in the Jordan Valley. In Jericho are the buildings of the German Sea Transport Company, one building partly destroyed by bombs.

   Wade has a fine eye for architectural detail of classical significance. He observes and photographs the Roman aqueduct that crosses the Ain-ed-Duk stream in Wadi Nouameia, Jordan. In Amman, Wade observes Es Salt, Wadi Hamman, a view six miles from the north of Amman and another of Wadi Amman with the railway station on the Hedjak railway. He records the appearance of a Turkish Hospital where sick and wounded are being loaded on to motor lorries. Four miles north of Amman, he notes the viaduct on the railway. It is the season for corn trading, and it is against this simple agrarian background that part of the army advances along the maritime plain.

For the final attack on Damascus, 12 mobile, surgical operating divisions came into action. Some of these mobile units were as many as 400 miles from the railhead that supplied the army. They undertook emergency surgery in a manner that became familiar in Africa during the Second World War. The Fifth Cavalry Division, for example, was accompanied by a surgical team commanded by Major Pirie Watson,[C] one of Wade's many Edinburgh friends and colleagues who were with the EEF.

   On 19th September 1918, Allenby's forces launched an attack in overwhelming strength and overran the dispirited Turks, driving them towards the hills or into captivity. By 21st September, the two Turkish armies west of Jordan had been broken, their munitions and transport destroyed in the narrow valley that led from Nablus to the river Jordan. The 4th Turkish Army was pursued into the Moab desert and cut down by the merciless nomads. Damascus was occupied on 2nd October. As the war moved towards its conclusion, Aleppo was reached on 26th October. It was the end. In Wade's words:

'Break through at 6 a.m. At 11 a.m. my small party followed the cavalry and until the Armistice was constantly on the move.'

There is a long camel convoy on the road to Tiberias. Wade approaches Acre and in Syria, sees the Dog River and the Lebanon. Sidon and the Ladder of Tyre follow. The convoy reaches Beirouth [*sic*]. The advance towards Tripoli ensues. They pass through Homs on the way to Aleppo.

   In the streets, Wade photographs a blind beggar, a fortune teller and scenes from the bazaar. The 'golden window' of the citadel is conspicuous. Soon afterwards, a squadron of Indian cavalry pass in formation. The railway is nearby but so is a travelling convoy of Bedouin. Baalbeck offers another opportunity to view ancient ruins of great beauty. From the summit of the Lebanon, he is near Malacca, accompanied by his colleagues, Mance and Smith.

   The journey to Damascus takes him through the Yarmack Gorge. The rail bridge is being repaired, but this does not prevent the passage of a supply train. In Damascus, he records the Barada River, views from the hospital and many others that include a courtyard, a town square and street scenes of great interest.

Towards the end of 1918, Wade visits Port Said, but early in 1919, he is again with the victorious army in Damascus. He sees the El Afulle station on the Haifa to Damascus railway. Scenes in the city include a court-yard, a town square and the Barada River. There is a further miscellany of illustrations of bombed transports at Jenin, the destroyed station at Deraa and an ambulance train on the Aleppo railway.

Weapons

The weapons employed in the Palestine and Syrian campaigns were heavy artillery, field guns, mortars, machine guns and rifles with bay-onets.[13–16] The magazine-loading Lee-Enfield rifle was a deadly weapon when aimed accurately from a distance of up to half a mile. Vickers machine guns directed at troop concentrations could inflict great numbers of injuries quickly. Grenades could be thrown in trenches as they were at Gaza. Shells destroyed concentrations of troops in the open, while howitzers were effective against an enemy dug into bunkers. A small proportion of wounds was attributable to dynamite, used by both combatants for the disruption of railways. For many months, the Turks, supported by Germany, had command of the air. At first they dropped darts. Later, small bombs were employed. Although the proportion of wounds caused by aerial attack was small, the slowly moving biplanes of 1916–18 could cause panic as well as injury among non-combatants and the nomadic peoples.

Transport of the wounded

In the course of the Palestinian campaign of 1916–18, it was axiomatic that the wounded should be treated quickly. It was also rec-ognized that they should be moved as rapidly and painlessly from the field of action as possible. It was for this reason that nine of every 10 casualties were evacuated from the battlefield to a CCS.

The majority of the wounded were carried at first by stretcher but sand sledges were also used. Many other casualties were borne by horse, camel (Appendix 2.1) or mule. Thereafter, road and rail trans-port conveyed them to the nearest ambulance hospital, a CCS or, finally, a base hospital. Unless casualties could be carried by the inland single-track railway, camel and motor ambulance and surgical units were compelled to use the primitive roads and, often, to cross the desert. A serious difficulty was that roads through the many mountainous areas, such as those of the Jordan valley, were narrow and of low quality. Some caterpillar track vehicles were in use. Seaborne transport was impracticable and casualties could not be evacuated by air. Although there were observation balloons, there were no large aeroplanes. So far as possible, those wounded who required long-term care were returned to the United Kingdom so that there was an incessant demand for ambulance ships (p 25, 135).

Figure 8.11 Transport of the wounded. *The key to successful care of the wounded was rapid transportation. Although railways were a determinant of strategy, roads of variable quality could be used tactically. In the Yarmack Gorge, as this photograph shows, bridges could be crucial to an advance*

Figure 8.12 The influence of camel transport. *Within months of the start of General Murray's advance to the Egyptian frontier, it was realized that horses, such as those brought by the Australian forces, could not be watered easily. Camels were therefore substituted for horses and horse ambulances converted to camel ambulances*

Figure 8.13 A camel ambulance. *Wounded soldiers could be carried by camel across ground inaccessible to motorized transport*

Figure 8.14 Camel transport in 1798. *More than a century earlier, Napoleon's Surgeon General, Dominique Larrey, employed camel transport for the wounded in precisely the manner adopted in 1916*

Figure 8.15 Sand sledge. *These simple devices could carry the wounded short distances across flat, sandy terrain*

Figure 8.16 Elephant transport. *Indian forces brought with them a number of elephants, which could tow guns and wagons when the ground was unsuitable for tractors*

Figure 8.17 Array of motorized ambulances. *Motorized transport came into its own after the capture of Jerusalem and during the 'Final Advance'*

Figure 8.18 A column of transport. *As the Turks withdrew, it became less hazardous to assemble increasing columns of wagons*

Figure 8.19 Failure of motor transport. *In spite of their apparent value, the conditions of desert sand often led to difficulty, although ambulances and cars could be dragged from the sand by steam tractor*

Figure 8.20 Transporting wounded by canal or river. *In the early operations of 1916, it was possible to carry many sick and wounded by river or canal. Overall, there were ten times as many sick as there were wounded*

Wounds

Wade held his own views of the treatment of war wounds, opinions derived from long and bitter experience in the field (Appendix 8.1). From an understanding of the weapons adopted by the combatants, it was possible to predict the most common form of injury. Shell and bullet wounds of the lower limb were commonplace and fracture of the femur represented a particularly large problem.[10,17] From February to November 1918, at least 5,000 new cases of fractured femur occurred in the British Army in France alone, accounting for 5% of all casualties. In 1916, Gray estimated the mortality of this injury at nearly 80%.[18]

Table 8.2 Proportions of wounds incurred by the Egyptian Expeditionary Force, 1916–20

Site of wound	Number of cases
Lower limb	2,156
Lower limb with amputation	48
Upper limb	1,319
Upper limb with amputation	18
Head and neck	704
Chest	230
Abdomen	134
Back	279

Of the wounds sustained in Palestine and Syria during 1916–20 (Table 8.2), 3,110 were caused by bullets, shrapnel,[D] bombs, bayonets or other weapons, while 1,584 were accidental or 'undefined'. In desert warfare, the most common forms of wound were those caused by rifle and machine-gun fire and high explosive shells. The presence of large numbers of horses and camels made local soil contamination common, but the desert campaigns were quite different from those endured in Flanders. Wounds suffered in the battles being fought across the moist agricultural lands of Belgium and France inevitably contained the spores of clostridia.[17] In wounds contaminated by spore-bearing soil, gas gangrene was very frequent and tetanus a constant threat to those who had not received anti-tetanus serum.[E] Sepsis was rife and erysipelas and 'pyaemia' common.[F] In Palestine and Syria, by contrast, the atmosphere was generally dry and hot and much of the soil relatively clean. Consequently, wounds were less often the site for the spores of anaerobic bacteria and, like those encountered in the South African campaigns of 1899–1902 (p 29), often healed quickly.

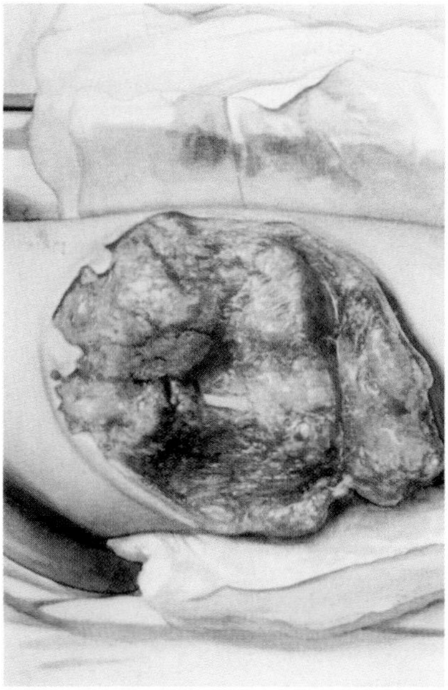

Surgical treatment of the wounded

Until the advent of antiseptic surgery, the delayed surgical treatment of battlefield wounded was hardly recognized. In the Franco–Prussian war of 1870, the Germans benefited from their adoption of Listerian principles of antisepsis whereas the French did not. Textbooks of that time state that, overall, barely one in five of the wounded survived. It came to be recognized that slow treatment exaggerated the risk of oligaemic and neurogenic shock, dehydration and limb ischaemia and predisposed to cellulitis, sepsis and gangrene.

Early surgical care was the first objective. Radiological techniques had become essential. So far as possible, minor injuries were treated locally, minimizing the demand for transport. Severe secondary haemorrhage represented a special danger. In immediate treatment, a 'rifle splint' had often been used but proved difficult to apply and had many disadvantages. Although Liston's long splint was substituted, this also was condemned.

It was for these reasons that the Thomas splint came into its own.[G] Its successful use

Figure 8.21 The Carrel-Dakin technique of wound salvage. *The figure shows a wound before treatment. The application of the technique was described by Abadie (1919). However, this method of perfusing a wound with a sterile isotonic solution was impracticable in the field*

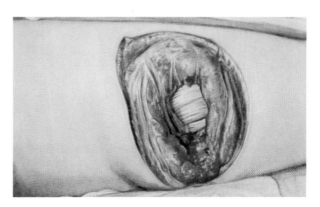

Figure 8.22 The Carrel-Dakin technique. *In this instance, an excellent result had been achieved*

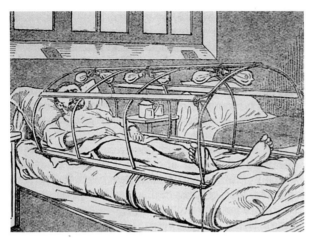

Figure 8.23 Treatment of shock. *Rest and warmth were emphasized in this 1918 drawing, but there is no evidence that fluid is being restored*

became one of Wade's principal purposes. The splints were light and easily applied. Thomas splints were of particular value for gunshot wounds of the femur, but they were also useful in the care of knee joint injuries and other fractures of the lower extremity. The Thomas splint enabled these injuries to be immobilized, protecting the wounded man against the incessant jarring movements that primitive transport caused and reducing the risk of delayed haemorrhage. The value of the Thomas splint was particularly apparent in situations where roads were virtually non-existent. From his experience at the Battle of Arras, April 1917, Gray had become convinced that the Thomas splint should be used routinely.[18] In comments made after the war, Wade strongly supported this opinion.[10] In Palestine, the case for the Thomas splint was pressed by the surgeons and readily accepted by General Allenby, who issued instructions for the manufacture and supply of these splints in great numbers. The benefits were seen quickly. In CCS's, the mortality from gunshot wounds of the lower limb fell from nearly 50% in 1916 to 15.6% in 1917. With the aid of this splint, men with fractured femurs could be transported safely for many miles on camels, in limbers or in the light Ford ambulances. They were taken for example to Corps Main Dressing Stations such as those on the banks of the Jordan, where the facility was close to advanced operating units such as that in which Wade served.

In the treatment of haemorrhagic shock, morphine was administered for the relief of pain. After the war, Wade described how the

Figure 8.24 Wade operating during the battles of Gaza. *By the time the battles of Gaza had ended, Wade had been recommended for the award of the Distinguished Service Order*

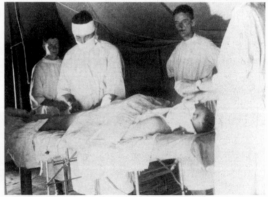

Figure 8.25 Another Edinburgh surgeon, Pirie Watson, in a tented operating theatre. *Wade's friend and colleague served throughout the campaign, leading an advanced surgical unit*

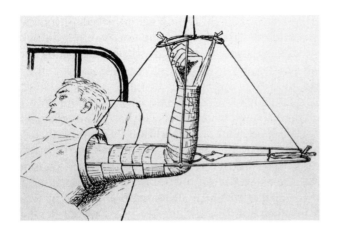

Figure 8.26 A splint for compound fracture of the arm. *The principles adopted in the design of the Thomas splint (p 154) were applied in 1918, ensuring immobilization of a missile injury of the arm*

Regimental Medical Officer (RMO) on active service was, in effect, the family doctor of his battalion. The RMO was expected to cover wounds, relieve pain, arrest haemorrhage, provide rapid and comfortable transport and minimize shock (Box 8.1).[11] Experience had shown that there were great dangers in the application of tourniquets. The Medical Officer was advised to grasp bleeding points with pressure forceps and to send patients to hospital with these haemostats applied. Minimizing shock depended largely on the thoroughness with which pain was relieved, haemorrhage arrested and rapid and comfortable transport provided.

Blood transfusion was impracticable and in Wade's 1921 lecture, was not mentioned.[10] In civilian practice in centres such as Edinburgh, an organized, central, public blood transfusion service did not become a reality until the mid 1930's (p 220). The safe storage of blood for use in civilian hospitals or by the military was not yet possible, and the administration of blood by direct, person-to-person transfusion was impossible in the field. Indeed, in the whole course of

---

Box 8.1 Hints for the prevention of wound shock in front line units of the first army in France, issued in 1918

- Control bleeding by firm bandaging, blood vessel ligature, packing wounds with gauze and the application of a tourniquet
- Combat cold – clothes, blankets, hot drinks, artificial heat
- Combat pain – efficient dressing and splinting, avoid redressing of wounds; careful carrying and handling; careful loading and driving of ambulances; silence; cheerfulness
- Morphine, but rarely in doses above ¼ grain
- Combat infection – dress wounds carefully, putting nothing in them; rapid evacuation
- Fluid to drink

the First World War, fewer than 200–230 transfusions are said to have been attempted. It was known that sterile saline could relieve shock but the preparation of dried plasma, to be reconstituted and used for the same purpose, had not yet been devised.

Surgical operations were often undertaken in tents near the battle lines. Thirty of Wade's operating cars (p 122) had been assembled prior to the Egyptian campaigns. They proved of use at Kantara and at the second battle of Gaza. However, climatic conditions determined that it was more practicable to use the cars as sterilizing units than as operating theatres. Instead of working with the Field Ambulance, one of Wade's mobile operating cars was therefore adopted by the Australians as a mobile advanced operating unit near the frontline.

The greatest surgical innovation of the First World War was delayed primary suture. However, the application of this principle to abdominal wounds proved disastrous, and attempts were soon made to undertake early abdominal surgery.[19] In Egypt, the facilities for specialized forms of treatment, including plastic surgery and neurosurgery, were limited by comparison with those available in Europe. Nevertheless, the surgical instruments and techniques available at this time were as good as those employed in concurrent civilian practice and not significantly different from many adopted in the Second World War. There were, of course, neither chemotherapeutic agents nor antibiotics.

Wade made no reference in his writings to battlefield anaesthesia. As in the Crimean, Franco-Prussian and South-African wars, chloroform, administered by open mask, was generally employed because of its non-inflammability.

Non-battle casualties

In the Palestinian and Syrian campaigns, endemic and epidemic infectious and parasitic diseases remained the scourges that they had always been. The two principal diseases that affected the troops were dysentery and malaria (Tables 8.3 and 8.4). Dysentery was particularly common during periods of trench warfare and in this situation, diphtheria was also identified. Flies were numerous in the latrines although the situation improved when incineration was introduced. Typhoid was commonplace and life-threatening[16]. Schistosomiasis (bilharziasis) was a frequent consequence of washing in water infested with the snail *Bulinus truncatus*.[20,21,E] Skin ulcers quickly followed the scratching associated with scabies and the ulcers often became infected. Sand fly fever and jaundice (infective hepatitis) were not uncommon and malnutrition was attributed to a deficiency of fresh fruit and vegetables. Taken with the large numbers of cases of skin and venereal disease, the non-battle casualty rate amounted to 741 of every 1000 individuals. During the period 1916–1918, the total number of such casualties reached the enormous figure of 503,377 (Table 8.4).

Table 8.3 Casualties incurred during the Egyptian, Palestinian and Syrian campaigns of 1915–18. Among 'Other Ranks', the ratio of battle to non-battle casualties was 1:10

Casualties	Officers	Other ranks	Total
Battle	3,570	47,881	51,451
Killed			7,394
Wounded			37,193
Died of wounds			2,993
Missing			2,486
Prisoners of war			1,385
Non-battle	17,977	485,400	503,377
Total	21,547	533,281	554,828

Table 8.4 Some causes of hospital admission for non-battle disease 1916–18

Disease	Number of cases	Deaths
Diarrhoea	34,493	16
Dysentery	14,844	484
Enteric fever (all forms)	4,118	148
Malaria	40,144	854
Venereal disease	31,051	0
Pneumonia	2,818	1,197

An armistice is declared

An Armistice was declared on 31st October 1918, only 12 days before the cessation of hostilities in Europe. After the Armistice, much of the army remained in Egypt. There was an opportunity for Wade to travel widely and he continued to use his camera freely. His pictures are a diary of his journeys.

Soon after the armistice, there is time to travel by boat, up the Nile. Memphis is the first objective; Wade views the Sphinx and visits the colossi of Luxor, Karnak and the Valley of the Kings. He passes Aswan and records the Aswan dam and Elephantine Island and sails on to Wady [*sic*] Halfa, where the vessel crosses the Soudanese [*sic*] border. Past Atbara, the photographs carry the reader to Khartoum, where Wade, like so many of his compatriots, is anxious to visit Gordon College, Omdurman and the Mahdi's tomb. He returns to Kantara on the Suez Canal, where he photographs an Army Service Corps' dump, the custom house and the swing bridge.

Figure 8.27 Scots wha hae! *The numerous Scottish units engaged in the campaigns of 1916–18 brought with them their pipes and drums and took every opportunity, particularly in the 'phoney' war of early 1916, of demonstrating their skills*

Figure 8.28 Armistice of 1918. *After the armistice of 1918, Turkish troops surrendered in very large numbers. In the background is one of the Egyptian Expeditionary Force's ambulance trains*

Figure 8.29 The litter of war. *Wade's photograph records the fate of one of the guns destroyed in the fighting*

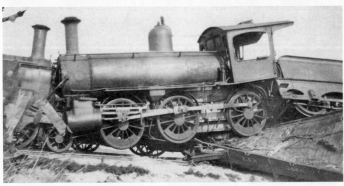

Figure 8.30 The detritus of war. *In the aftermath of the Palestinian and Syrian campaigns, many damaged railway engines lay on or near the single-line railway that the Germans had created so painstakingly before the war*

Photographs taken in Amara (Al' Amarah), on the road from Basra to Baghdad, suggest strongly, but do not prove, that Wade visited the Mesopotamian field of operations. There is little doubt that some of his close colleagues had been stationed there.

Among his records are 14 further photographic prints labelled 'Turkish photographs'.[H] They include one of General Kress von Kressenstein, and their nature suggests strongly that the photographs were taken by a Turkish prisoner who may have given them to Wade. He was in the habit of acquiring mementos from patients he had treated.

Figure 8.31 Turkish troops firing from a front-line trench. *This is one of many photographs believed to have been obtained by Wade from Turkish wounded for whom he and his fellow surgeons cared*

Figure 8.32 Turkish surgical unit. *The Turkish armies had considerable surgical support. However, water-borne infection, skin disease, malaria and malnutrition ravaged their forces and contributed to a decline in morale*

Figure 8.33 The Turkish command. *During the early phase of the Egyptian and Palestinian campaigns of 1916–18, the Turks remained well established in Jerusalem and Damascus. Here, Wade uses captured Turkish photographs to show high-ranking officials driving through Jerusalem*

Soon afterwards, Wade embarked for the voyage home, and in late May 1919, arrived back in Scotland.

A peace treaty with Germany was finally signed on 28th June 1919. As we have seen, Wade had been elevated to the Order of the White Eagle of Serbia and, in the Victory Honours, was made a Companion of the Order of St Michael and St George (CMG). Many letters of congratulation attested to the wide respect in which he was held for his selfless devotion to duty. He already had been awarded the Distinguished Service Order and had been twice mentioned in Dispatches (p 318).

Complete release from military duties was another matter. On 17th March 1919, the long-serving WS Caw, Treasurer and Clerk to the Managers of the Royal Infirmary of Edinburgh, the RIE, thanked Wade for a letter enquiring about his release from the army. Mr Caw addressed Wade as: Colonel Henry Wade, AMS, c/o Director of Medical Services, 1st Echelon, Egyptian Expeditionary Force. He told Wade:

'The Managers applied for your release through the proper channel (the Scottish Medical Service Emergency Committee, the SMSEC) on November 26th 1918. Three of the other officers named have now returned to duty here.'[22]

However, the matter remained in doubt. On 13th March 1919, Caw explained to TH Graham, Secretary SMSEC, Glasgow, saying that Wade had told him that he had no knowledge of any application having been made for his release. Two days later, TH Graham replied:

'An application has already been made to the Ministry of National Service for the release at the earliest possible moment of Dr Comrie and Mr Wade.'

The following week, Caw reassured Wade and he was finally demobilized on 7th July. On 8th September 1919, the Managers of the RIE reappointed Wade to the position of Assistant Surgeon unanimously. The post was for five years, with effect from 8th November.

In an ironic twist to the tale, on 8th July 1919, Wade's bankers, Holts (Army Agents and Bankers), sent him his demobilization gratuity statement.

'On account of the gratuity due to you on demobilisation as per the enclosed statement, we beg to advise you that the account has credit for £786.11.11d. The statement shows a gratuity for the period 10/9/14 to 15/5/19 to be 372 days pay at 45/– a day = £837/–/–d.'

This amount was judged by the War Office to be a sufficient reward for five years of military service in the face of the enemy. It was not assessed so generously by the Inland Revenue (Chapter 9).

In an epilogue, Wade wrote to Geddes and Seif, Luxor, Egypt, on 19th November 1919 to ask them to make enlargements of his photographic collection. The *Luxor Photo Stores* confirmed on 3rd December that they would do his work and would charge 10 piastres for each print. They said quaintly:

'Luxor now is very longing to see Colonel Wade and any of his friends who may be desiring to make her a visit.'[1]

Chapter 9

Peace returns, practice resumes

1919–51

At eleven o'clock this morning came to an end the cruellest
and most terrible war that has ever scourged mankind.

(Lloyd George, in a speech to the House of Commons, 11th November 1918)

Nearly two years in South Africa, together with five years in the
Mediterranean and the Middle East, meant that, by his 43rd
year, Henry Wade had spent one quarter of his adult life in
regions of war. He had sailed from Newcastle to the Mediterranean in
1915. He returned to Scotland from Syria in May 1919. Britain had
been devastated by conflict. Now it was plunged into the worst pandemic since the Black Death. The influenza outbreak that began in
1918, attacking armies entrenched in the Flanders mud, as well as a
malnourished civilian population, killed great numbers. In total,
150,000 people perished in Britain.

Large numbers of letters to and from friends and colleagues were
now the order of the day. Writing to George Fraser of Dundee on 15th
June 1919, Wade said:

'The fighting days of the Scottish Horse Mounted Brigade Field
Ambulance are over'[1]

Memories of the long road from Hebron to Beersheba, on which it was
wise to carry a revolver,[2] were fading, but, as Fraser recalled:

'You once said to me: some of the places you have seen will
never leave you.'[3]

For the millions who had survived the horrors of the war, the return
to peace was difficult and demanding. An Armistice had been declared
on 11th November 1918. The covenant of the embryonic League of
Nations was completed on 14th February 1919, championed by an ail-
ing American President Wilson. It was not until 23rd June 1919 that
a Peace Treaty with Germany was signed at Versailles. Russia remained
in turmoil, Germany in chaos. British troops left Murmansk but
retained a presence in Cologne until 1926. In the Middle East,

Chapter Summary
• After the war
• Surgical practice
• The nursing home
• Equipping the nursing home
• Relationships with general practitioners
• Nature of private surgery
• Relationships with patients
• Patients' fees
• Patients' questions
• Relationships with ex-service men and women
• Relationships with companies
• The world without
• The future

Mesopotamia (Iraq) benefited from British protection, but French soldiers were in conflict with the Syrians at Baalbek.

The country was in economic disarray. Tens of thousands, returning to their homes and families after long periods of absence, searched for employment. Army officers who had survived trench warfare became bus drivers, naval commanders who had braved Atlantic submarines and North Sea raiders set up small corner shops. Royal Air Force pilots slaved as civil service clerks while the medical profession, seeking to learn civilian skills, struggled to re-establish hospital contacts and to rebuild their practices.

Against this confused and disturbed background, punctuated by the dramatic scuttling on 21st June 1919 of the German High Seas Fleet at Scapa Flow, war leaders were starting to publish their memoirs and artists, architects, writers and musicians their compositions, plays and books. Confidence in a nebulous future was threatened by Keynes' *The economic consequences of the peace* but the spirit of hope was uplifted by Somerset Maugham who wrote *The moon and sixpence*. HL Mencken published *The American language* and Pablo Picasso, at the height of his powers, completed the design of sets for Diaghilev's *Three cornered hat*. Almost unnoticed, the death occurred of the last of the pre-Raphaelite brotherhood, William Michael Rosetti. Edward Elgar's cello concerto received its first performance as Edwin Lutyens designed the Cenotaph for Whitehall.

After the war

Henry Wade knew he was trebly fortunate. He had suffered ill health but recovered both from dysentery and malaria.[A] Unlike many of his friends and colleagues, he had survived the war and still owned a fine house at 6 Manor Place, Edinburgh. The house had been empty but was intact. He had a secure consultant appointment to the Royal Infirmary of Edinburgh, the RIE, and support from the Royal College of Surgeons of Edinburgh, the RCSEd. Moreover, he was now gaining proper public recognition for the services that he had given freely over a period of five years. He received many warm letters on the award of the Companion of the Order of St Michael and St George. On 7th June 1919, DP Hartley wrote to congratulate Colonel Wade on this new honour.[4] A month later, Wade thanked Hugh Ferguson for his generous words and commented 'We saw a good deal of the war together'.[5] Professor Edwin Bramwell added his laudatory voice.[6]

Henry Wade was a realist. He had neither wife nor family. To an extent, this alleviated the problems that now faced him. He was ambitious to succeed in his chosen profession, and an early step was to make sure that his qualifications were properly recorded again in the *Medical Directory*, which was now available for 18/–d.[7] He was conscientious, hard-working, skilled and responsible and soon became a member of the Emergency Medical Service of the Department of

Health for Scotland. There were to be no short cuts and no easy options on the road to success. But, like so many, he had to deal with petty bureaucracy and with administrators who, having avoided conscription, found themselves in positions of authority in local and national government.

Returning to his home at Manor Place with the honorary title of Colonel, Army Medical Service, there was an appreciative and gracious welcome. Wade received unexpected gifts from a variety of sources. The presents ranged from a brace of pheasants and books to a Melton Mowbray pie for Christmas.[8] Kindly invitations varied from luncheon with the Purse Bearer to His Grace the Lord High Commissioner and dinner at the University Club with TF Dewar to a weekend with Jean McLean Hunter, tea with Katherine Cameron and a recital from Miss Lucy Herbert. Mrs Hunter sent a report of the Dumfries Burns Club Centenary:

> 'The best record I have ever seen in any paper of such a function.'

Like so many other ex-servicemen and women, Wade was faced with challenges of a kind he had not encountered since 1914. The insurance values of his house and furniture were about to increase to £2,500 and £2,000, respectively. He sought the advice of his elder brother, Thomas Callander Wade WS, on the best action to take.[9] One reason for these increases was Wade's wish to improve the quality of the fittings. He was anxious to install a large alabaster or Mexican onyx pendant close to the roof of one of his large rooms and asked Faraday and Sons of Wardour Street, London, whether they could send a pair of electric candlesticks similar to those provided previously.[10]

The RIE had survived the vicissitudes of the war and was rapidly regaining both strength and vitality. Its responsibilities are described in Chapter 10. Henry Wade quickly resumed his duties at this, the largest of the country's voluntary hospitals. Like his fellow consultants, he received no salary and indeed was forbidden by the terms of his contract to accept payment for his services – a constraint explained by Wade to a parent who enquired about the fee for an operation in the RIE on his daughter who was an arts student.[11] Wade's hospital responsibilities were not confined to the RIE. He continued to serve the Leith Hospital. In many other parts of the country, new buildings and new services were springing up and, on 26th

Figure 9.1 Colonel Henry Wade. *On his return to Britain in May 1919, at the end of his service in Gallipoli and then in Egypt, Palestine and Syria, Wade was demobilized. His release came on 7th July but he was not freed from his obligations to the Scottish Medical Service Emergency Committee until 2nd September. This portrait was made during the intervening period*

December 1922, he was invited to become a consultant surgeon to the recently opened Peebles War Memorial Hospital.

Surgical practice

In peace and war, Wade had already displayed to the full the qualities of the successful surgeon – knowledge, manual skill, stamina, honesty and humanity. It was hardly surprising, therefore, that his exceptional services should be in demand from people in many walks of life and many counties. There was much to be done in catching up on pre-war practice. With increasing frequency during the years 1919 to 1923, patients were referred to Wade by more than 50 general practitioners from many parts of Scotland and the north of England. His experience in the army and the fact that he had served with numerous general practitioners and surgeons who now asked for his advice and help, contributed to an increasingly busy life. A large proportion of these general practices were in Edinburgh, but others were to be found in towns as widely separated as Bo'ness and Inverness, Hawick and Manchester, Polmont and Nottingham, London and Wick. Military, naval, business, legal and commercial interests were evident, as well as civilian. Finally, there was his extremely well-known and increasing expertise in surgical urology, a speciality that he was soon to exploit to the full (Chapter 12).

The nursing home

After his return to the United Kingdom in 1919, it was only to be expected that Henry Wade would continue to develop a private practice of his own. He was not poor, but he earned little from his appointment to the RIE and his principal source of income would continue to be his individual surgical practice. His patients were first seen at 6 Manor Place and it was here that his secretary worked and his business correspondence came. However, 6 Manor Place was equipped neither for clinical investigation nor for operative surgery. For these purposes, Wade was obliged to use the operating theatre suites of the Queen Mary Nursing Home at 29 Chalmers Street, Edinburgh, and the Royal Scottish Nursing Home which had premises at 48 Moray Place and 20 Torphichen Street.

A more ambitious plan was called for. The concept envisaged a Nursing Home of his own. To prosecute this plan, he joined forces with his friend and colleague David Wilkie (p 42). Together, they went into partnership to establish a new clinic. On 16th May 1921, they purchased 35 Drumsheugh Gardens, Edinburgh, from the trustees of the late Mr Holmes Ivory WS. In legal terms, they were 'Trustees for a joint adventure', that is, partners. The purchase included the 'pleasure ground in front of the said garden'. The price was £3,800. The words of the instrument of sale are illuminating:

'Disponed by Trustees of the deceased Holmes Ivory, to Henry Wade, Surgeon, residing at 6 Manor Place, Edinburgh and David Percival Dalbreck Wilkie, Surgeon, residing at 56 Manor Place, Edinburgh, aforesaid survivor, as Trustees and Trustee for a Joint Adventure for the establishment and carrying on of an Institution in Edinburgh under the name of the Private Clinic.'

Thirty-five Drumsheugh Gardens, now the Bonham Hotel, was well placed in the most central and affluent part of the city. Wade and Wilkie converted the building to allow modern operative surgery. The property bore the simple title '*Private Clinic*'. To an enquiring patient, Wade explained that by using the word Clinic:

Figure 9.2 35 Drumsheugh Gardens, Edinburgh. *In partnership with David Wilkie, Wade purchased 35 Drumsheugh Gardens on 16th May 1921. It was the first step in a bold move to establish a Private Clinic. Subsequently, 36 Drumsheugh Gardens was bought in 1923, 34 Drumsheugh Gardens in 1928. After Wilkie's death in 1936, Wade added the top flat of 33 Drumsheugh Gardens*

'I mean to convey to all who are interested the information that it is a variety of Nursing Home concerned primarily with the investigation of disease or its treatment by special means such as are not available except in the most completely equipped modern hospital.'

The Clinic was ready by 26th April 1922. It was staffed, among others, by a Miss Grant to whom patients reported. She seems to have been the receptionist and secretary. The nursing staff included a Miss Pike, the matron, and a Miss Cameron. The arrangements for financing the Home were made with care. On 29th November 1922, Wade wrote to Thomas Stevenson Esq, stockbrokers of Glasgow, saying:[12]

'Since I was last in communication with you I have embarked on the venture of purchasing, equipping and organising a certain variety of Nursing Home. This is now completed and gives every promise of being a success...and is entirely free of debt.'

Wade and Wilkie's work prospered, and the activities of the Private Clinic expanded steadily. By 27th December 1923, the partners were in a position to buy 36 Drumsheugh Gardens from Helen Scott Watt or Fleming for a price of £4,000. In 1928, the Private Clinic expanded further and on 4th July, Wade and Wilkie bought 34 Drumsheugh Gardens for £4,000 from Sir George Aitken Clark Hutchison KC, MP.

The fact that Wade and Wilkie were able to finance their projects without having to borrow money provides a clear indication of their professional success and financial skill. Allowing for inflation and the change in the value of currency, the charges for private surgery in 1922 were comparable with those in 2005. Thus, a 'bladder operation' and aftercare cost 30 guineas (£31.50). When it is remembered that a living wage for a manual worker in 1920 was no more than £2 a week, this charge can be seen to be equivalent to one of £3,000 to £4,000 in 2005. Only one year before his retirement from the staff of the RIE in 1939, one of Wade's letters indicated that the lift required attention, confirming that his private practice continued actively.

David Wilkie died from cancer in 1938. On 28th November 1939, the various properties that formed the Private Clinic, 34–37 Drumsheugh Gardens, were 'conveyed' to Wade as the surviving partner. He became the sole proprietor of the nursing home. After the Second World War ended, Wade purchased the top floor house at 33 Drumsheugh Gardens for £1,700. The date was 24th November 1945. Wade was still described as residing at the Private Clinic, 35 Drumsheugh Gardens. The vendor was Mary Dorothy Forsyth, the widow of James Alexander Low. The price was £1,700. On 14th January of the following year, 1946, Wade bought the second and third floor house at the corner of Drumsheugh Gardens and Rothesay Place for £3,000. The purchase included the basement house at 37A, later called 1 Rothesay Place.

The years passed, and Wade's activities lessened. On 13th August 1951, he conveyed all the properties in Drumsheugh Gardens and Rothesay Place to the University of Edinburgh. The price shown on the search sheet, £30,000, was deleted and the comment 'adjudicated' substituted, a procedure that was adopted to show that the property was a gift rather than being sold for a specific price on which stamp duty could be calculated easily.

Equipping the nursing home

The new Home included a lift for patients,[13] consulting rooms, an operating theatre and accommodation for postoperative care. There were single and shared rooms, with the facilities reflected in a differential scale of charges. There was no laboratory but X-ray apparatus was installed. Many of the necessary scientific tests were made at the Laboratory of the Royal College of Physcians, the RCPEd, although the occasional conduct of examinations *post-mortem* necessarily demanded the facilities of the RIE or of the Procurator Fiscal's mortuary.

The practical business aspect of the nursing home called for a substantial investment in the most modern office equipment. Wade had purchased a Dictaphone recording machine in 1911. In 1919, the machine was due for overhaul: it was essential that medicated air filters be added to prevent moisture gathering on the speaking tube and glass.[14] Wade was in contact with a wide range of manufacturers. Within two months of his release from the army, he asked Down Bros to repair 'an accompanying instrument'. When AG Taylor called on 10th November 1919, he arranged to have an instrument made to hold the special test tubes that Wade used for collecting urine samples from ureteral catheters. Wade lent him the apparatus he used. Later, he asked:

> 'Have you been able to make the instrument? I would like the original returned. Not only was it useful but it was made for me by a prisoner of war on service in the East. I treasure it as a memento of his military service.'

Mr Taylor replied that the new instrument had had to be replated. However, he returned the model lent by Mr Wade. Bruce Green, 14, 16 and 18 Bloomsbury St, WC, offered dry batteries:

> 'They are suitable for illuminating all surgical instruments and appliances' at 4/9d each plus 6d postage.'

Wade wanted two. In 1922, Wade asked Charles Thackray of the Instrument Department, Great George St, Leeds:

> 'When will the special X-ray catheter you are having made for me be ready?'[15]

Thackray responded:

> 'One variety has come through as they should be – but those that should have been as the original sample are not at all right – they are not correctly marked.'

Wade returned the unmarked X-ray ureteral catheters. They were unsuitable. He asked for a definite pronouncement from the French makers as to whether the special catheters were or were not being made. Thackray told Wade that the ureteral catheters should be delivered in a month, adding:

> 'By this time you should have received the set of Record syringes and Young's boomerang needle.'

Wade had indeed received them. On 13th February 1923, he remitted £7/15/–d.[16]

The question of X-ray plant arose. In December 1922, Mr R McLeod wrote from M Schaerer, SA, 41 Berner's St, WC, to say that he was now handling the finest deep therapy X-ray apparatus, the original Erlangen symmetrical apparatus as used by Professor Wintz of Erlangen and Dr Morton of London.[17] He added:

> 'I hear that you were thinking of installing apparatus of this sort in Drumsheugh Gardens.'

Wade responded:

> 'The Drumsheugh Gardens installation was set aside but may possibly materialise.'

However, other new designs were evolving. Wade's choice of surgical instruments and equipment was influenced strongly by the visit he made in 1920 to the United States. On 19th October 1922, Wade wrote to Claude Violi c/o Dr Harvey W van Allen, Springfield, Massachusetts, USA, to say he had heard of the successful use of the Potter-Bucky diaphragm and to ask for particulars.[18] He received a pamphlet that explained that stereoscopic plates could be made in any size and any position; that with this instrument, secondary radiation was reduced greatly, limiting the haze seen in radiographs of the thicker parts of the body; and that gall stones could be detected readily. The urinary tract 'could be taken with clearness on a single plate'. Mr Violi added: 'the Potter Bucky diaphragm is now only $200.00'.

There was talk of a microscope but the Wade papers do not make clear why a neighbour from 10 Manor Place, perhaps a professional colleague, apologised for the trouble he had caused looking for one and explaining:

'I emptied all the drawers and cupboards.'[19]

On 24th October 1922, Wade thanked the Charles Wilson Surgical Instrument Company, 300 North Howard St, Baltimore, MD, for the sphincterotome and vesical tractor ordered through Dr Geraghty. He sent $24.23 in payment.[20] Early in January 1923, he wrote to the Wappler Electric Co Inc, Electric Medicine Apparatus, 162–184 Harris Avenue, Long Island City to say:

> 'On June 30th 1920 I bought from you in New York a size 15 French Otis Brown Examining and Irrigating Cystoscope. Can you provide one with the additional attachment for a single ureteral catheter?'

Soon the Clinic was attracting attention not only from inquiring practitioners and their anxious patients but from nursing publishers. In September 1922, Miss Jean Speedy from the *Nursing Times* asked if she could make a visit to 35 Drumsheugh Gardens in order to write an article about the establishment.[21] Apologetically, she confessed later that she had not been able to do full justice to its excellence.

Figure 9.3 Portrait of Henry Wade. *The date of this portrait is not certain. It was believed to have been made during the 1920s*

Relationships with general practitioners

Wade's letters illuminate the nature of private surgical practice in the early post-war years. It was in the nature of things that individual practitioners tended to refer their patients to surgeons they knew and trusted.[22] The relationship was reciprocal. Among Wade's closest practitioner colleagues was Dr Barrie of Hawick. Wade's correspondence with Dr Jeffrey FRCS of Jedburgh and Dr Barrie exemplifies the style of this trust.[23,24] The conditions dealt with ranged from the most serious to the trivial.

On 17th October 1919, Wade recounted to Dr Barrie the story of one his most notorious cases, of which an account is given in Chapter 3. William Waugh, aged 27 years, had had a sarcoma of the upper end of his right humerus removed on 12th August 1913:

> 'About one half of the upper end of the bone was removed and the reduction made good by implanting a portion of the femur from another patient.'[B]

Another patient, Miss Barrie, was Dr Barrie's niece. She had ill-defined loin pain and was under the care of Dr Jeffrey. On 18th October 1920, Dr Jeffrey wrote to Wade about accommodation for Miss Barrie in the Queen Mary Nursing Home, Edinburgh. Dr Barrie had telephoned the nursing home himself. After the necessary investigations were over, Wade wrote again to describe the urinanalysis. There was no suggestion that cystoscopy or pyelography had been undertaken. He concluded that a stone might be present and that there might be slight ureteric damage. There was no mention of further investigation or treatment.

On another understandable note, Wade wrote to Dr John Jeffrey on the same date to say that:

> 'The cheque was most gratifying.'

In the early post-war years, before Wade's Private Clinic was opened, a nursing home was not always easy to find. The case of a Miss Rutherford illustrates the difficulty. On 11th February 1920, Wade was obliged to tell Dr Barrie that he would not be able to obtain a single room at the Queen Mary Nursing Home for 7–10 days.[25] He suggested that she could be admitted to another home. In reply, Dr Barrie explained that Miss Rutherford was prepared to wait for the vacant ward at the Queen Mary. Then on 16th February, Wade wrote to say that a room had been found earlier than anticipated. A week later, he wrote again to explain to Dr Barrie the nature of the operation on Miss Rutherford. Dr Barrie could not be present in person.

> 'A long appendix was removed. The large caecum was plicated, its dimensions reduced, and the caecum fixed 'in its normal situation'.'

The correspondence with practitioners often dealt with social and financial problems. Thus, a patient from Wick was being sent to see Wade in Edinburgh, and her doctor wisely warned him:

> 'The lady in question is somewhat addicted to bouts of drinking.'

In another note, Pryce M Campbell of Polmont asked on 24th January 1920 whether he should be inoculated against 'tropical fevers': he had been appointed to the Sudan.[26] However,

> 'I cannot attend for an injection on Saturday February 7th since I am 'booked' for the rugby international.'

Nature of private surgery

The letters sent and received by Henry Wade during the years 1919–23 tell us the nature and variety of the surgical operations for which patients chose private care. In very general terms, life-threatening procedures and operations of the most complex kind were conducted in the large hospitals, where the laboratories and the X-ray (the Electric Diagnostic) Department were readily available. Lesser operations, frequently a matter of comfort and convenience, were diverted to the private clinics and nursing homes, which were the choice of those who could afford them.

The letters written by Wade and received by him during the period June 1919 to March 1923, make it clear that Wade investigated and operated on a wide range of conditions (Table 9.1). The number of cases, however, was small as judged by modern standards, and this accords with the records of the Leith Hospital, where no more than three operations were performed each day. The practice at 35 Drumsheugh Gardens came to include much general surgery and orthopaedics. Diseases of the alimentary system were particularly frequent, so that acute and chronic appendicitis; femoral and inguinal hernias; duodenal ulcer, sometimes perforated; haemorrhoids; and tumours of the parotid salivary gland, tongue, stomach and colon were encountered. There was a correspondingly large representation of disorders of the urinary system, in which Wade had begun, many years previously, to express an especial interest. They included renal infections and calculi, bladder cancer and benign nodular hyperplasia of the prostate together with its complications. Cystoscopy was practised increasingly.

An example of the kind of case that Wade treated came from correspondence with Dr Huddleston who wrote on 18th December 1919 about a Mr Anderson. The patient, Dr Huddleston explained, 'has marked urinary trouble'.[27] Dr Huddleston told Wade that Professor Meakins had advised admission to the Leith Hospital. After a delay of 17 days over the Christmas and New Year period, Wade arranged to see Mr Anderson. Examination showed that:

> The outlook for Mr Anderson is by no means satisfactory. He has an intractable cystitis, which has produced infections of the renal pelves and urethra. He had an urethral stricture for which he was treated in the RIE 25 years ago. However, the main underlying cause is a chronic interstitial fibrosing prostatitis. At the moment, he is profoundly toxic and if something is not done to improve his condition, it is sure to prove fatal at no very distant date. I propose bladder drainage tomorrow. The prospect of ultimate recovery is poor.

On 27th January 1920, Henry Wade wrote again to Dr Huddleston to say that Mr Anderson had died 'at the end of last week'. An autopsy

Table 9.1 Nature of the disease in cases referred to Henry Wade's Private Clinic, January 1919 to June 1923

Affected system	Disease
Skin	• Pre-auricular: epithelioma (squamous carcinoma) • Eyelid: squamous carcinoma • Cheek: papilloma
Nose	• Infra-orbital sinusitis; lymph nodes: tuberculous • Abscess
Alimentary	• Parotid gland: sarcoma, carcinoma • Tongue: carcinoma • Tooth: cyst of canine fossa • Stomach: carcinoma, gastroptosis (2) • Duodenum: perforation (3) • Liver: haemangioma, pedunculated • Appendix: acute, gangrenous; subacute and chronic inflammation • Colon: carcinoma (2) • Intestine: hernia, inguinal; haemorrhoids • Lymph nodes: tuberculosis
Urinary	• Kidney: tuberculous pyelonephritis (3); calculus; pyelitis; pyelitis with secondary cystitis; mobile kidney • Ureter: calculus, bifid • Urinary bladder: cystitis; carcinoma (2); varicosities; incontinence • Prostate: chronic interstitial prostatitis (3) • Urethra: discharge • Penis: squamous carcinoma
Genital	• Testis: recurrent acute orchitis • Breast, female: carcinoma (3) • Uterus: chronic cervicitis
Gunshot wounds	• Thigh, with sciatica • Chest wall • Mediastinum • Site unstated: discharging
Bone and joint	• Knee: semimembranosus bursitis; torn cruciate ligament; torn semilunate fibrocartilage; tuberculous synovitis • Wrist: injury • Metacarpophalangeal joint: injury • Ulna: malposition of healed fracture • Leg straightening: in pernicious anaemia with subacute combined degeneration • Leg, jaw: chronic osteomyelitis • Skull: late effects of injury • Spinal deformity: not detailed

showed a very large carcinoma growing from the floor and right wall of the bladder and invading neighbouring lymph glands. The right kidney was reduced to one eighth of the normal size due to ureteral obstruction. In this case, the exact diagnosis was unobtainable, partly because of the patient's weak condition, partly because of the limitations on investigation imposed by the small technical resources of the time.

Tuberculosis of the cervical lymph nodes was still prevalent among the young, so it is not surprising to find 'neck glands' being operated upon frequently. A variety of small tumours that Wade treated included carcinoma of the tongue, sarcoma of the parotid salivary gland, squamous carcinoma of the eyelid and a 'lump' behind an ear. Wade maintained a brisk interest in orthopaedic disorders and dealt with diseases of the arm, leg and ankle, such as torn cruciate ligaments. Knee joint meniscectomy was undertaken and the consequences of head and neck injury were investigated. Wade had records of the work that he had done before the war, and he often wrote to general practitioners to enquire about the fate of their patients.

Laboratories (p 74) were in use for diagnosis but not in the way or on the scale that has become the custom in modern times. Much of the work conducted for individual surgeons was undertaken by the Laboratory of the RCPEd where Dr James Dawson and his wife Edith (p 84) had established a reputation for their profoundly skilled and painstaking reporting of biopsies. Thus, on 28th April 1922, Mrs Jeannie S Shearer sent Wade a cheque for 35 guineas and asked him to explain the nature of the tumour removed from her young son, Ernie.[28] In a prompt reply, Wade told her that the pigeon egg-size mass was a sacral dermoid. It was enucleated without difficulty and had been examined by the RCPEd laboratory. Dr Dawson's report stated:

> 'The tumour is a myxofibroma without any signs of teratoma. It will not recur.'

Wade agreed with this opinion. Mrs Shearer expressed her immediate gratitude and told him that she would send the report to Cairo, where her husband was working.

Relationships with patients

Behind a gruff, sometimes stern exterior, Wade hid a kindly manner, a deep sense of responsibility towards his patients and a sensitive understanding of their suffering and of their personal and financial problems. LDG wrote on 12th November 1919 to thank Wade for his kindness to 'my dear mother at the close of my father's life'. She quoted her father who said:

> 'I like that doctor. His face is one I can trust.'

When a young boy, Robert A wrote in 1919 to tell Wade of his good recovery and expressing the hope that he may be as kind and gentle as Wade when he grows up. Wade replied, thanking him for his present and, apropos surgery, advising him that:

'It is not so much the work you have got as the way you do it.'

On 15th February 1919, a friend thanked Wade for advice and comments, adding:

'The woman was dismissed and my son awakened by his foolishness. His overstrain will respond to small doses of bromide.'

Later in the same year, a Mrs D wrote to say:

'I'm keeping awful well.'

A Mr W Sandilands was very sorry not to see Wade before leaving the nursing home. He felt as if he owed his very life to Wade's wonderful skill.

'I shall not readily forget your kindness.'

On 10th June 1922, John Young wrote from *Young and Chapman, Silk Mercers, Woolen and Linen Drapers, Hosiers, Glovers and Haberdashers, Dress making, Millinery, Mantle making, Family mourning, Flannels, Blankets, Sheetings, Bed quilts, Table clothes, Towelings, Curtains etc.* to say:

'Many thanks for your kind attention. Katherine is making good progress towards recovery. However, I've had a hurried call from Edinburgh to say that my eldest boy is down with appendicitis and must be operated on at once. He is making good progress.'

But patients were not always so understanding, and an army major, writing from the Caledonian Club, Edinburgh, commented that:

'I am far from satisfied that the operation on my secum [*sic*] and appendix will restore me to health.[29] Dr T gave me a much more thorough examination than either you or Dr R.'

But Wade retained his practical common sense and replied:

'You have had a general toxaemia and should place yourself in the hands of a physician.'

Mrs Sherriff of Larbert wrote on 10th July 1922 to say she was unhappy about her orthopaedic boots:

'The left is comfortable but the right hurts me terribly.'

Even by late October, it proved difficult to arrange a time when Mr Cochrane, the procrastinating bootmaker, could be present.

From time to time, patients were asked to attend 'meetings of medical men', a way of persuading a patient to be seen at a clinical conference or, perhaps, to take part in a clinical teaching session in the presence of students.

Patients' fees

Very often a patient's letter containing a fee, usually a cheque or money order, would be accompanied by a note of thanks and by questions relating to the condition that had been treated. Wade's records show that the smallest fee charged during the years 1919–23 was two guineas (£2/2/–), the largest 100 guineas.

On 17th October 1920, Mrs Falconer King, Coilvar, 43 Stirling Rd, Edinburgh, had pleasure in sending Mr Wade a cheque for professional services, while Jane King of 4 Morton Street, Joppa, wrote on black-edged paper:

'I am sorry you have had the trouble of sending a second account. I shall forward it as I did the first to Messrs McKenzie Innes and Logan WS, Melville St.'

At much the same time, J and F Anderson WS, 48 Castle Street, Edinburgh, wrote to say that they:

'should esteem it a favour if you would let us have a note of your fee for the operation on Lieutenant Gen Sir James Wolfe Murray (deceased).'[30]

Replying, Wade begged leave herewith to enclose a note of his fee of 100 guineas, which J and F Anderson paid promptly. On 8th September 1919, Mrs WS Normand of Ardwick, Callander:

'begs to enclose cheque for 2 guineas for professional services rendered today to baby.'

James Shaw of Brae Villa, Haddington, sent a cheque for ten guineas on 19th December 1922 for personal fees and 'home' charges:

'I feel sure that which you have done will soon make me quite fit again.'

Robert L Walker wrote from the Manse, Ravensbourne, Dunedin, New Zealand, on 15th September 1922, enclosing a postal order for 25 guineas.[31] He would have settled before leaving the country but he:

'had many things to think about. I am perfectly well and have had no trouble with the rupture since the operation and since seeing you have got married again.'

With tongue in cheek, Wade replied:

> 'I am very pleased to learn of the satisfactory result that has fol-
> lowed your treatment.'[32]

The settlement of accounts was not always so easy.[33] On 27th June
1922, a Mr JAF Sinclair asked Wade to debit Thomson and Co, 28
Bernard Street, Leith, with nursing home and home and medical
expenses. The letter was followed by one on 3rd July from Miss CA
Pike, Matron, 35 Drumsheugh Gardens, Private Clinic, requesting W
Thomson to pay Mr Sinclair's account. On 5th July, W Thomson of
Ben Line Steamers Ltd then sent Miss Pike a cheque for £40/19/–. On
29th September, Wade posted a note of his fee to Thomson's for an
operation carried out on 9th June. On 6th October, he was told that
Mr Sinclair now resided at the Old Ship Hotel, Leith. On 10th
October, he again requested Sinclair to settle his account.

The following day, Thomson's explained that they were not responsible for this charge and referred Wade to Mr Sinclair himself.
Replying, Wade informed Thomson's that Sinclair had been referred
to him by Dr Lyon Brown of Hong Kong, that he had agreed to pay a
fee of 50 guineas and that the expenses would be borne by 'your firm'.
Wade asked for Mr Sinclair's present address. By 1st March 1923, however, Wade had had no response to a letter sent to Leith. Meanwhile,
Thomson's had been told that Mr Sinclair had gone to Glasgow. They
did not know his address. He had now been traced to the north of
Scotland and, in a last, desperate attempt to recover his money, Wade
wrote on 15th March 1923 to Stafford Place, Wick, but without result.

Every surgeon, physician or general practitioner who has conducted
private practice has been faced periodically with the dilemma of how
to deal with patients who cannot pay for their care. Wade's response
was understanding and, for the most part, generous. Thus, on 3rd
March 1920, Gertrude Bunyan wrote that:

> 'I have received your fee but hadn't thought the amount would
> be so large.'[34]

In reply, Wade said:

> 'The fee charged for the operative treatment you received was
> rendered on the assumption that you were so situated as to be
> able to afford my ordinary fee for such treatment.'

Wade suggested that she call to discuss an 'adjustment'. In spite of
this, Gertrude Bunyan said that the very utmost she could afford was
20 guineas. Wade thereupon resolved the matter by writing to say that
he enclosed a note discharging – that is, abolishing – the fee. Other
patients who could afford to pay were reluctant to part with their
money. On 23rd March 1920, Dr Dingwall Kennedy of Wick wrote to

Wade about a wealthy patient who he had considered for the operation of gastrojejunostomy.[35] Dr Kennedy said:

> 'Just charge your ordinary fees. If he weeps about his financial position just mingle your tears with his but at the same time mingle his gold with yours.'

Patients' questions

An important part of a surgeon's practice is the responsibility of dealing with the many questions that arise in patients' minds before and after surgery. In Wade's practice, patients would ask, for example, about the possible recurrence of a hernia, the outcome of the removal of a tumour, urinary frequency or the alleviation of back pain. Very often, Wade's advice would take the form of encouragement, support or reassurance.

It is in the nature of human affairs that errors occur and that ill-luck may accompany good. No surgeon can pursue his or her career for a lifetime without suffering from misfortune or committing error. It is only to be expected that, occasionally, patients remain dissatisfied with their diagnosis or treatment. Despite his operation on 1st June 1922, a Captain Walker, with whom a sometimes querulous correspondence of 21 letters and telegrams extended over one year, explained that he 'cannot hold the water any better'.[36] His general practitioner, Dr Campbell of Inverness, had prescribed sulphurated quinine and strychnine; he had also 'passed the bougie again last Saturday', although 'the stricture at the top is very tight and the urine still contains a small amount of pus'. But two months later, an unhappy Captain Walker wrote that he was still in trouble with pain at the neck of the bladder 'where you cut it'. Two weeks later he felt compelled to say 'the medicine you prescribed made me much worse as regards the frequency of passing water'. He had therefore been taking a cottager's remedy: ginger, cream of tartar and Epsom salts. Fortunately for Wade, Captain Walker was well enough to accompany his frail mother (she had had a stroke) to Monte Carlo, and the saga ended when Wade's account for 10 guineas was settled.

In another domestic drama, a friend, Miss BH Wilson, wrote from Falkirk to ask Wade to see:

> "one of our maids', Margaret McEwen, who has swallowed a long pin.'[37]

Although her local medical adviser recommended 'wait and see', Margaret complained of chest pain. But all was well, and 12 days after the accident, Miss Wilson reported to Wade:

> 'The pin has duly appeared and Margaret is keeping it as a memo.'

Thoughtfully, she asked Wade whether a financial contribution should be made to the RIE, thereby revealing that the domestic servant had been taken by Wade to the hospital, presumably for radiography. Wade did not think a payment was required. He added:

> 'Your contribution to the welfare of the community in its widest sense has always been a very large one.'

This was an indication that Miss Wilson, like thousands of others, was active in fundraising for the voluntary hospital. James Watt of 8 Charlotte Square, Edinburgh, wrote to say that:

> 'I am seeing you this afternoon (23rd January 1923) 'at the request of Sir Harold Stiles.'

Mr Watt had been troubled for a year or two with passing stones, and he was sending two boxes of them to Mr Wade.[38] He commented:

> 'They seem both the same although the later have a touch of white.'

Mr Watt's earlier stones were reported, on analysis, to be uric acid. In another, undated pencil note, J Angus Gillan said:

> 'I should like to see you about a small pain I have now and then. I don't want to alarm the family but I think it may be appendicitis. Could you see me when you are along tomorrow? I can make some excuse or ring up when you come here only please get me and not Mother or Father.'

Relationships with ex-servicemen and women

In part because of his fame as a surgeon, in part because of his recognition as a national hero, Wade was often called upon for advice regarding matters that arose as a result of the war. On 31st July 1919, on behalf of Mr Orr Deas of Earlsferry, his wife Elie thanked Wade for his wartime help. She said:

> 'He has been before a Board and has been granted 4 weeks leave.'

On 17th September, Colonel Innes commented that he would shortly come before a medical board at the 2nd Scottish General Hospital, Craigleith. He wondered whether there would be a vacancy in an Edinburgh nursing home at that date.

On 24th October 1919, Wade wrote to Miss Braidwood that:

> 'Before the War I operated on your late brother, Alexander Braidwood.'

Wade had been advised by Dr Allan Gray to send a note of his fee, however late. He apologized to Miss Braidwood, explaining that he had been on active service for five years.

A letter from the secretary to the Admiralty told Engineer Commander HV Whyham RN on 28th February 1920 to report to the Royal Naval Hospital, South Queensferry. On 4th March, Wade informed the Admiralty that Commander Whyham was at present an inmate of the 48 Moray Place Nursing Home Edinburgh, where he had been operated upon for haemorrhoids four days previously.[39]

There were other less clinical demands on Wade's time and patience. Hugh Ferguson, an ex-serviceman who had probably been with Wade during the war, was seeking a German rifle to use on his farm:

'There is plenty of work, rabbit killing, for me until spring when the vermin killing begins.'

Wade responded on 12th November 1919 that:

'I will try and do what I can about the matter...and make enquiries to see if there is any possibility of getting one.'[40]

Relationships with companies and insurance companies

Before the opening of the Drumsheugh Gardens Nursing Home, the Clinic, and for many years afterwards, Wade acted for companies and insurance agencies that referred patients to him. He also responded to requests from commercial companies such as Jenners of Princes Street, Edinburgh, to treat members of their staff. The company paid for his services.[41]

In one instance, Thomas Wardley was recommended to him by the Cumberland Coal Owners Mutual Indemnity Company Ltd in October 1922 for an X-ray to be carried out at 4 pm as arranged with Dr Stewart.[42] In a further case, JE Skelton of Whitehaven, Cumberland, asked Wade on 19th March 1923 for the necessary certificate he needed for the Druids Society, of which he was a member. The Society required a specialist's certificate before considering his claim. Mr Skelton had been given light work for six weeks (because of his knee) on the recommendation of the compensation board. On 15th February 1923, Wade asked Ms Shaw, Matron of the Queen Mary Nursing Home, to send a note of nursing home charges for Mr Graham's maintenance to the Scottish Mine Owners' Defence and Mutual Insurance Association Ltd, 11 Maygate, Dunfermline. Four days later, he asked her to add the enclosed account for a vaccine to the bill of Mr Nicolson, so that he might recover the money from the Cumberland Coal Owners. During the same week, on 6th December

1919, an agent sent a cheque for £21 in payment of a fee. The agent was acting on behalf of *Mitchell Hughes of Pittenweem, Fishcurer and Commission Agent for all Classes of Herrings*.

On 24th April 1922, the cashier of the Fife Coal Company, Mr Henry Rutherford, asked Robert Philp to call on 'Dr' Wade at 2 pm on the 28th for an examination.[43] He explained to Mr Philp: 'We will either advance or refund your expenses'.

The world without

On account of the senior and distinguished position that Wade had reached when the war ended, he was often asked for advice on matters that could extend beyond the practice of surgery. He was, for example, an active member of the British Medical Association (BMA) and took part in its meetings in Edinburgh and Glasgow. In the summer of 1919, Wade received the agenda for the Edinburgh meeting of Thursday 26th June. The items included a review of the scale of fees payable under the Midwives (Scotland) Act; a discussion of chemists and the supply of medicines after hours; the Bills for Registered Nurses; and the proportion of fees payable to doctors absent on His Majesty's service. The Chairman of this meeting was JL Lackie, the Vice Chairmen W Stewart and J Ritchie. The Senior Secretary/Treasurer was GK Paterson and the Junior Secretary JD Comrie.[44]

In November 1919, Mr WE Warne, Financial Secretary of the BMA, WC2, London, wrote to Wade accepting that he, Henry Wade, had been absent on active service for five years.[45] He would not have stopped the dispatch of Wade's *British Medical Journal* had he known. Mr Warne made an oblique reference to a 'colonial rate of subscription', noting that Wade's subscriptions for 1914, 1915 and 1916 had been paid on his behalf, a letter indicative of the trouble caused by administrators who had not been on active service to those returning from the war.

Then there were questions relating to teaching. A Mr WT Buchan was an ex-serviceman. He had clearly accepted advice from Wade and had enrolled for a postgraduate course at the School of Medicine of the Royal Edinburgh Colleges, the SMRC (p 246):

> 'I aim at a clinical M.D. I hope to see you at Surgeons' Hall or at the Royal Infirmary.'

Correspondence with Mr AA Bowlby elicited a typical response from an irrascible Wade.[46] It was proposed that the Consulting Surgeons of the Armies of Great Britain should present the American College of Surgeons with a mace to endorse their mutual respect. Wade thought that this idea was not sensible. It would, at any rate, cost each British surgeon £7 or £8. The mace itself, he described scathingly as 'a useless bauble'. Nevertheless, the plan went ahead and on 11th October 1920, a commemorative parchment endorsed with the names of the

President of the American College of Surgeons, GG Armstrong, and the past President, William J Mayo, bore the College seal and testified to the gift.

The future

While these consultations and negotiations were continuing, much of Wade's time was directed to his responsibilities in the RIE, where many patients each day awaited surgical diagnosis and treatment. The state of the hospital, the changes that had taken place in its structure and activities since 1903, and the nature and number of the operations performed are described in Chapter 10.

CHAPTER 10

The changing face of the Royal Infirmary of Edinburgh

1919–39

Surgeons must be very careful when they take the knife!
Underneath their fine incisions stirs the culprit – Life!

(Emily Elizabeth Dickinson, *Complete Poems*, 1891)

The work of the Honorary Medical and Surgical staff is yearly
becoming more onerous.

(Report regarding the affairs of the Royal Infirmary of Edinburgh, 1930)

eturning from the army, Wade discovered that civilian hospital
practice had altered little since 1914. But there were differences
in attitudes. In the cynical post-war era, revolution was in the
air, fuelled socially by a reaction to wartime suffering and austerity,
politically by the rise to power of Lenin in Russia and the National
Socialists in Germany. Wade had learned by bitter experience that
there was no 'dynamic equilibrium' in disease. Diseases evolved both
abruptly and gradually; surgical practice was compelled to change in
conformity with these natural phenomena.[1] Surgery and medicine
were drawn remorselessly into an endless evolving cycle[2,3] and hospitals altered as demands for care fluctuated.[4,5]

This chapter outlines the state of the Royal Infirmary of Edinburgh,
the RIE, during the second phase of Wade's life, the years 1919–39,
and sets the scene for a description in Chapter 11 of the surgical work
that he undertook during this period.

After the ravages of the First World War, aerial ambulances, blood
transfusion,[6,7] chemotherapy, antibiotics (p 224) and intravenous
anaesthetics[8] would transform surgical practice. In the background
were heated debates on the role of women in medicine, the provision
by the state of health care, and domestic matters that ranged from the
compulsory registration of dentists to child nutrition. In the years
that followed, very many far-reaching changes would take place, not
only in the practice of surgery and in the closely associated fields of
medical care but also in medical biology, laboratory medicine and, by
no means least, hospital construction itself. Directly or indirectly,

Chapter Summary
- **Assistant Surgeon again**
- **Surgeon-in-Ordinary**
- **The hospital**
- **Radiology flourishes**
- **Hospital wards**
- **Operating theatres**
- **The work of the hospital**
- **Hospital staff**
- **Cost of surgical care**

these changes influenced both Wade's surgical work and his personal life and prospects.[9,10]

As Chapter 8 shows, the Managers of the RIE first applied for Wade's release from First World War military service through the Scottish Medical Service Emergency Committee on 26th November 1918. However, confirmation of his freedom came only on 2nd September 1919. A large part of Henry Wade's life had already been dedicated to his principal hospital, the RIE[11,12] and an increasing proportion to private, consultant practice. Now he was anxious to resume his hospital commitments.

Assistant Surgeon again

Six days after Wade's release from the army, on 8th September 1919, Mr WS Caw, Treasurer and Clerk to the RIE, wrote to Wade:

> 'I have pleasure in informing you that this afternoon the Managers unanimously re-appointed you as an Assistant Surgeon for a further period of 5 years from 8th November next.'

Wade remained Assistant Surgeon to the Leith Hospital where, in 1920, he was promoted to full Surgeon.[A] Among the other positions Wade resumed on his return from the army was that of Consultant Surgeon to the Ministry of Pensions at Craigleith Hospital, Edinburgh, later to be the Western General Hospital. In the same year, he and John Struthers were appointed HM Inspectors of Anatomy for Scotland (Kaufman, personal communication).

Then came the intermission referred to in other parts of this work. Early in 1920, Wade was granted leave to visit the United States of America (p 170). As the result of an invitation extended to him before the war, he had planned to travel as early as 11th October 1919 with his friend and colleague, Dr Arthur Henry Havens Sinclair.[B] However, the visit was postponed until the early part of 1920. Wade wrote to Mr Caw, now Interim Superintendent of the RIE, telling him that, during his absence in America, his colleagues Mr JW Struthers[C] and Mr JM Graham[D] would be able to carry out his duties. In the absence of Professor Alexis Thomson (p 344), Wade said Mr Struthers would be responsible for wards 9 and 10 of the RIE, while, on 10th April, Mr Graham would assume this task.

Surgeon-in-Ordinary

The years passed, and on 17th November 1924, Wade's increasing seniority culminated in the position of Surgeon-in-Ordinary to the RIE.[E] The appointment was for five years from 1st January 1925 and carried with it the charge and complete management of wards 5 and 6. At last, he was a 'Chief'.[F] Wade was therefore one of seven senior surgical consultants responsible for the organization and work of entire surgical units (Table 10.1). Meanwhile, his expertise in urological surgery had been recognized widely, and he had been granted control of the Electric Diagnostic Theatre.[G] His first assistant was Mr RL Stewart,[H] his Clinical Tutor Mr JJM Shaw.[I] The name of a second assistant, Mr David Band, now appeared.[J]

Table 10.1 Honorary surgical staff of the Royal Infirmary of Edinburgh, 1924, 1929 and 1939. There were seven senior surgeons (Surgeons-in-Ordinary); these included the two Professors of Surgery. The others were granted the status of Senior Lecturer in Clinical Surgery of the University. The hospital also had nine Assistant Surgeons; all were Lecturers in Clinical Surgery of the University and each was granted a two-year probationary appointment

Year	Honorary surgical staff		
	Consulting Surgeons	**Surgeons-in-Ordinary**	**Assistant Surgeons**
1924	AG Milller	AA Scot Skirving	John Fraser
	CW MacGillivray	Professor Sir Harold J Stiles	JM Graham
	JM Cotterill	GL Chiene	A Pirie Watson
	CW Cathcart	WJ Stuart	FE Jardine
	FM Caird	JW Struthers	JNJ Hartley
	JWB Hodsdon	Professor DPD Wilkie	WQ Wood
	Sir David Wallace	**Henry Wade (Wards 5 and 6)**	JJM Shaw
	JW Dowden		Walter Mercer
	Alex Miles		WA Cochrane
1929	CW MacGillivray	GL Chiene	A Pirie Watson
	JM Cotterill	WJ Stuart	FE Jardine
	CW Cathcart	JW Struthers	WQ Wood
	Sir David Wallace	Professor DPD Wilkie	JJM Shaw
	JW Dowden	**Henry Wade (Wards 15 and 16)**	Walter Mercer
	Alex Miles	Professor John Fraser	WA Cochrane
	Professor Sir Harold J Stiles	JM Graham	K Paterson Brown
	AA Scot Skirving		R Leslie Stewart
			T McW Millar
1939*	Sir David Wallace	Professor John Fraser	Walter Mercer
	Professor Sir Harold J Stiles	JM Graham	K Paterson Brown
	WJ Stuart	A Pirie Watson	R Leslie Stewart
	Henry Wade	FE Jardine	T McW Millar
	Alex Miles	WQ Wood	DS Middleton
	GL Chiene	Professor JR Learmonth	WAD Adamson
	JW Struthers	JJM Shaw	John Bruce
			JR Cameron

*The RIE also had an Associate Assistant Surgeon (WA Cochrane) and an Associate Neurological Surgeon (NM Dott).

In the summer of 1924, fate stepped in once again. On the verge of promotion, the possibility that Wade might be elevated to a University Chair of Surgery arose not once but twice.[K] However, it was not to be.

The Chair of Systematic Surgery had fallen vacant when Alexis Thomson (p 344) resigned in 1923.[13]. The choice of a successor was intimately connected with an offer to the University of Edinburgh by the Rockefeller Foundation, minuted on 6th December 1923, to give £35,000 to support the building of new clinical laboratories. The purpose was to support the work of Professor Meakins, who had been closely involved in the development of a laboratory for Clinical Chemistry. However, Meakins had accepted the Chair of Medicine in Toronto, and it was agreed to transfer the offer to the Chair of Systematic Surgery. Murray Lyon was appointed to succeed Meakins.

On 16th January 1924, representatives of the University Court met with Managers of the RIE, including Sir James Hodsdon, to discuss these proposals. On 22nd May 1924, the Dean of the Faculty of Medicine, Professor Lorrain Smith, confirmed the Faculty's agreement to support the Chair of Systematic Surgery. He hoped that the successful candidate could take up the position by the autumn term. The University Court agreed the appointment on 17th June 1924 and the Rockefeller representatives accepted their decision two weeks later. Within three days, David Wilkie had (p 42) submitted his *curriculum vitae* to the University Principal, Sir Alfred Ewing. On the same day, he was offered the Chair. One week later, on 15th July 1924, he accepted.

In the following year, Sir Harold Stiles retired and another younger and distinguished colleague, John Fraser,[L] was elected to the world-famous Regius Chair of Clinical Surgery.

The hospital

Wade found himself once more in an enormous and increasingly complex township. The early years of the RIE (Chapters 1 and 3) have been described.[11,12] The effect of the First World War on the hospital had been serious but not crippling. At the outset of hostilities, many patients had been evacuated to safer parts of the country. As the campaigns in Flanders, Gallipoli, Egypt and Mesopotamia took shape, there was a gradual return to peacetime activity. A greater threat to the country's survival had been the naval blockade, so that, even in 1919, the supply of all foods was not wholly restored to normal.

The foundations on which the efficient work of the RIE rested were the buildings and their services. Unlike many hospitals of its time, such as those of Chicago and San Paolo, the RIE did not have the advantage of a single tall structure within which communication by lifts ('elevators') was rapid and efficient. In a single day, a member of the medical, surgical or nursing staff might walk many miles. Capacious lifts with grills as doors were installed within the three-storey buildings but there were no other moving stairs or mechanical aids to carry the handicapped, the sick or their relatives. The transport of patients and the medical and surgical work within the RIE were therefore still as physically demanding as they had been in 1903 and remained slow and inconvenient.

Much new construction had taken place during the 40 years since the 'New' Infirmary opened; more would soon follow. Disquiet was growing about the state of the maternity service. The accommodation in Lauriston Place had become woefully inadequate and a decision had been taken to erect a new building. By 1923, it had been decided that a new maternity hospital of at least 250 beds was required urgently. The ambitious structure, which would accommodate the gynaecological patients from the Jubilee pavilion (Chapter 3), was to be drawn into the confines of the RIE. There was one drawback. Access to the necessary land had to be negotiated with the Merchants' Company who would need to find an alternative site for a new George Watson's College for Boys. A deal was struck in 1926 but the foundation stone of the new maternity hospital, later to be called the Simpson Maternity Pavilion, was not laid until 22nd May 1935 when the Duke and Duchess of Kent performed this ceremony.[11] Construction proceeded apace, and the building was opened in 1939. The hope that the pavilion could absorb the gynaecological patients proved to be unrealistic and the final number of maternity beds was only 125.

A new departmental block was also constructed for the diagnosis and treatment of skin and venereal diseases. It was connected with an open corridor that linked the wards for gynaecology with the principal medical ward blocks. As soon as this essential new structure was occupied, many surgical patients were moved to wards 4 and 5. They came to include orthopaedic surgery, a Cinderella subject, for which provision had long been sought. Ward 3 was designated for the receipt of police cases and for patients with delirium tremens (DTs). The ward was not for cases of 'insanity' or other mental ailment. The RIE, like all large hospitals, had contingency plans against the possibility of large fires; explosions; rail, air or sea disasters; or for unexpected outbreaks of epidemic disease. There was a chronic shortage of accommodation in the wards that dealt with the surgery of ear, nose and throat disease but despite requests, Ward 4 could not be released because of the shortage of nurses.[14] The provision of a comprehensive dental surgical service was the responsibility of the Dental Hospital built in 1930. The details of this Hospital and its work are beyond the scope of the present book.

Heating, lighting, cleanliness and safety were at the heart of the work of the hospital. The coal-fired, steam boilers that supplied heat and power to the entire gigantic edifice had begun to fail. It became necessary to replace them. The opportunity was taken not only to install new boilers, which eventually became oil-burning, but to rebuild the boiler house itself. Accommodation in the power station

Figure 10.1 The laundry of the Royal Infirmary of Edinburgh, 1926. *Much of the labour is manual and the staff is large*

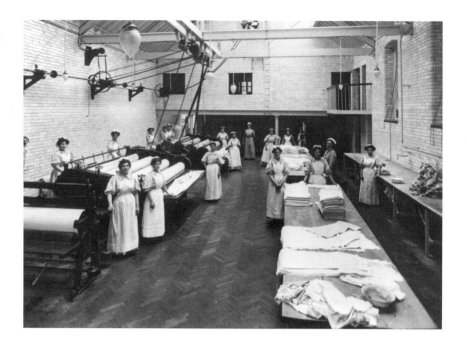

was provided for the hospital maintenance and engineering staff. The alterations extended to the Pathology Department and the mortuary, which, together with the hospital chapel, were substantially reconstructed.

Radiology flourishes

The space provided for Radiology beneath the operating theatre of the Professor of Clinical Surgery was proving woefully inadequate. To accommodate the exponential growth in demand for radiographs of all kinds, a vacant site between the medical and surgical pavilions was found, and a sophisticated new building was opened on 9th October 1926 at a cost of £48,587. The structure took into account the increasingly understood hazards of exposure to ionizing radiation. Analogous changes were made in provisions for radiotherapy. The quickly growing use of radium for the treatment of cancer had led to an urgent need for the expansion of facilities for this work. Wade made particular use of this form of treatment, and his colleague JJM Shaw was given responsibility for its organization. Beechmount House, Corstorphine, designated as a radium centre, was recognized by the Radium Authority as a National Radium Centre for Edinburgh and the South East of Scotland. Subsequently, the complex and massive equipment needed for this work was taken into the new Department of Medical Radiology of the RIE but the administration and organization of the Departments of Radiotherapy and of Diagnostic Radiology were not separated physically until after the Second World War.

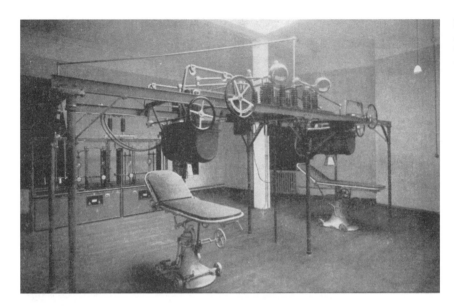

Figure 10.2 Radiology.
X-ray apparatus in the early days of the Department of Radiology, accommodated in the building opened in 1926

Hospital wards

The hospital wards were very naturally of the greatest concern to Wade and his colleagues. Each unit comprised two wards, one male, one female; a nearby operating theatre; and associated rooms and offices. During Wade's 15 years as Surgeon-in-Ordinary, many alterations were made in ward structure.

Within the wards, account was taken of convenience for the staff and comfort for the patients. There was great delay in replacing the cumbersome screens that had to be moved up and down the wards to give patients privacy. The screens concealed procedures that ranged from spinal puncture to the laying out of the dead and were a particular burden for the nurses. The cumbersome objects had to be moved many times each day and night. Only in 1953, in response to pleas by Miss Marshall, the Lady Superintendent of Nurses, did the Medical Committee give permission for the installation of bed curtains on rails in a single ward and then only on an experimental basis. Similar curtains were placed in the medical wards within a year but, by 1957, they had not yet been adopted in the surgical wards.

In 1925, the remaining open fires so characteristic of older hospitals were finally bricked up and the heating system replaced by radiators.[15] There was a central catering department, but much of the patients' food was made, or at least prepared, in kitchens that adjoined the wards, where dietary needs were under the direct supervision and control of the ward sisters. These essential rooms were modernized and improved progressively.

**Figure 10.3 1920s ward
with open fire and nurses.**
*In the centre of the ward is an
open coal-burning range and a
grand piano. There are no
individual screens around the
beds*

Operating theatres

Following the Listerian revolution, the universal aim of institutions
such as those of the New York Hospital was 'to make surgery as safe as
if it were being done in the most luxurious home', a phrase that
recalls attitudes to surgery in the early years of the nineteenth century. In spite of dramatic advances in anaesthesia and the adoption of
antisepsis and asepsis, the architectural design of operating theatres
changed little between 1903 and 1939.[16]

In the theatres of the RIE, a spacious floor accommodated a single
operating table. In Listerian days, these tables had been of teak. Many
came to have a marble structure, but the availability of stainless steel
changed their design radically, and they were now equipped with
drainage systems. The walls of the theatres were lined with ceramic
tiles and the floors formed of tiles or cement. Heating was provided
from the distant hospital boilers by means of radiators, to which hot
water was conveyed by low-pressure, wide-bore pipes. There were no
thermostats. At first, ventilation depended on windows reduplicated
to make a form of double-glazing, a style much more frequent in con-
tinental countries such as Prussia and Russia where the winters were
long and bitter. Later, fan systems were installed and the air brought
into theatres through wire or fibre mesh that excluded insects. Air
conditioning, in a strict sense, was still very unusual although it had
been adopted in warmer climates such as those of the southern States
of the USA. Lighting was largely by electricity, although the use of
daylight was still widespread.[17] New theatres incorporated illumina-
tors that minimized glare and shadows.

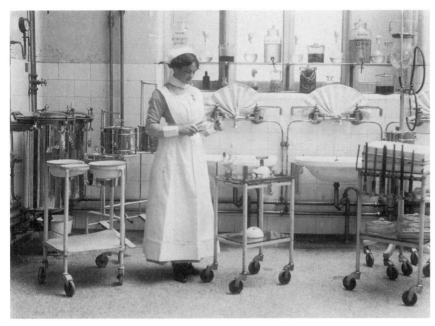

Figure 10.4 Operating theatre of Wards 7 and 8. *The wards were those of the Professor of Clinical Surgery. The illustration depicts the style of clothing worn by the operating theatre nurses and the trolleys and basins employed during the first half of the twentieth century*

Soon after Wade's promotion in 1924 to the charge of wards 5 and 6 of the RIE, he asked for large and costly changes to his operating theatre.[18] The Managers were sympathetic until they discovered that new electric light fittings would cost £80 and a new operating table £119: the total estimated cost was £307. In 1929, a similar situation arose after his move to take charge of wards 15 and 16. Again, Wade asked for extensive alterations to the theatre. The hospital Managers agreed that it was not satisfactory that patients should be anaesthetized in the sterilizing room; however, it was also accepted that space in the students' room adjacent to the sterilizing room should not be given up.[19] The front row of seats would therefore be removed from the operating theatre itself while, to improve working conditions, a Scialytic lamp would be installed in the theatre at a cost of £78.[M] Matters moved slowly however. It was not until June of that year that these recommendations were finally approved. Even then, they had to go to the House Committee for endorsement.[20]

The work of the hospital

In the years between 1900 and 1939, increasing clinical demand and a continual rise in the number of patients being admitted, led to greater hospital work loads and augmented costs. A very large proportion of this work came from the daily attendance of multiplying numbers of outpatients, that is, patients from 'outside' (Tables 10.2–10.4). The numbers of outpatients rose steadily. In 1929–30, the annual number was 65,689, in 1937–38, 75,622. In 1939, fewer

Figure 10.5 Operating theatre of Wards 13 and 14. *For comparison with Figure 10.4. The theatre is that used by the Professor of Systematic Surgery. At the rear are raised benches used by students and postgraduates as they watched the operations*

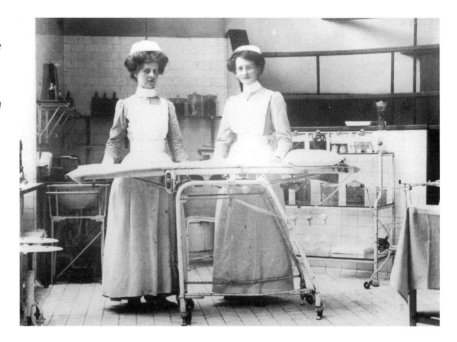

patients came with the advent of war. During Wade's time as Surgeon-in-Ordinary, the revolutionary concept of mixed male and female out-patient clinics was mooted by Professor Edwin Bramwell.[21]

Cases of Accident and Emergency were brought to the outpatient entrance of the RIE, adjoining the lower, surgical corridor. Each night, one of the seven surgical units or 'charges' was designated to receive patients who required urgent care. The junior staff of this unit attended to emergencies as quickly as they could, reaching decisions on whether simple treatment was possible – perhaps within the out-patient operating theatre – or whether immediate admission to the wards was necessary. In times of demand, for example, during holiday seasons such as Christmas and the New Year, additional beds were placed in the centre of the 'receiving' wards, allowing greater than normal numbers of patients to be accommodated.

During the years 1924–39, the period when Wade was Surgeon-in-Ordinary to the RIE, he was responsible for the surgical treatment of nearly 14,000 patients. To these figures must be added those he investigated in the Electric Diagnostic Theatre (p 230) and the many he saw as outpatients. An indication of the challenges faced by Wade, and of the volume of work with which he and his fellow consultants grappled, can be gained by examining the records for some of the years of the 1920s and 1930s.[22] It is of interest to compare the number of admissions to the RIE in 1924–39 with those of modern times which are summarized on p 353.[N] In making this comparison, it should be noted that, with increased surgical specialisation, the methods of expressing hospital admissions and numbers has altered radically in recent years (Table 10.5).[23]

Table 10.2 Bed occupancy, deaths, duration of stay and bed costs in the 1741 and the 1879 Royal Infirmaries of Edinburgh, for the years 1836–37, 1854, 1879–80, 1891, 1928–29 and 1936–37[11,25]

Variable	Robertson's Close Hospital		1741 Royal Infirmary Edinburgh		1879 Royal Infirmary of Edinburgh		
Year	1729–30	1836–37	1854	1879–80	1891	1928–29	1935–36
Total inpatients	35	4,164	4,397	5,315	*	19,889	21,568
Inpatients treated and discharged	30	3,829 (335)	*	4,857	*	18,972	20,612
Available beds	6	373	*	420	*	1,006	1,117
Patients in hospital/day	6	435	*	648	648	956	965
Number of deaths/year	*	*	*	458	*	1,244	*
Inpatients treated in surgical wards	7	NA	245	2,310	2,624	14,229	15,076
Mean duration of stay in surgical wards (days)	36.9	*	42	29.9	25	13.8	13.8
Mean cost of occupied bed/year (£)	2.8	25	21	60	63	150	175

NA=not applicable.

Table 10.3 Number of patients admitted to the RIE for the years 1924–29 and the number of deaths

Year	Patients admitted	Deaths[21]
1924	14,908	1,025
1926	16,138	1,107
1927	17,843	1,115
1928	18,779	1,084
1929	19,001	1244

The duration of time spent in hospital was usually much less for surgical than for medical patients. In 1924, the average time for medical patients was 22 days and for surgical patients 19 days. The corresponding figures for 1929 and 1930 were 16.7 and 17.0 days for medical patients and 13.90 and 13.7 days for surgical patients.

Delays in the admission of patients to hospital exercised physicians and surgeons severely throughout Wade's lifetime. Waiting lists were also a continual source of concern to the hospital Managers, who worried about rising costs. In 1924, 1,729 people were waiting for admission to the RIE. In 1929, the figure reached 2,494, and, in 1936, it was 2,971. Again, the delays were selective: they were greater in specialities

Table 10.4 Number of patients treated in the Royal Infirmary of Edinburgh during Henry Wade's time as surgeon in charge of wards, and the cost of hospital care

Year	Patients treated in hospital	Outpatients treated	Deaths	Surgical patients treated	Nurses	Hospital income (£)	Ordinary hospital expenditure (£)
1925	15,755	NA	1,052	10,164	354	109,931	127,751
1926	17,024	NA	1,107	11,586	373	107,201	NA
1927	18,713	NA	1,115	13,187	382	111,495	140,539
1928	19,680	67,623	1,084	14,466	383	117,191	136,831
1929	19,889	NA	1,244	14,229	NA	114,898	143,684
1930	20,543	65,689	1,262	14,606	415	118,560	151,765
1931	20,123	64,081	1,129	14,370	416	122,847	155,766
1932	20,049	66,266	1,197	14,438	417	118,081	157,065
1933	20,159	69,444	1,263	14,491	437	117,912	148,200
1934	19,849	66,792	1,249	14,303	439	112,510	156,896
1935	20,695	67,583	1,314	14,524	428	128,649	156,698
1936	21,568	72,543	1,354	15,076	460	129,020	169,694
1937	21,951	73,400	1,369	15,047	472	136,762	177,044
1938	22,895	75,622	1,362	15,747	473	140,882	187,859
1939	21,896	73,499	1,306	15,295	499	156,423	195,225

NA=not available

where surgery was in demand. Thus, because of the very long delays in providing treatment for patients with suspected tonsillar disease, much attention was directed to the needs of the Department of Otolaryngology (ENT). In 1924, 829 patients were on the waiting list. The majority of them were young people judged to require an operation for the removal of tonsils and adenoids. A comparable situation had arisen with the Department of Dermatology. Again, it proved impracticable to release Ward 4 of the RIE to accommodate these patients, as this was now the only 'relieving ward' held vacant for possible emergencies.[24]

Hospital staff

In 1919, the RIE was confronting the ravages of war and struggling to revive its earlier image of modernity and efficiency. To meet the demands of the patients and their doctors and to maintain its buildings, the hospital now employed thousands of people. One result of the 1914–18 war had been a loss of staff: thus, 61 nurses from the RIE were enlisted into the armed forces in 1914–15,[11] and, by the following year, 14 of the honorary consultant staff were absent. For these and other reasons, the work of the hospital diminished significantly during this time.

In 1928, Sir James WB Hodsdon retired, and in June of that year Wade moved from wards 5 and 6 to those of wards 15 and 16. He was reappointed to this new charge on 18th November 1929, with effect from 1st January 1930. Wards 5 and 6 were taken over by Mr James Methuen Graham.

Wade and his surgical colleagues were now supported not only by physicians, obstetricians, dermatologists, radiologists, radiotherapists and many others but also by laboratory and scientific staff. There was a close association with the Departments of the University Medical School. In 1930, in the laboratories, for example, were Dr James Davidson, Senior Pathologist and Dr WR Logan, Bacteriologist. The University's Professors of Pathology and Bacteriology, A Lorrain Smith and TJ Mackie, held honorary hospital appointments. In the following year, Lorrain Smith was succeeded by A Murray Drennan, while RF Ogilvie became an Assistant Pathologist. Davidson was followed by WG Millar in 1934 and, in 1935, with the continuing rise of neurosurgery, a new appointment of Neuropathologist was created for Dr H Biggart. In the same year, Mr WAD Adamson and other surgeons worked as Assistant Pathologists in the manner chosen by Wade in 1906. The supporting staff of the hospital did not enjoy large salaries. In 1926, an Assistant Bacteriologist's salary was £250 per annum, while Dr James Davidson, then Senior Assistant Pathologist, received £350. Nevertheless, the prestige of the RIE was high and recruitment was not difficult

In his surgical 'charge', Wade, like each of the other senior surgeons who had the responsibility for wards, enjoyed the indispensable and continuous support of a Nursing Sister, whose overriding authority not only influenced but directed much of the day-to-day work of the unit. The Ward Sisters dwelt beside their wards with living and bedroom accommodation cheek by jowl with the ward itself. This arrangement meant that her knowledge and skills were available to inexperienced House Surgeons at all times, an arrangement that was generally beneficial to the patients under the Ward Sister's care but sometimes inconvenient or even embarrassing to a young Resident.

The role of the nurse had changed beyond all recognition.[11,12,25] By 1923, the hospital staff included 342 nurses. Their salaries formed a very large part of the costs of the hospital administration. By 1930, their number had risen to 415 and by 1939 to 499, a 46% increase (Table 10.4). The rise in numbers was in close accord with the increased number of inpatients treated. Nursing was, and remains, a profession not devoid of occupational hazard and there were periodic outbreaks of influenza and streptococcal tonsillitis. Occasionally, so many nurses were sick that Ward 4 had to be opened to receive them. Generally, however, the proportion of the nursing staff absent through ill health was approximately 4% of their total number.

Very similar considerations influenced the approach to nurses' accommodation. Living as they did within the confines of the hospital was only a slight relief from the arduous and lengthy days they were expected to give to the care of their patients. In due course, a new building would take the place of the accommodation at Archibald Place, where several adjoining houses had earned the name of the 'West Home', and of temporary housing in George Square, rented from the University of Edinburgh. There was quiet accommodation for the night staff at Woodburn House, Canaan Lane, Morningside: night nurses were conveyed to and from this site each evening and morning. Travelling in the dark, their brightly lit bus was a vivid reminder to the local inhabitants of the immense benefits they derived from their hospital. The nurses, in their red capes, appeared as 'angels of mercy' but laboured long hours for little financial reward, with short holidays and the occupational hazard of frequent exposure to diseases such as tuberculosis.

An old proposal that accommodation for the nursing staff could be built between individual hospital pavilions had been rejected. As the number of nurses grew, it appeared to be essential to house at least 400. Construction of a fine new nurses' building started in 1936 and was completed in 1939. The new edifice suffered from the same financial constraints that had limited the size of the Simpson Maternity Pavilion, and the number of rooms in the ambitious new Florence Nightingale Home was ultimately 260, not 400, as had been planned.

The RIE was administered by a Committee of Managers, on which the Town Council, Royal medical and surgical Colleges and other organizations were represented. Every year, a full report was published.[O] The Managers met weekly or fortnightly. The minutes of their Committees are preserved in the Special Collections of the University of Edinburgh Library.[P] The Managers conveyed their policy through a series of bodies that included the Medical Managers Committee, the Law Committee, the Nursing Committee and an influential House Committee.

By modern standards, the administration of even the largest hospital was the immediate responsibility of a remarkably small number of dedicated and long-serving individuals headed by a Medical Superintendent. In 1914, the Superintendent was Lieutenant Colonel Joseph (later Sir Joseph) Fayrer RAMC. With the outbreak of war, he was granted leave of absence, and his place was taken by the Secretary/Treasurer of the Royal College of Surgeons, Mr MacKenzie Johnston FRCSEd.[26] Mackenzie Johnston carried great burdens, as he was appointed simultaneously to the Committee of Management of the RIE. Lt Colonel Fayrer resumed his duties in 1919, but died in office in 1924, when he was succeeded by Colonel George David St Clair Thom CB. Colonel Thom passed away on 7th April 1935. His place was taken by Lieutenant Colonel Alexander Dron Stewart FRCSEd.

The Superintendent was supported by a Treasurer/Clerk and by a very small number of assistants. Both the Superintendent and the Clerk were directly responsible to the Board of Management, who, in turn, worked closely with the financial bodies which undertook fundraising and the allocation of resources. The administration of the RIE and the conduct and efficiency of the committees also depended heavily on the shoulders of the Treasurer/Clerk: Mr William Strathie Caw. He retired in 1929, having served the Infirmary for 49 years. He was succeeded by Mr Henry Maw.

The Superintendent, in effect the Chief Executive or Managing Director, was always concerned that the 'rounds' conducted by Honorary Consultants should not interfere with the practical care of patients. In 1935, the Superintendent wrote:

> 'Will members of the honorary staff please ensure that ward work is finished by 1.15 p.m. daily.'

The hospital necessarily employed a large army of technical and scientific staff, a Master of Works, stokers for the coal-fired boilers, porters and cleaners. On 25th January 1928, it was recorded that a part-time ward secretary received £1/10/–d weekly and a masseuse £3/10/–.

Cost of surgical care

For those accustomed to the ways of the twenty-first century, it is difficult to believe that, until 1948, the Scottish teaching hospitals, the centres of medical teaching and training, remained charitable institutions.

During Wade's years as a senior consultant, the annual costs of the RIE rose from £120,000 to £150,000, a figure equivalent to more than £100,000,000 today. It was a 'voluntary hospital', that is, a hospital entirely dependent on public subscription. No government money was provided, and every penny needed to pay for the maintenance of the buildings, the staff and the costs of patient care had to be raised by public subscription. Consultants were not permitted to accept direct payment for their services. Their assistants received small gratuities but were largely dependent on the generosity of their seniors, who employed them in the private practices in which they, the consultants, laboured for their livelihood. Many young surgeons undertook teaching. Those who were sufficiently qualified and talented, young Wade among them, made their way on to the teaching staff of the Extramural School of Medicine of the Royal Edinburgh Colleges, as explained in Chapter 13. Such a privilege gave status and brought a small financial reward in the form of lecture fees.

The corollary of a bar on the acceptance of consultant fees determined that very many grateful patients, their relatives and friends gave generously to the hospital itself. It is of considerable interest that the amount of money attracted to the hospital in this way varied very greatly between different Surgeons-in-Ordinary, every one of whom worked on comparable contracts, each, in theory, undertaking similar volumes of work. In the 1920s, the reasons why Wade's patients gave an annual sum that was only two-thirds, or sometimes no more than half, of that donated by the patients of Professor David Wilkie or by those of Professor John Fraser[l] is not immediately apparent. When the volume of work of these distinguished surgeons is examined, Fraser is found to have been a particularly rapid operator, slightly faster than Wilkie[29] and significantly faster than Wade. It is also possible that Wade was devoting relatively more time to his Private Clinic. Yet Wilkie was a partner in the same practice and was supporting if not undertaking, a considerable volume of experimental surgical research and giving generously of his time to charitable causes.

Table 10.5 Costs of the Royal Infirmary of Edinburgh, 1729–2000

Year	Cost (£)
1729–30	98
1836–37	6,727
1879–80	27,818
1922–23	110,150
1928–29	143,684
1935–36	169,694
1999–2000*	106,000,000

In 2000, the mean cost of treating surgical patients within the specialities was: £1,205 for Otolaryngology (3,585 cases), £2,008 for General Surgery (7,691 cases), £1,145 for Gynaecology (2,337 cases), £817 for Ophthalmology (1,252 cases), £1,610 for Orthopaedics (4,765 cases), £2,130 for Surgical Paediatrics (1,865 cases), £1,038 for Urology (4,644 cases).

*Otolaryngological, urological, surgical paediatrics and accident and emergency cases are recorded as having been treated separately, under the auspices of the Lothian University Health Trust.

Wade was closely concerned with the cost of **looking after** his patients. The cost of caring for a patient in the RIE for 1836–37 had been £25, for 1879–80 £60, for 1928–29 £150 and for 1935–36 £175. By the year 2000, this figure had risen to £1,421. Expressed in terms of the individual patient, the average cost of a patient in 1939 was £3/5/1d per week. The mean cost for a whole episode of treatment was £7/11/1d. The cost of the voluntary hospital in terms of ordinary expenditure was £140,539 in 1927. It had risen to £177,044 by 1937 and to £195,225 by the outbreak of World War II.

Until 1947, when the voluntary hospitals were absorbed into the embryonic Scottish National Health Service, their costs had been met by voluntary subscription. Money was raised by public appeal, aided, for example, by a League of Subscribers. Members of the League were committed to supporting the hospital by annual contribution. The records of their contributions, and those of the many hundreds of individuals, trades, collieries and churches in all parts of the country and overseas that supported the RIE, occupied at least two-thirds of the Annual Reports of the hospital for the years 1919–39. A large proportion of the money needed to balance the budget came from the thousands of voluntary contributions solicited each year from individual people, grateful patients, businesses, offices and charitable organizations in Scotland and elsewhere. In 1937, £136,762 was raised in this way, in 1939 £156,423.

Something of the financial constraints that limited the work of the voluntary hospitals of the time can be learned from a minute that records that, at the time of his appointment as Surgeon-in-Ordinary in 1928, Mr JM Graham wrote asking for a cabinet and a typewriter. The Committee of Medical Managers replied brusquely that as 'a typewriter has not been issued to any of the surgeons hitherto, one should not be provided for Mr Graham'.[27]

Wade was also concerned greatly about the cost of ill-health **to** patients. In the 1920's and 1930's, the loss of working time caused by injury was very great, although it was clear that, generally speaking, exercise and graduated work facilitated a return to normal activity. In 1912, Wade found that the non-operative treatment of fractures in patients over the age of 15 years meant incapacity for 27.6 weeks.[28] Of these patients, 9% were permanently disabled. In the case of fractured femoral shaft, the lost time could be as much as 33.6 weeks and 11.7% of these patients were incapacitated permanently. The corresponding figures for fractured tibia and fibula were 26.7 weeks and 8.1%. A study of 22 injuries comprising seven fractured femurs, 14 fractured lower legs and one of both showed that the financial loss for each patient was £4,490: £2,932/11s/5d was paid in insurance compensation, while the employers paid an additional £1,558. At that time, an average wage for a working man was of the order of £1–£2 per week.

The challenge faced by Wade and his associates of labouring under the conditions described in this Chapter is outlined in the following pages.

CHAPTER 11

Surgeon at work: operative surgery and surgical care

1919–39

> I must confess that highly, and very highly, as I esteem the honours which have been conferred upon me, I regard all worldly distinctions as nothing in comparison with the hope that I may have been the means of reducing in some degree the sum of human suffering.
>
> (Joseph Lister, in a speech conferring on him the Freedom of the City of Edinburgh, 15th June 1898)

Like his august predecessor, Wade devoted his life to the care of his fellow men and women. The hospital at the centre of his work, the Royal Infirmary of Edinburgh, the RIE, is described in Chapters 1, 3 and 10. Now the procedures that he used to recognize and treat disease are considered. No surgeon can practice without experiencing occasional failure but it was accepted that Wade's diagnostic acumen and operative skills were exceptional. As a consequence, he was much sought after by anxious patients or their relatives, sometimes as a 'court of last appeal'. The fame he achieved and the respect and acclaim he was accorded were unsolicited and unsought. They illustrate his character perfectly.

The records[A] of the patients on whom Wade operated during the years between the two world wars illustrate his methods and the organization that made their application practicable. Coincidentally, they shed a penetrating light on the social and domestic conditions of the time, telling us of the poverty and malnutrition so common in Scotland. They hint at a lack of organization of hospital services and show how the 1914–18 war led to an influx of wounded and scarred men and women who required surgical care. They also reveal the not unexpected existence in Scotland of infectious and tropical diseases brought from far-flung theatres. Wade's hospital case notes are reminders of how the expectation of life among the civilian population was little more than it had been in 1903,[1] demonstrating graphically the degree to which the prevalence of disease in the early twentieth century western world differed dramatically from that of the twenty-first.

Chapter Summary

- Diagnosis
- Radiodiagnosis and radiotherapy
- Anaesthesia
- Surgical instruments
- Operative surgery
- Blood transfusion
- Resuscitation
- Postoperative infection
- Chemotherapy
- Postoperative care
- The daily round, the common task
- Retirement

Figure 11.1 Henry Wade.
Wade is shown in this photograph at the height of his fame as a urological surgeon

In spite of the improvements in nutrition that followed the end of the First World War, infection, particularly tuberculosis, remained a great threat. To guard against this 'white plague', there was neither any screening programme nor any form of antibiotic therapy. Indeed, the death rate from tuberculosis in 1920 had become as high in the villages as in the cities.[2] A contributory factor was overcrowding and the fact that, among the many poor, large families were commonplace. Infant mortality remained high, and many children died in childhood from scarlet fever, diphtheria, measles, poliomyelitis and whooping cough or were left with intractable conditions such as bronchiectasis and mitral valve stenosis, for which, in Wade's time, there were no surgical remedies. Although vaccination against smallpox was obligatory, prophylactic immunization (p 207) against the fevers of childhood was not endorsed. The complications of 'German' measles, rubella, were not recognized. The spectre of syphilis, a residue of the First World War, haunted surgical as well as medical practice. Cancer, for the most part a disorder of adult and older persons, was a smaller relative problem in Wade's time than it has now become.

Despite these intractable challenges, better anaesthesia, improved radiographic methods and the successful introduction of blood transfusion contributed to an air of surgical optimism. New techniques now encouraged more ambitious procedures than had been possible before 1914,[3] and the lessons of war benefited practice greatly. One result was that increased numbers of patients sought surgical care. In Scotland, the voluntary hospitals provided much of this service, so that, as Chapter 10 shows, they came under growing pressure for money and space (p 199).[4] Another consequence was the expectation, among patients and their medical practitioners, that a surgical operation would hint not at death or deformity but at the restoration of health and vitality. The hospital was no longer the 'cauldron of disease' that it had been until the 1870's but a 'temple of cure'.

Diagnosis

The key to success in surgery has always been the swift and precise identification of disease. Wade pursued this ideal relentlessly.[5] In surgery, as in internal medicine, the scene for responsible diagnosis was set by eliciting an exact history from a patient – a verbatim record of the onset and pattern of the illness, the style of a patient's life, the diet, an account of previous illnesses and of any family history of disease, travel and accident. A meticulous physical examination of the patient followed.

After examining a patient, Wade selected as many as were necessary of the available laboratory tests of the blood, urine and tissues. Occasionally, the cerebrospinal fluid was investigated. Simple laboratory tests were made in a room adjacent to the hospital wards – a 'side room', where a bench, fitted shelves and cupboards accommodated the apparatus and reagents needed to examine the urine for sugar and albumin, to measure the level of haemoglobin in the blood and to inspect the stools. However, more sophisticated studies were in increasing demand. For this purpose, samples were dispatched to the hospital laboratories, accompanied by handwritten request forms. The second quarter of the twentieth century was becoming the era of the clinical laboratory scientist. Larger hospitals such as the RIE could afford to delegate tasks in clinical chemistry, bacteriology, haematology and tissue pathology to a growing cadre of specialists. Smaller voluntary and municipal hospitals such as the Leith Hospital were often compelled to place the burden of these varied techniques on the shoulders of a single individual, a 'jack of all trades'.

A new clinical laboratory was associated with Ward 21 of the RIE. **Clinical chemistry** became of crucial significance. In 1929, the hospital engaged a professional chemist, Dr CP Stewart, and a small technical staff. One limitation on the number and rapidity of the chemical measurements that could be made was the fact that they were manual and time consuming. Automation was not initiated until the late 1950s. The van Slyke glassware for blood urea assays, for example, had scarcely changed since 1903, while the cumbersome measurement of blood glucose levels still depended on the precipitation and weighing of an insoluble product. Requests for the repeated, rapid measurement of these substances, particularly during the night, conveyed an air of unreality. As Wade's case notes demonstrate, such requests were made infrequently: it was safer to be dangerously ill in the daytime than at night! There was not yet any form of blood gas analysis, and the rapid assay of electrolytes, essential for the regulation of the metabolic disturbances so common in surgery, was generally impracticable.

Bacteriological tests were frequent and of great and growing value. They were monitored by the watchful eyes of the Medical Research Council,[6] the Public Health Laboratory Service[7] and its Scottish counterparts. In Edinburgh, diagnostic work on behalf of the City of Edinburgh was conducted in the laboratories of the Usher Institute of Public Health, which opened in 1903. In 1928, this work was transferred to the laboratories of the Medical School. The First World War greatly accelerated understanding of infectious diseases but outbreaks of enteric fever, the conditions of typhoid and paratyphoid, might compel the closure of whole surgical wards, as could epidemics of food poisoning. Further infectious diseases that demanded bacteriological attention urgently included outbreaks of infection among medical and nursing staff and the inadequate sterilization of the suture material catgut, described on p 224.

Even in Edinburgh, more obscure infections and their consequences sometimes had to be treated. One legacy of foreign military campaigns was the need to be able to call on experts who could identify reliably the parasites of malaria, bilharziasis (schistosomiasis), kalar-azar (leishmaniasis) and other **parasitic diseases**. Cases of rabies, 'dog-bitten patients', were dealt with by the Laboratory of the Royal College of Physicians of Edinburgh, the RCPEd.[8] Particularly during and after the First World War, increasing numbers of cases of venereal disease were encountered in surgical practice. In November 1914, the President of the RCSEd agreed with the Deputy Director General of the Army Medical Services that lectures on this topic should be given to the troops by surgeons who were members of the Council of the College.[9]

Virology was still in its infancy. Many of the 'filterable' viruses that threaten surgery in the twenty-first century were entirely unknown, their existence unsuspected .[10]

The study of blood and bone marrow disease, **haematology**, was largely the province of physicians. Many of Wade's patients suffered from anaemia in addition to the condition that had led them to seek his advice, and he was well aware that disorders of the blood could prejudice the outcome of any operation he performed. The search for defects of blood constituents in surgical patients was therefore mandatory. It was made by measuring haemoglobin concentrations, by counts of white blood cells and platelets, and by assays such as those determining the erythrocyte sedimentation rate, the packed cell volume and the clotting and bleeding times.

Wade spent several years in pathology laboratories (Chapters 4 and 5) and was an enthusiastic exponent of the value of evaluating tissues by **biopsy** (p 78) before undertaking a definitive operation. It was an approach of particular importance in the recognition of cancer, renal and hepatic disease, and disorders of the skin and skeleton. In Edinburgh, the Laboratory of the RCPEd (Chapter 5) played an important part in providing this service, which it shared with the laboratories of the RIE. The staff of the hospital laboratory were often members of a University Department. In an approach to a diagnostic problem, a certain dichotomy could be recognized. Thus, in two consecutive patients, tissue from the first might be directed to the Laboratory of the RCPEd, while tissue from the second could be submitted to the Laboratory of the RIE. The first, perhaps a case of urinary disease, might be reviewed by Dr James Dawson (p 84) on behalf of the Laboratory of the RCPEd, while the second, possibly tissue from a patient with alimentary disease, would be reported by Dr James Davidson, Assistant Pathologist to the RIE. The evidence suggests that Wade invoked the RCPEd Laboratory in cases of special, research interest and the RIE's laboratory in cases of a more routine nature.

Diagnostic cytopathology, the microscopic examination of individual cells as opposed to pieces of tissue (Chapter 5), was practised rarely.

In twenty-first century surgery, it has become unthinkable and unethical to undertake the diagnosis, prophylaxis and treatment of a patient without taking into account the principles of **immunity**. This was not necessarily so in the period from 1920 to 1939. In all of the cases of accident or injury that Wade treated, tetanus was of course recognized as a threat. From his extensive wartime experience, he knew the disease could be prevented by passive immunization, the administration of an anti-tetanus toxin antiserum manufactured in the horse. Anti-tetanus serum was therefore injected into all threatened patients immediately after they were admitted to his wards in the RIE. During the First World War, the ravages of gas gangrene had also begun to be countered by the preparation of antisera to other spore-bearing anaerobic bacteria. By 1939, Wade's House Surgeon was instructed to administer anti-gas gangrene and anti-tetanus sera to every patient in whom the development of such an infection was considered possible.

The control of tuberculosis by public health measures was a further matter of great significance to Wade. Tuberculosis of the urinary tract (Chapter 12) was among the most common conditions he treated. It had long been known that sensitivity to tuberculosis could be assessed by observing the results of an intradermal Mantoux test. The test was employed as a means of eliminating this diagnosis in patients who, suspected of tuberculous disease, could be shown to yield a negative reaction. In theory, the administration of the vaccine designated BCG (*Bacille Calmette et Guérin*), which was made in 1921,[11] could offer protection to those of Wade's patients who had not yet encountered the tubercle bacillus. However, the routine administration of this vaccine to children at risk did not come until some years after Wade left hospital practice. The possibility of tissue and organ transplantation had been explored before the First World War. Wade had used a graft successfully in the treatment of a malignant tumour of bone (p 51) although the basis of transplant immunity was not yet understood. He was, of course, not the first to attempt bone grafting.

Radiodiagnosis and radiotherapy

Throughout Wade's lifetime, the demand for radiographs increased steadily. In the 1930s, the rate of increase in the number of radiographs was 12 times that of the number of patients admitted to the hospital. A significant part of the demand for radiology came from Wade's work in the Medico-Electric Theatre – the Electric Diagnostic Theatre (p 230). Wade's expertise in urological surgery (Chapter 12) was widely recognized. In 1923, when he was still an Assistant Surgeon, he was granted direction of the Theatre (pages 208 and 230); the appointment was renewed annually.[12] In this unit, he carried out procedures such as cystography, retrograde and (later) intravenous pyelography (Table 12.1).[B] There were frequent calls for new or ancillary equipment.[13] Wade's appointment was confirmed in 1924 after he had become Surgeon-in-Ordinary to Wards 5 and 6. Subsequently, the word 'Electric' was abandoned and the theatre became simply the 'X-ray Diagnostic Theatre'.

> The records of the diagnostic theatre are contained in a series of loose-leaf files. On average, there are two files for each year, each with approximately 150 entries. Thus, it is possible to calculate that no more than one or two patients were examined each day, with an individual entry for each patient bearing a reference number, the patient's name, age and sex but often only a brief clinical history. In 1925, occasional reports were still written by hand. In September 1925, for example, Wade's secretary was apparently on holiday; since a series of reports was in his own writing. The sheets were headed 'Urological Reports' and carried a subheading 'Cystoscopy Examination'. The diagnostic theatre was also used for the examination of patients suspected of having gall-bladder and associated diseases. Cholecystography was often undertaken, but the reports were written quaintly on 'Urological Report' forms.

In the regulation and conduct of the work of the Electric Diagnostic Theatre, Wade was fortunate to have Mr RL Stewart as his First Assistant and Mr JJM Shaw as his Clinical Tutor. Moving to Wards 5 and 6 in 1924, the name of a second assistant, Mr David Band, appeared. Conventional radiology was of quickly increasing significance in diagnosis (p 190). To meet this demand, Wade collaborated with Dr Hope Fowler and Dr Woodburn Morrison and submitted annual reports on the work undertaken and the apparatus used.[14,15]

Anaesthesia

The RIE was dilatory in appointing a full-time, professional anaesthetist.[16] Even in the 1930s, it was still acceptable for fourth- and fifth-year medical students to be called on at short notice to administer anaesthetics to patients approaching major operations such as thyroidectomy. For 20 years after the Managers of the RIE had acceded to the request to designate Clinical Surgical Tutors to supervise anaesthesia (Chapter 3), no attempt was made to have an anaesthetist appointed officially to the RIE. The Lord Advocate then drew attention to the danger of allowing unqualified medical students to give anaesthetics without proper medical supervision. As one result, in 1932, Dr Sheena Watters was appointed to cover emergencies. Two more anaesthetists were designated for this purpose in 1933; one was Dr John Gillies, who was later to achieve fame for his part in the operations conducted on King George VI.

Throughout the years when Wade was Surgeon-in-Ordinary to the RIE, the agents used for general and local anaesthesia, as well as the techniques by which they were applied, were evolving quickly.

General anaesthesia

For general anaesthesia, Wade and his colleagues still preferred ether and chloroform.[17–19] They remained the mainstays of general anaesthesia until the time of the Second World War. New gases, such as cyclopropane and halothane, had been shown to be safer than chloroform or ether but these agents were not used universally. Wade and his colleagues preferred nitrous oxide ('laughing gas') for minor procedures and for many dental operations. The gas was cheap and relatively safe, while induction was rapid and recovery equally so. In 1926, the cost of Boyle's apparatus for this form of anaesthesia was no more than £35 (£35/5/6d).[20] There was particular concern about anaesthesia for those in a state of 'shock' or likely to enter this state, and agreement that nitrous oxide/oxygen should be used for all such patients.[21] A special trolley was kept for this purpose in Professor John Fraser's operating theatre adjoining Wards 7 and 8 of the RIE.

By means of a syringe, an anaesthetic agent could be given into a vein. For this purpose, ether and chloroform had themselves been tested. There were obvious advantages in not having to place a mask over a patient's face and to compel an individual to inhale an irritating vapour. However, Wade did not hurry to take advantage of the novel intravenous barbiturates that had been synthesized in the 1920s. Ultra-short-acting agents, such as evipan (1932) and pentothal (1934), were compounds that could be administered intravenously. They entered surgical practice in Edinburgh as Wade's time as a senior surgeon to the RIE drew to its close.

Muscle relaxants, such as curare, came into widespread use only after Wade's retirement from the RIE. As an adjunct to safe anaesthesia, however, he often used intratracheal intubation (Chapter 3). New and improved equipment had evolved for this purpose, and a Reavel two-way electrical pump, bought in 1928 for £12 (together with £13/10/–d for accessories), offered advantages. It came into use in the following year.[22] The equipment was adopted by Wade for operations such as the excision of pharyngeal or oesophageal carcinomas. Oxygen was generally given simultaneously.

Local anaesthesia

For local anaesthesia, spignocaine, novocaine and lignocaine were among the agents developed during Wade's years. He selected them for spinal and epidural anaesthesia. There was awareness that the Crown Agents had expressed concern about the safety of cocaine.[23]

Consideration had also been given by the Scottish Board of Health to a total ban on the manufacture of the heroin widely employed in analgesia in cases of intractable pain.[24]

Occasionally, wider issues related to the hazards of anaesthesia would arise. On 26th January 1925, the Superintendent of the RIE, Colonel Fayrer, sent a circular carbon-copied letter to Mr Wade saying:

> 'I shall be glad if you will kindly let me know if you have any cause of complaint regarding the quality of the anaesthetic ether supplied to your wards.'

Next day, Wade responded:

> 'During the past 3 months I have operated on a large number of patients anaesthetised with ether. There have been no serious complications or any increase in post-operative complications.'

However, because bronchitis had occurred among both hospital and private patients, it was agreed that 'ether of the utmost purity should be used and its general use reviewed'.

Surgical instruments

As the years passed, Wade employed an increasing variety of instruments for preliminary diagnosis. They included cystoscopes, gastroscopes, sigmoidoscopes and bronchoscopes. They were of rigid, inflexible construction and incorporated small tungsten filament light bulbs connected to transformers and thus to an electricity supply. They were cumbersome to use and difficult to sterilize. For inspection of the ear, nose and throat, head mirrors from which electric light was reflected were replacing those dependent on daylight or gas light. Auroscopes of unitary construction then came to incorporate battery-operated electric light bulbs.

Continual advances occurred in the design of scalpels, forceps, scissors and retractors. The eminent neurosurgeon, Norman Dott (p 51), was a pioneer of instrument innovation. The detachable blades of Morton's steel scalpels were coming into use,[25] and the new science of plastics had been born. Its applications in surgery were predictably limitless. Suture materials of new design and composition were formulated. Hypodermic and other small syringes were generally still made of glass and steel although the plastics industry was evolving quickly. The sheets, gowns and tubes so widely used during operations were made almost entirely of rubber, as were tubing and cannulas. Towels and swabs were of linen or cotton.

The sterilization of surgical instruments was the responsibility of each individual surgical unit. Towards the end of the nineteenth century, a new class of instruments became available that was able to withstand the heat needed for proper sterilization. They replaced the handmade instruments with ivory or ebony handles that had served so well until that time. Following Lister's example, many surgeons employed hot-air ovens to sterilize the new steel scalpels, scissors and retractors necessary for operative procedures. This was the technique Lister had adopted in the preparation of instruments required for his experiments on bacterial cultures. In the Glasgow Western Infirmary, the eminent surgeon William Macewen was fortunate in having an instrument manufacturer sensitive to his personal requirements.[26] Towels and sheets were sterilized by steam. Autoclaves were coming into general use, but the days of a central sterilizing department and the commercial packaging and sterilization of plastic devices by irradiation lay in the distant future.

In the years before 1939, the small instruments so often used in side-room procedures were sterilized by boiling. This was the normal practice prior to injections, blood transfusion, the aspiration of blood or other fluids, and spinal puncture. The instruments were boiled in stainless steel containers, over the flame of a Bunsen burner.

Operative surgery

When Wade succeeded to the charge of Wards 5 and 6 in 1924, the impact of an organized blood transfusion service, chemotherapy and better anaesthesia had not yet been felt, but there was a steady increase in the volume of work, perhaps in part a reflection of the transition from war to peace. In addition, there were innumerable advances in the practice of surgery[27–30] and coincidental changes in the patterns of disease. Every one of these developments contributed to an inexorable growth in the demand for his services. Among the 14,000 patients under Wade's care in the RIE during the years 1924 to 1939 were many cases of abscess, carbuncle, cellulitis, haemorrhoids, appendicitis, cholecystitis and cholelithiasis. The operations of appendicectomy and cholecystectomy were commonplace and pyloroplasty was coming into use. Patients with cancer were seen less often than today – the mean age of the population was less – but some forms of malignant disease, particularly gastric carcinoma, were relatively common. Thyroidectomy for neoplasm or goitre was performed regularly. Beyond these 'general' procedures were many operations within Wade's field of urological surgery. They included prostatectomy, nephrectomy and lithotripsy. However, the pattern of disease and the nature of the operations performed in his Private Clinic at 35 Drumsheugh Gardens, Edinburgh, were significantly different from those undertaken in the RIE. They are tabulated in Chapter 9.

In the period from July 1917 to July 1922, the record books[C] for Wards 5 and 6 of the RIE listed the register number of each patient admitted to the wards; the date of admission; the patient's name, age and sex; the date of any operation; and the result, which could be 'cured', 'relieved' or 'died'. The operating theatre books also recorded 'remarks', which indicated the anaesthetic used and the surgical procedure. At the top of each page was the name of the House Surgeon, whose task it was to complete these notes. Their quality varied with the interest and aptitude of each individual Resident.

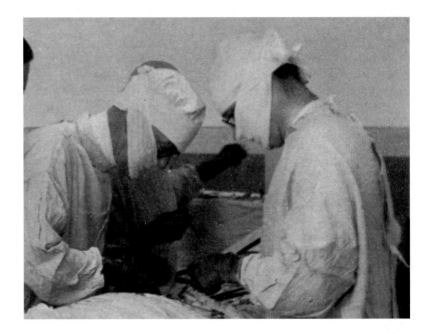

Figure 11.2 Wade in his operating theatre. *In many illustrations of surgeons in the theatres of the first half of the twentieth century, it is not easy to be certain of a surgeon's identity because of the caps and masks that were worn with increasing regularity*

The increase in the numbers of patients subjected to surgery continued (Table 10.5). During the years 1917–22, 1,900 operations were performed in Wards 5 and 6 of the RIE, a number that represented 32 procedures each month. It is reasonable to assume that considered (cold) operations were performed on weekdays only and likely that only one to two days were 'operating days'. On this basis, the average daily operating list was probably of two or three major cases, together with the inevitable cluster of minor procedures. In the years that followed, Wade himself undertook 504 of 1,144 operations (43%) in Wards 5 and 6; the remainder were performed by his colleagues who included David Band, JJM Shaw, IL Dick, WAD Adamson, RL Stewart, DS Middleton, TMcW Millar, WA Cochrane, J Jeffrey, FG Gibbs, TI ('Tamas') Wilson and WA Morton. From 1931 to 1938, 2,300 operations were performed in Wards 15 and 16, a figure representing 33 each month. Of these, Wade again performed two of every five procedures, his signature added to the pages of each of the volumes of operation records.

The nature of Wade's operations continued to cover a very wide field of disease. Moreover, the wards catered for accidents and for emergency admissions: there were many cases of fracture, laceration, dislocation and other injury. There was a predominance of patients with gastrointestinal disorders. The overall mortality was 10%. Those who succumbed were, on average 40 years of age and were often suffering from gastric, intestinal or urinary disease but death in young people with bone infection, osteomyelitis, was surprisingly frequent. The mean duration of hospitalization was 24.7 days but many patients required readmission.

As Chapter 10 recounts, the Managers of the RIE were constantly troubled about the growing waiting lists for admission to the RIE, a problem exacerbated by the length of time spent by patients in the hospital. The problem of duration of hospital stay is exemplified by the following case.

A woman aged 35 years was admitted to Ward 15 on 3rd December 1934. She had spinal tuberculosis, suffered from kyphosis and complained of dysuria. The bladder urine contained tubercle bacilli. Wade undertook nephrectomy. A pathologist confirmed the presence in the renal tissue of widespread tuberculosis. The patient was discharged after 69 days but was readmitted to Ward 15 on 2nd April 1935. A sinus had formed at the site of the nephrectomy. Under nitrous oxide and oxygen anaesthesia, Mr Jeffrey curetted the sinus and packed it with bromo-iodo-phenyl paste (BIPP). The edges of the sinus were 'approximated'. She returned again to Ward 15 on 20th September 1935. A letter describing her case to her practitioner was signed by Professor DM Dunlop. The sinus was again curetted with a sharp spoon. Pus and purulent debris escaped, and BIPP was rubbed into the site. The patient left hospital after 26 days. On 25th July 1936, her practitioner reported that she had suffered from pain and swelling in relation to the bladder for eight weeks. Excretion urography was performed. Three days before her next operation, the patient began to receive ¼ gr morphine daily; it was administered as a suppository together with ¹⁄₁₀₀ gr atropine. On 17th September 1936, the right ureter was transplanted. She left hospital after 46 days. On 28th April 1938, she was readmitted once more. She had begun to complain of abdominal pain. Many adhesions were found at laparotomy. They were divided by Mr I Aird. She was transferred to Ward 6 on 5th May 1938 and discharged after 31 days. However, she continued to experience abdominal discomfort and received advice on taking an alkali mixture after meals. On 5th December 1938, she returned to Ward 16 under the care of Mr Wade, having developed an abscess in the left loin. The abscess was drained. Non-haemolytic streptococci were isolated from the pus. A bacteriological report was signed by Dr CG Wallace. On 26th March 1941, the patient described acute lumbar pain. A pyelogram was unsuccessful. At the same time, she found that she could not hold items in her hands. Rectal examination revealed a large cold pelvic abscess.

The final outcome of this protracted case was not recorded.

Neurosurgery

The new and quickly evolving subject of neurosurgery, the surgery of the central and peripheral nervous systems, had been given a dramatic impetus by the pioneering work of Macewen.[26] Macewen initiated much brain surgery and was influential in persuading surgeons to adopt an aseptic – as opposed to an antiseptic system. In this work, his practice of boiling the materials and instruments used in his operations was gradually accepted. He readily adopted the method of steam sterilization introduced by Bergmann in 1886 and published the results of his great success in the treatment of brain abscess, first in 1879 and then in 1893, in a classic work entitled *Pyogenic infective diseases of the brain and spinal cord.*[31,32] His report of the successful surgery of an intracranial neoplasm was epoch making.[33] By 1920, the subject had been advanced dramatically by Harvey Cushing (1869–1939).[34] His new techniques for brain surgery, in part based on his extensive experience during the First World War, had begun to be adopted in civilian practice. Among the Edinburgh surgeons who benefited from Cushing's knowledge, skills and experience, none became better known than Norman Dott (p 52).

Relatively few cases requiring neurosurgical care were treated in Wade's wards. Accidental injury accounted for most of those in which operation was attempted.

> A man aged 36 years was admitted to Ward 15 after slipping on the road and falling on the side of his face. In spite of the accident, he was able to walk home. Later, his wife could not rouse him. He was unconscious on admission. Extradural haemorrhage was diagnosed. Under local anaesthesia, Mr JJM Shaw raised a temporal flap and found an extensive clot measuring approximately 6 × 3 inches. Bleeding from the middle meningeal artery could be seen but was not stopped by diathermy. The dura mater was sutured. At the end of the operation, the patient remained unconscious. He died soon afterwards. A necropsy, limited to the head, revealed a two-inch long temporopareital fracture of the skull.

Cardiac and vascular surgery

Although Carrel had transplanted both veins and arteries in 1905,[35] this was not a field in which Wade claimed experience. Subsequently, Carrel undertook the first successful heart operation, an operation conducted in a dog.[36] It was only in 1916 that Ionescu advanced cardiovascular surgery further when he experimented with sympathectomy for angina pectoris.[37] In 1935, Carrel's first extracorporeal artificial heart pump was tested.[38] By this time, clear signs were emerging that the largest hospitals would need surgeons who could specialize in this field of surgery. Wade was not among them.

Thoracic surgery

Surgical approaches that demanded the opening of the chest were limited by the inadequacy of techniques for safe anaesthesia. Not until the end of the Second World War could rapid progress be made.

A man aged 32 years was admitted to Ward 6 on 10th November 1925. He complained of persistent cough for three weeks following a right-sided pleurisy six weeks previously. Under nitrous oxide and oxygen anaesthesia, Mr Wade incised the chest wall at the level of the 9th rib. Three pints of pus escaped. In an earlier, preoperative aspiration, pneumococci had been identified. The patient was discharged after 35 days.

Gastrointestinal and biliary surgery

The most immediate advances in surgery that resulted from the introduction of antisepsis and asepsis were experienced in the fields of gastrointestinal and orthopaedic surgery. Not surprisingly, Wade gained considerable experience with the necessary techniques. By the 1920s, it had become possible to approach with some hope of success conditions that 30 years previously would have been inoperable. The most frequent procedures remained those for hernia and appendicitis.

A man aged 35 years was admitted to Ward 6 on 25th April 1925 with a perforated, acutely inflamed appendix. The appendix was removed by Mr JJM Shaw under chloroform and ether anaesthesia. The abscess was drained and he left hospital after 27 days.

A man aged 68 years was admitted to Ward 6 on 10th November 1925. He complained of a swelling at the back of his tongue, which he had first noticed 18 months earlier. Under chloroform and intratracheal ether anaesthesia, Mr Wade inserted a gag into his mouth and removed the left half of the tongue. A histological report on 16th October 1925 described commencing invasion by a squamous neoplasm. On 20th November 1925, the report was amended to read 'early squamous carcinoma of the tongue'. The patient left hospital after 12 days. No mention was recorded of radium or X-ray therapy.

A woman aged 59 years was admitted to Ward 5 on 2nd March 1926 with a history of progressive difficulty in swallowing. She had been referred to Mr Wade on 18th February 1926 by Dr JS Fraser, who, with Dr JD Lithgow, was otolaryngologist to the RIE. Dr Fraser said, 'I do not think the case is a very favourable one for surgery'. On 11th March 1926, under chloroform and intratracheal anaesthesia, Mr Wade undertook the excision of an extensive carcinoma of the oesophagus and lower part of the pharynx. The oesophagus was divided a short distance below the edge of the tumour and a tracheotomy performed. A pathological report by Dr James Davidson (Volume XXIX, No 740) described a rapidly growing squamous epithelioma. Two days after the operation, the patient's pulse rose rapidly to 112 and her temperature to 104.8°F.

A man aged 31 years was admitted to Ward 6 on 3rd January 1925 complaining of the gradual onset of abdominal pain. A perforated peptic ulcer was diagnosed. The perforation was closed, and he underwent pyloroplasty by Mr JJM Shaw. He was discharged after 15 days.

A woman aged 67 years was admitted to Ward 16 on 30th December 1939 complaining of epigastric pain, nausea and vomiting. The pain was worst in the gastrohepatic region and was referred to the back on inspiration. There was abdominal distension. The House Surgeon, Dr James M Drennan, wrote in the notes: 'She is too fat!' In 1931, the patient had been in Professor John Fraser's wards with

continued

cholecystitis and was found to have an extraperitoneal abscess but no calculus. Efforts to resuscitate her failed, and she died without any satisfactory diagnosis. An autopsy by Dr Colin Campbell confirmed that death had resulted from acute necrotising pancreatitis with cholelithiasis, dilatation of the common bile duct, intrahepatic cholangitis and tuberculous pyometra.

A male aged 63 years was admitted on 27th December 1924 complaining of abdominal pain and the inability to defecate. A rectal biopsy was performed by Mr JJM Shaw. Biopsy confirmed the presence of rectal adenocarcinoma. Colostomy was undertaken on 6th January 1925, and, as usual, nepenthe was given as an analgesic in the postoperative period. The patient was discharged on 15th January 1925 but readmitted on 1st April 1925, when it was decided that no further treatment was indicated.

Urinary surgery

Henry Wade's extensive experience of urological surgery forms the substance of Chapter 12. The problems faced by the few who specialized in urology are exemplified by the cases below.

A 76-year-old woman with intractable urinary infection (chronic pyelocystitis) [*sic*] was investigated by cystoscopy. Wade wrote: 'The best line of treatment would be 1. to confine the patient to bed; 2. to regulate the action of the bowels; 3. to increase the intake of fluids; 4. to administer an alkaline bladder sedative; and 5. possibly, to use an urinary antiseptic' (Case 8576).

A woman aged 39 years was admitted to Ward 5 on 15th January 1925. She had had 10 children and two stillbirths. Of the surviving children, one had died of whooping cough and two of diphtheria. A urinary bladder tumour had been operated upon in Ward 17 in June 1924. She now had haematuria and frequency. The patient remained in hospital for three days, during which further fulguration of the bladder lesions was undertaken by Mr Wade. She was readmitted on 30th March 1925 but died nine days later. A post-mortem examination revealed that the tumour was a vesical squamous carcinoma.

A woman aged 26 years was admitted to Ward 5 on 25th April 1925 with the complaint of left lumbar pain. She had been anaemic for 18 months and had been confined to bed for four weeks. Nephrectomy was performed by Mr Wade on 12th May 1925. A calculus was found, together with evidence of old tuberculous pyelonephrosis [*sic*]. The patient suffered considerable postoperative shock. She made an apparent recovery on 15th May but the following day suffered a sudden collapse. She died at 7.45 am. An autopsy revealed a pleural effusion together with gastric dilatation.

A male painter aged 41 years had fallen on 11th October 1926 and fractured a rib. He was shocked. Under stovocaine intrathecal anaesthesia, Mr Shaw exposed and sutured a lacerated kidney.

Endocrine surgery

Continuing advances were being made in the surgical treatment of thyroid, adrenal, pituitary, ovarian and testicular disease, although relatively few cases were referred to Wade.

A woman aged 44 years was admitted to Ward 5 with a thyroid swelling. She had exophthalmos, palpitations, excitement and weakness, signs and symptoms of thyrotoxicosis. Under chloroform and ether, Mr Wade exposed the thyroid by a Kocher's incision and removed the anterior part of the gland. She was in hospital for 19 days. On 29th October 1926, a pathological report from the hospital laboratory, signed J Davidson (p 197), reported a toxic adenoma 'passing into malignancy'.

A man aged 53 years was admitted to Ward 6 on 2nd May 1925 with the complaint of pain and swelling of the right testis. The Wasserman reaction was negative. He was operated on by Mr Wade on 7th May 1925 under chloroform and ether anaesthesia. The organ was removed. Histological examination by Dr James Davidson revealed clear evidence of testicular tuberculosis. The patient left hospital after 61 days.

Orthopaedic surgery

When he returned to Britain in 1919, Wade's outlook had widened. He realized that orthopaedics was a subject in its own right. Wade often quoted Sir Robert Jones who had advanced the revolutionary view that all fractures, whether recent or old, united or malunited, should be in the care of a special Orthopaedic Surgeon. It was a concept slow to take hold in Edinburgh. The Council of the RCSEd noted in 1918 that, 'Orthopaedics had been removed from the list of optional subjects for the Fellowship examination in 1900 and they did not see any sufficient reason for replacing it at the present time'.[39] For some years, matters proceeded slowly, and, in 1928, the Managers of the RIE remained cautious. They observed that 'Facilities in the RIE do not warrant an Orthopaedic Department'. In suggesting that there was a place for a University Lecturer in Orthopaedics, they speculated that the University would be aware that a scheme was being developed for the establishment of a Cripples' Hospital for southeast Scotland.[D] Their views were updated in 1934, when an Orthopaedic Department was at last opened in the RIE.

In 1921, Wade recounted some of his wartime experiences of orthopaedics to a civilian audience accustomed to dealing with miners' injuries.[40] He recommended that an 'outfit' for surgeons who dealt with colliery accidents should include a knee flexion piece for attachment to a Thomas splint, pressure pads for correcting local lateral displacement, a pair of Pearson's callipers, a pot of Sinclair's glue, a bent Thomas splint and a Sinclair skate.

Wade treated orthopaedic patients with a wide variety of disorders. The first case, bridging pre- and post-First World War practice, is repeated from Chapter 3, pp 51–52

A man aged 27 years had fallen playing football in August 1913. There was numbness, immobility and pain in an arm. X-ray showed a pathological fracture of the upper end of the shaft of the humerus. The fracture had healed satisfactorily, although stiffness persisted and movement was restricted. Two years later,

continued

the emergence of a swelling led to the diagnosis of myeloid sarcoma, although the tumour was not examined microscopically. An exploratory operation revealed a centrally situated tumour. The head and upper portion of the shaft of the humerus, including six inches of bone, were excised. Prior to the operation, an amputation for senile gangrene had been performed on a man aged 67 years and a six-inch long segment of the lower end of the femoral shaft removed under aseptic conditions. This bone graft was implanted in continuity with the glenoid cavity of the younger man. No plates or screws were used to secure the implant because of the danger of ischaemia. Subsequent review showed new bone fixing the graft in position. Wade believed that the new bone had arisen in part from the bone cells of the implanted femur. The patient successfully resumed his occupation as a mill worker within two months of the graft. Re-examination in November 1919 confirmed that the implanted bone remained firmly united to the recipient's humeral shaft. Later, the patient, whose case is referred to in Chapter 9 (p 171), developed a sarcoma at the site of the graft and died.

A man aged 39 years was admitted to Ward 6 on 3rd May 1925. He had been thrown from his motorcycle and had fractured the tibia and fibula of his right lower leg. The leg was placed in a box splint. He was discharged after 31 days.

A male aged 46 years was admitted to Ward 6 on 2nd January 1925 with the complaint of an ill-fitting boot. The patient gave a previous history of tuberculosis of the lungs, back and neck glands. Tuberculous disease of the foot was identified. On 16th January 1925, Syme's amputation was performed under chloroform and ether anaesthesia. The patient left hospital after 39 days.

A boy aged 11 years was admitted to Ward 6 on 11th October 1926 with pain and redness of an area over the lower tibia. Osteomyelitis was diagnosed, but no treatment was prescribed other than rest.

A man aged 48 years was admitted to Ward 56 with a painless swelling of the right abdomen. Fourteen years earlier, a 'spot' had been removed from the same place. Six years ago, an egg-sized swelling was excised; it had recurred, again in the same place, six months later. Under chloroform and ether anaesthesia, Mr Wade removed the mass, which was the size of half a clenched fist. A pathological report from the Laboratory of the RCPEd described an extensive, infiltrating fibrosarcoma. The patient remained in hospital for 27 days.

Trauma

The Accident and Emergency services that have become customary in the twenty-first century were woefully lacking in the early years of the twentieth. Improved transport, speedy evacuation, resuscitation, anaesthesia, blood transfusion and antibiotic treatment were matters for the future.

A man aged 18 years was admitted to Ward 6 on 6th October 1925. His motorcycle had run into a lorry. He was in profound shock, was unconscious and was bleeding from the mouth, tongue and nose. There was a compound fracture of the left thigh. He died soon after admission.

A man aged 17 years was admitted to Ward 6 on 9th October 1925. He had fallen from a scaffold in Princes Street. He complained of pain in his back. Paralysis was suspected, but his bladder function was unaffected. He had a fractured clavicle. He made a steady recovery and was discharged after 14 days.

A man aged 56 years was admitted to Ward 6 on 7th November 1925. He had been run over by a lorry. A tourniquet had been applied to the right leg by the police. A compound fracture of the tibia and fibula was identified. Under chloroform and ether anaesthesia, Wade's assistant, Mr RL Stewart, cleaned the fracture site with Eusol (Edinburgh University Solution of Lime). The leg was splinted and held in traction in a Thomas splint. The patient was able to leave hospital after 13 days.

Breast surgery

Attempts at the radical removal of breast cancers can be traced to the earliest records of surgery. No better example of the challenge presented by mastectomy in the days before the introduction of general anaesthesia and antisepsis can be found than in Dr John Brown's searching tale of *Rab and his friends*.[41] By 1926, numerous successes had been recorded, based on the pioneering work of Halsted, Handley and many others.[42,43]

A woman aged 57 years was admitted to Ward 5 on 25th February 1926. Two years earlier she had noticed a dimple at the site in the breast where there was now a palpable lump. It was above and lateral to the nipple. No glands were palpable in the axilla. She had had 15 pregnancies, 10 of which went to full term and eight of which were living. On 1st March 1926, Mr Wade undertook a radical mastectomy. The pathological report by Dr James Davidson from the hospital laboratory, described a widespread scirrhous carcinoma of the breast with extensive involvement of the axillary glands. The patient left hospital after 19 days without further treatment.

Surgery of the lymphoreticular system

Few cases of lymphoma are recorded in Wade's notes but tuberculous lymphadenitis was still rampant.

A woman aged 23 years was admitted to Ward 5 on 31st May 1926 with cervical lymphadenitis. She gave a previous history of recent diphtheria. In the past she had had rheumatic fever and chorea. On 1st June 1926, under chloroform and ether anaesthesia, Wade scraped the inner walls of the abscess and shelled out two lymph nodes. A report by Dr James Davidson revealed tuberculous caseation. The patient remained in hospital for 11 days.

Plastic surgery

The dramatic advances that took place in plastic surgery were largely accomplished after Wade had retired from the RIE. However, Wade's colleague, Mr JJM Shaw made pioneering contributions to this new speciality.

A woman aged 25 years was admitted to Ward 5 on 4th June 1925. She had had a brown hairy mole on the dorsum of the hand since birth. She was a pianist. Under chloroform and ether anaesthesia, Mr Shaw excised the naevus by means of a complex procedure, and the patient returned home after 20 days.

A man aged 71 years was admitted to Ward 6 with a growth on his left hand. It had appeared two years earlier, and, as it grew, he removed it himself with a razor. He had worked for 30 years in a gas company, where he was involved in extracting by-products of coke burning. He had previously had growths on both sides of his face, and 16 growths on his right hand had been treated with radium. Under chloroform and ether anaesthesia, Mr JJM Shaw excised the present growth and repaired the defect with a skin graft taken from the anterior abdominal wall. The patient remained in hospital for 25 days. A pathological report by Dr James Davidson described a squamous epithelioma (carcinoma) of the skin of the hand.

A woman aged 70 years was admitted to Ward 5 complaining of a spot beside the right eye. It formed a scab and became sore. On 27th May 1926, the lesion was excised fully by Wade and the skin replaced by a Thiersch graft taken from the right thigh. A pathological report by Dr James Davidson revealed: 'great hyperplasia of the squamous epithelium which now shows the deeper invasion of malignancy. The cells are actively proliferating'. It was not possible to state whether the tumour was a basal cell carcinoma or a squamous carcinoma. The patient left hospital after 23 days.

Ophthalmological, otolaryngological and gynaecological cases

Patients with ophthalmological, otolaryngological or gynaecological disease entered Wade's practice only occasionally.

A boy aged 6 years had been shot accidentally with an airgun pellet in his right orbit. On 4th March 1926, Mr Wade and Mr RL Stewart together attempted to locate the pellet, which could be seen by X-ray. Exploration of the injured orbit was not successful, and the patient left hospital after 11 days.

Blood transfusion

Wade took a particular interest in the development of a centralized Edinburgh blood transfusion service. For much of his time in the RIE, patients subject to major operations were at risk of death from blood loss. Wade realized the immense importance of providing blood for those under his care. As late as 1929, however, there was no reliable means by which he could fulfill this purpose. He knew that by the end of the First World War, no more than a few hundreds of transfusions had been possible.

A successful transfusion of blood from one human to another had been made in 1818, and both Joseph Lister and William Macewen had undertaken the procedure successfully. However, there were many hazards. Their nature became clearer after Karl Landsteiner showed that when the red blood cells of one individual were mixed with the serum of another, the cells often but not invariably clumped, a process of agglutination.[44]

> Landsteiner demonstrated that all humans could be categorized by the presence or absence of two antigenic substances found on the red blood cells. The antigens were designated A and B. On the basis of the presence or absence of one or other or both, four blood groups – A, B, AB and O – were identified. The prospect of safe human transfusion seemed increasingly realistic, although the full complexity of human blood groups and their inheritance was not appreciated fully until after the discovery of the rhesus (Rh) factor in 1940.[45]

A crucial limitation on the practice of transfusion was the lack of any technique that allowed blood to be stored. Person-to-person transfusion was the only practicable approach,[46] either by aspirating small amounts of blood from a vein of a donor and injecting the collected blood little by little into a vessel of the recipient, or by connecting the circulations of the donor and the recipient directly, as they lay side-by-side. Then, in 1914, it was discovered that sodium citrate could prevent the coagulation of blood held outside the body although blood could still not be stored. In 1916, the refrigeration of blood to which glucose had been added provided the answer to this intractable problem. The transfusion of stored blood now became pos-

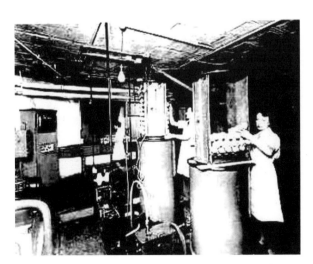

Figure 11.3 Blood transfusion centre. *Plasma is being freeze-dried*

Figure 11.4 Detail of the apparatus for freeze-drying plasma

sible although its widespread use depended on the organization of a panel of donors.

In 1918, few had realized that blood transfusion would be of immense importance in civilian surgery. There was little support for a service. An exception to this disinterest was the attitude of Mr (later Sir) Geoffrey Keynes through whose efforts a small panel of donors was recruited in southeast London. In Edinburgh, the subject was advanced by Mr James Graham (p 352), who performed 46 transfusions on 39 patients between 1913 and 1919. In 1929, members of the Royal Medical Society established an informal panel of donors for the RIE. The panel existed for two years. The initiative was then seized by JR Copland. He enlisted an army of volunteers, the Holyrood Order of Crusaders. His panel was first called upon in 1931. When the Crusaders withdrew their support in 1936, a meeting of eminent citizens was sustained by the Lord Provost and the Edinburgh Blood Transfusion Service was formed. It was at this meeting that Wade, now President of the Royal College of Surgeons of Edinburgh, the RCSEd, stated that the blood for transfusion: 'must be the free will offering of men who love their fellow mortals'. The Edinburgh service came into being only a few months after Marriott and Kekwick's description of 'continuous drip' transfusion, a practical approach that set the pattern for all subsequent developments in transfusion technique. On 9th February 1940, the Scottish National Blood Transfusion Association was constituted at a meeting in St Andrew's House, Edinburgh.

A partial solution to the problem of correcting blood volume lay in the infusion of isotonic saline or gum saline, as described in the next of Wade's cases. A further development, which came too late for Wade, was the infusion of reconstituted, freeze-dried plasma as a sub-

Figure 11.5 Administration of blood by transfusion. *In this illustration, Dr H Scarborough is shown giving a transfusion. The blood is contained in an open-ended, glass infusion flask of the kind used before plastic containers came into use*

Figure 11.6 Blood for transfusion being moved by car in 1936. *The car is an Austin 12.*

stitute for blood. It was a technique that proved invaluable in the Second World War. However, this approach could not influence the oxygen-carrying capacity of a patient's blood.

A miner was trapped by a fall of coal in 1934. He sustained a fractured femur and a compound fracture of the tibia and fibula. After the femur had been placed in traction, the tibia and fibula were set in plaster. 'On coming from theatre he was given 900 cc of gum saline and 400 cc of saline'. However, he developed pneumonia, and the traction was temporarily stopped. He recovered and four months later was able to move in walking callipers.

Resuscitation

Techniques of resuscitation had advanced significantly since 1914 (Chapter 5) but they bore little resemblance to those practised in the twenty-first century.

On 12th November 1931, a man aged 52 years was admitted to Ward 16 under Wade's care. He had been wounded by shrapnel in the left leg in 1918. The wound had suppurated, and there was a large deforming scar. A first operation was undertaken. Anaesthesia was induced by ethylene dioxide and continued with chloroform and ether. The callus was excised from the leg ulcer and 12–15 conical 'pinch' autografts applied, taking skin from the left thigh and applying them directly. However, only three of them 'took'. A second operation was performed on 7th December 1931, but the patient stopped breathing. Artificial ventilation was attempted with oxygen and carbon dioxide. Cardiac massage was adopted via the abdominal route. Strychnine was injected subcutaneously, and ether was placed on the tongue. Adrenaline was injected into the heart, but the patient did not revive. An examination *post-mortem* revealed adherent pericarditis and evidence of right apical fibrous tuberculosis. It remained uncertain whether these changes were sufficient to cause death: the influence of chloroform was suspected.

Postoperative infection

Epidemic infection is a constant threat when large numbers of people congregate, particularly when they share sources of food and water. Hospitals are especially vulnerable and have often been described as 'cauldrons of disease'. The high rates of infection that complicated operations before the First World War were largely attributable to a persistent lack of understanding of the modes of bacterial transmission. The importance of the washing and scrubbing of hands; the wearing of gloves; the use of caps, masks and gowns; and the avoidance of manual contact with non-sterile objects were learned by bitter and prolonged experience.

Wade carefully considered the problems of disinfection in the treatment of orthopaedic war wounds contaminated by soil and detritus.[40] In the early part of the 1914–8 war, it had become clear that chemical disinfectants were of slight value. Watson Cheyne's antiseptic paste was unsatisfactory but Eusol (Edinburgh University Solution of Lime) was valuable. Although the Dakin–Carrel method of infusing wounds and injuries proved impracticable on a field of battle, wounds benefited from normal saline-hypertonic saline solution (*sic*) washes as well as from salt packs. Carl Browning advocated the use of flavine in a 1 in 5,000 solution, but there were disadvantages: flavine stopped suppuration but delayed wound repair. Another material that proved popular and of value was bromo-iodo-phenyl paste (BIPP) and flavine: it was the brainchild of Mr Rutherford Morison. The paste could not be used to fill an entire wound cavity, but a small amount, rubbed carefully into every corner of a wound after arresting bleeding, cleaning, excising and disinfecting with spirit, was of value. Encouraging results were obtained, especially in potentially infected gunshot wounds of the knee joint. The paste could be used during the period in which a patient was being transported to hospital.

The spectre of infection spread by faulty methods of sterilization raised its head in 1927 when a number of cases of tetanus were reported. Professor TJ Mackie, Professor of Bacteriology of the University of Edinburgh, was responsible for the overall conduct of the painstaking bacteriological investigations that followed. He found that the culprit was catgut, in which tetanus spores remained after inadequate sterilization. As a result of his studies, recommendations on the preparation of catgut were made known to the Scottish Board of Health.[47]

Chemotherapy

During Wade's lifetime, innovations in chemotherapy and antibiosis revolutionized the treatment of disease. He read with enthusiasm of prontosil rubrum and of the emergence of the sulphonamides.[48] The world of surgery was not immediately aware of the significance of the discovery made by Alexander Fleming,[49] who had observed in 1929, the antibacterial activity of *Penicillium notatum*. Indeed, more than 10 years passed before an extract, penicillin, became available for use in the treatment of infection. By 1942, sufficient had been produced by bulk fermentation for human use. It was immediately employed for the treatment of the wounded accommodated in wartime Emergency Medical Service hospitals such as Bangour (p 284), where Wade was Director of Surgery.

Subsequently, Wade observed the advent of streptomycin,[50] the first agent with significant activity against *Mycobacterium tuberculosis*, although there is no evidence that he used it himself. Streptomycin was followed by the so-called broad-spectrum antibiotics, aureomycin and chloromycetin.[51] After Wade's retirement from hospital practice, but within the period in which his Private Clinic was still active, the dramatic report of the anti-inflammatory action of the adrenal corticosteroid, cortisone, was published.[52] The properties of this new compound were described at the very moment when a new form of antibiotic, neomycin, became available.[53]

Postoperative care

Understanding of nutrition was growing quickly, not only because of the discovery of an increasing number of vitamins and other essential food factors, but also because of the employment in the larger hospitals of professional dieticians trained to assess the optimum diet for individual patients and staff.

The demand by surgeons for the skills of physiotherapists increased, particularly because of the long overdue creation of a Department of Orthopaedic Surgery. Accommodation for a new generation of these skilled and professional workers was initially on the second floor of the new X-ray Department of the RIE.

The daily round, the common task

Texts, notes, drawings and photographs cannot give a full impression of the arduous work shouldered by Wade and his colleagues. Wade's surgical work was interrupted quite naturally by periods of vacation. However, the 1930s was a period of particular interest in his career because of his visit to Australia (Chapter 14) and then, in 1935, on account of his two years as President of the RCSEd, of whose Council he had been a member of since 1925. The fact that there was very little decline in the number of operations he performed during these particularly busy times is a reflection of his character and tenacity.

Figure 11.7 Ward in the RIE in 1937. *There are still no curtains around the patients' beds, and relative privacy is ensured only when heavy screens are moved manually, by nurses, from other parts of the ward*

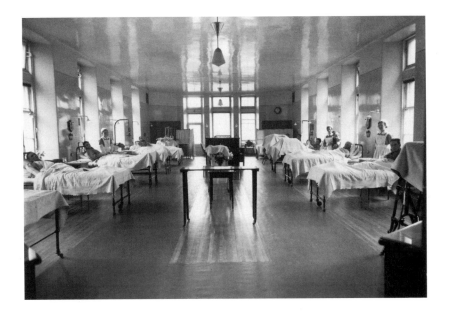

Wade's days were long and arduous. It is possible to reconstruct one from the recorded words of his immediate colleague, the late Noel Gray.

Setting off from his weekday home at 6 Manor Place, Wade walked the short distance to 35 Drumsheugh Gardens. After winter weekends, when he might travel from Pilmuir House, Haddington, he favoured a long heavy coat with an Astrakhan collar. Having talked to the matron, nursing sisters and his secretary, Wade would visit each resident patient and assess their progress. He was often accompanied by his First Assistant and his Clinical Tutor. Moving to a changing room, he would dress in boots, gown, cap and mask. He then began the tedious but demanding task of the scrubbing of hands, a meticulous routine that was the best guarantee of avoiding the spread of infection during an operation. Donning rubber gloves, he entered the operating theatre. By the time he reached this room, the patient would have been anaesthetized, the anaesthetic, usually chloroform, administered by his assistant or, occasionally, by a senior student. The theatre staff would be dressed in the same style. An operation, perhaps appendicectomy, was preceded by sterilization of the surface of the patient's skin. Iodine in alcohol, thioflavine or later, methiolate were used for this purpose. Sterile linen towels were draped around all parts of the patient's body near the area where the operation was to be performed, which was left exposed. The operation over, the surgeon and his colleague's rested briefly.

After completing the morning's 'list' of operations, Wade drove to the RIE. There is no record of the kind of car he preferred, but many senior surgeons chose a Rolls Royce, not infrequently purchased second-hand. Wade owed much to the loyal staff who looked after his cars – William Innes and James Smith – and he left each of them £50 in his Will.

In the RIE, where he arrived at about 11 a.m., a very similar routine to that of the Private Clinic was repeated. First, he visited his patients in the wards a cup of tea preceding the ward round. On operating days, a substantial 'list' of operations followed. The ward operation books give a reasonably exact record of their number and nature (see above). On average, the operating theatre of Wards

continued

15 and 16, in which Wade laboured from 1928 to 1939, accommodated two to three major operations on each of the designated operating days. Wade undertook more than 40% of them himself. There were, in addition, many minor cases often dealt with by his Assistants.

After such a morning, Wade might expect to return to Manor Place at 1.30 to 2.00 p.m., to be confronted by an afternoon during which he would see a list of private patients in consultation. Letters and messages followed.

The price to be paid for owning and managing a Private Clinic was that sudden demands on his time, in the form of surgical emergencies, might arise by day or night. Once a week, a similar call on his time might be expected from the RIE, although, for the most part, the cover provided for urgent admissions to the Infirmary was given by his Clinical Tutor or his Assistant Surgeon.

Saturday mornings were occupied by clinical teaching 'rounds' in the RIE (Chapter 13), when his great knowledge and experience were offered to a dedicated and expectant group of postgraduates studying for their examinations. On Saturday afternoons, when there were few requirements to attend committee or RCSEd Council meetings, Wade retreated to Pilmuir House (Chapter 15).

Retirement

Wade left the honorary staff of the RIE at the end of 1939, eight years before the advent of the Scottish National Health Service.[2] His retirement was obligatory; it was effective from 29th December. Marking the occasion on behalf of the Board of Management of the RIE, Professor Gulland expressed their appreciation of Wade's long and loyal services to the hospital. As was the custom, he now became a 'Consulting Surgeon'. Through his new responsibility for the Emergency Surgical Service at Bangour Hospital (p 284), his commitment to his nursing home and its private practice, his valued role in the RCSEd and his membership of advisory committees, however, he remained close to the 'coalface' of contemporary surgery. The hospital in which he had grown up, knew and loved would continue to change but he was sufficiently mature and wise to appreciate that institutions do not stand still. He watched with intense interest as surgery moved into the age of the graft, the 'keyhole' and the genome.

Figures 11.3–11.6 are reproduced by permission of Dr AHB Masson and the Edinburgh and South East Scotland Blood Transfusion Association

Figure 11.8 Henry Wade in 1939. *The photograph shows Wade at the time of his retirement from the RIE, a relaxed but solitary figure, contemplating his departure from his alma mater. There is little in the hospital records to demonstrate that he enjoyed a farewell dinner, reception or presentation*

Figure 11.9 The central tower and clock face of the Royal Infirmary of Edinburgh. *A nostalgic view of Wade's hospital as it was in 1939, the year of his retirement*

CHAPTER 12

Innovation in surgical urology: a master craftsman

1912–39

Some men there are love not a gaping pig;
Some that are mad if they behold a cat;
And others, when the bagpipe sings I' th' nose,
Cannot contain their urine.

(Shakespeare, *The Merchant of Venice*)

In the early years of the twentieth century, specialism in surgery was on the increase. It was one consequence of the ability of surgeons to operate painlessly and with relative freedom from the threat of postoperative infection. Wade insisted on describing himself as a 'general' surgeon, that is, one who could perform any of the most frequently required operations for any of the most common conditions. In practice, through interest, experience and opportunity, he became a pioneer and specialist in the difficult and demanding field of surgery of the urinary tract.[1-3]

The origins of urological surgery, or surgical urology, can be traced in some of the earliest historical records. Cutting for the stone, lithotomy, was the most ancient operation undertaken for the relief of a specific surgical condition.[4] The reasons lithotomy was attempted were two-fold: first, the presence of a stone in the urinary tract was among the most painful and distressing of conditions afflicting mankind. Moreover, cutting for the stone, although an excruciating ordeal, was sometimes successful. Consequently, lithotomy was practised by ancient Hindu, Greek, Roman and Arabian surgeons and formed one of the five great operations of surgery described and skilfully illustrated by Charles Bell.[5] The practice of lithotomy was so important to the Incorporation of Barber Surgeons of Edinburgh that they considered establishing a Chair of Lithotomy in 1741.[6,A]

Wade was captivated by surgical urology first, because of the time he spent as a demonstrator in anatomy (1902) and pathology (1903); second, because of the studies of experimental glomerulonephritis that became part of his MD thesis;[7,8] and third, because of his work as

Chapter Summary
- Urological diagnosis
- Surgery of the kidney
- Surgery of the ureter
- Surgery of the urinary bladder
- Surgery of the prostate gland
- Royal Society of Medicine

Assistant Pathologist (1906–08) to the Royal Infirmary of Edinburgh, the RIE, where he encountered many cases of urinary disease.

Wade was responsible for the post-First World War development of surgical urology in Edinburgh. Together with Jacobs of Glasgow, he was accepted as the Scottish pioneer of this speciality. Early in his consultant career, Wade formed a close working relationship with some of the leading American experts in this field. An invitation to visit Professor Hugh H Young dated back to their meeting in 1913. The advent of the First World War interrupted Wade's plans. However, the chance to travel to the Johns Hopkins Hospital came to fruition in 1920.[B] The influence of the Americans on Wade's work was very great. As Chapter 9 describes, he took advantage of his visit to the USA to approach a number of instrument companies and to order from them the latest equipment needed for his new work in Edinburgh.

In the years of a consultant practice that extended from 1909 to 1939,[9,10] Wade was constantly aware that systemic illness and metabolic dysfunction might be early evidence of urinary disease. The challenge of diagnosing urinary disorders, he believed, should be understood by general practitioners.[11] The signs could be obscure so that loss of appetite, for example, might be the first evidence of urinary dysfunction caused by hydronephrosis. Urinary obstruction could upset the 'renal equilibrium',[12] invoking incipient uraemia. With Dick,[13] Wade reviewed the problems of pre-renal, renal and post-renal anuria. Renal secretion ceased when the blood pressure fell to 50 mm Hg. The intravascular injection of a soluble salt could be diuretic, but water was dangerous and sodium chloride ineffective. However, hydrated sodium sulphate (Glauber's salt) was restorative.[13]

Urological diagnosis

In urological surgery, as in every other responsible medical and surgical practice, precise diagnosis necessarily preceded exact surgical treatment. Wade, demanding, meticulous and skilled, used every available method for the investigation of his patients (Table 12.1). After recording a full history, he made a complete urological examination. The value of the Electric Diagnostic Theatre (the EDT) became increasingly evident. The theatre (Chapters 10,11) came into its own after the end of the First World War.

Patients suspected of having urinary disease were referred to the EDT from every one of the seven surgical 'charges' of the RIE. Some surgical units received many more such patients than others, so that in the late 1920s, for example, Mr JW Struthers of Wards 9 and 10 sent numerous patients for investigation, while Mr JM Graham of Wards 15 and 16 submitted relatively few. This pattern of referral was an index of the professional interests of the individual surgeon. Many patients were referred to the EDT by Professor John Fraser but very few indeed were sent in the name of his Assistant Surgeon, Mr Walter Mercer, who was already developing his particular specialities of thoracic and

Table 12.1 Diagnostic methods used by Wade for the investigation of urinary disease during the years 1909–39

Technique	Procedure
Urine analysis	Urinanalysis was conducted in the 'side room' of a hospital ward
Urine culture	Bacteriological studies were becoming frequent; a guinea pig might be injected
Blood	Chemical analyses, such as assays of blood urea and blood glucose, were made by hand; they were slow and of limited variety. The functional activity of the kidneys was examined by measuring urea excretion or by a phenolsulphonphthalein test
Radiography	To demonstrate the urinary bladder, for example, radiograms were made with the tube at right angles to the plane of the pelvic brim
Cystoscopy	Using the best instruments, cystoscopy, performed without anaesthesia, allowed the examination of the urinary bladder and ureteric orifices
Ureteral catheterization	Ureteral catheterization was frequent. Estimates of pelvic capacity were by renal lavage
Chromocystoscopy	Chromocystoscopy was of value in searching for ureteric calculus. Four cm^3 (ml) of indigo carmine was injected intramuscularly. Within 7–10 minutes, a jet of coloured urine was normally propelled from each ureter
Retrograde (infusion) pyelography	By 1899,[13] opaque styletted catheters were used as aids to post-cystoscopic radiography. The renal pelvis was visualized by introducing a radio-opaque medium through a ureteric catheter. Later, the method was employed to measure the volume of the pelvis. Radio-opaque collargol, argyrol, silver iodide or thorium nitrate were introduced gently, by gravity or syringe, into the renal pelvis until the patient complained of slight discomfort. These agents were replaced in 1918 by 20% sterile sodium bromide
Intravenous (excretion) pyelography	Radiographic examination of the urinary tract was enhanced by the injection of a contrast medium into a peripheral vein. Uroselectan, abrodil and hippuran (sodium ortho-iodohippurate) were chosen. Uroselectan contained 42% iodine
Quantitative excretion urography	Uroselectan was precipitated from acidulated urine and weighed. Renal function was assessed by the amount. Normally, most was excreted 1.5–3 hours after injection
Biopsy	Needle biopsy was rare but help could be obtained from open biopsy

orthopaedic surgery. From time to time, depending on the interests of individual consultants, patients for urological investigation were also referred to the EDT from physicians, from the gynaecological wards, from Dr Lees of the Department of Venereal Disease, from the neuro-surgical wards (Wards 19 and 20) and from general practitioners.

In the period 1925–30, the number of patients with suspected urinary disease examined in the EDT was approximately two each day. However, it is not possible to determine precisely how many patients were investigated by Wade himself or by his immediate colleagues JJM Shaw and David Band.

The investigation of an individual patient began when, two days before their examination in the EDT, the subject was given potassium bromide as a mild sedative. By this time, the usual sequence of enquiry had been the macroscopic, microscopic and bacteriological analysis of the urine, the analysis of the blood and finally preliminary X-rays. Cystoscopy followed, a procedure conducted with an inflexible instrument in which a source of electric light was incorporated.

> The Museum of the Royal College of Surgeons of Edinburgh, the RCSEd, (Chapter 6) has many of Wade's instruments. They include a series of his cystoscopes. The older instruments are of the simple Nitze design: one was manufactured in Berlin by Louis and Lichtenstein and another in the USA by ACMI. It bears the date of a patent – 1908. Two further instruments are urethroscopes: one a Wyndham Powell design made by Down Brothers and the second a Ringleb design constructed by Georg Wolf of Berlin. There is a lithotrite and evacuator and an incomplete Young's roungeur. One operating cystoscope is of Drapier make and originates from E Krauss of Paris. Finally, there is Wade's individual test tube holder, the source of which is described in Chapter 9.

Retrograded pyelography followed. Specimens of urine were collected at various times during each study. The reports recorded in the EDT books invariably included details of the subsequent bacteriological investigations. Generally, the records included the name of the referring surgeon and the ward from which the request came. Although the records showed each patient's name, age and sex, the pages were not signed and the name of the surgeon conducting the examination was not noted.

Cystoscopy[14] might be followed by retrograde pyelography. Wade valued laboratory techniques highly when confronting diagnostic problems such as haematuria,[15,16] pyuria, suspicious X-ray shadows,[17] unexplained renal hypertrophy, abdominal swelling and loin discomfort.[9] He wrote, however, 'I have never found any value in the nature of the cells present as a means of localizing the site of a lesion of the genito-urinary tract'. To stress the significance of X-rays, Wade quoted two cases where cystitis had persisted undiagnosed for several years in spite of cystoscopy. When radiograms were at last made, renal tuberculosis was revealed in both.

As instrument design improved, the use of cystoscopy assisted diagnosis increasingly. In 1922, Wade reported that he had carried out more than 1,000 investigations by ureteral catheterization without complication.[9] The procedure was

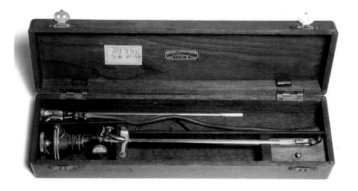

Figure 12.1 Cystoscope. *The Museum of the Royal College of Surgeons of Edinburgh contains 20 cases of surgical instruments belonging to Wade. Among them is a large collection of illuminated cystoscopes. Two of these sets are of the Nitze design; they were manufactured in Berlin*

difficult with impermeable stricture of the urethra; with severe prostatic hypertrophy; with ureterovaginal fistula; if an inaccessible ureteral orifice was the result of an opening into a diverticulum; if a visible ureteral orifice could not be catheterized; and in the presence of inflammation. In 1920, the simplest and safest way of demonstrating that both kidneys were 'functionating' [*sic*] was chromocystoscopy (cystochromoscopy). Where a calculus was the cause of partial ureteric obstruction, 'the pigmented urine escaped like smoke from a slow-burning fire'.

Retrograde (infusion) pyelography

When retrograde (infusion) pyelography was employed, the principal renal diseases recognized were infection, tuberculosis, calculi and tumours. Congenital abnormalities included single functionating [*sic*] kidney, horseshoe kidney, cystic disease, and pelvic and unilateral fused kidney. The broader term antegrade urography described the percutaneous injection of a contrast medium into the renal pelvis or calyces (antegrade pyelography) or into the urinary bladder (antegrade cystography) by means of a needle or catheter.

Wade emphasized the importance of a proper understanding of the anatomy of the renal pelvis.[18] Minor variations included two ureters opening independently, close to each other, or the presence of three major calyces. He employed 'infusion' urography without harm in more than 4,000 patients.

Intravenous (descending or excretion) pyelography

Intravenous (descending or excretion) pyelography was introduced in 1929.[19,20,21] The entire kidney could be outlined. Wade and Band[19] and Wade[22] wrote warmly of the technique. 'Excretion' urography proved useful for determining the function of a remaining kidney when unilateral nephrectomy was being considered. Interpretation of the appearances could only be by 'one well trained in recognizing pyelographic appearances: the method should not be depended on as a routine means of demonstrating the cause of disease. Rather its province is more to demonstrate the effect of disease'. The procedure was painless but difficult in adults 'of unstable mind' [*sic*]. It offered the first means of visualizing the urinary tract in early childhood.

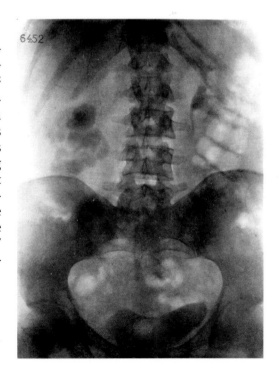

Figure 12.2 Excretion urogram made in 1930. *This is Figure 3 from Wade and Band.[19] The original caption reads: 'Excretion urography. Tuberculous disease of the right kidney'. The work described in this paper was undertaken within a year of the first report of the technique from von Lichtenberg's clinic*

Laparotomy

Finally, Wade accepted that laparotomy was sometimes essential to confirm the presence of a functionating [*sic*] contralateral organ. Nephrectomy without such an investigation was only justified if there was accidental rupture and haemorrhage or if acute fulminating suppurative pyelonephritis endangered life.

Surgery of the kidney

Tuberculosis

Before the end of the Second World War, tuberculosis was rife in Scotland. Renal, urinary bladder and epididymal tuberculosis were therefore closely familiar to Wade. A substantial part of his practice concerned their surgical treatment.

The symptoms centred on urinary frequency and discomfort; bladder capacity was diminished. Diagnosis did not rely on demonstrating mycobacteria in the urine although in 26 of Wade's cases the organism was found. After cystoscopy, bilateral ureteral catheterization was undertaken. There was a risk of misdiagnosing bilateral disease if the selective examination of urine from both kidneys was not practised. Rarely, suprapubic cystotomy might be required but Wade did not favour 'this French practice'. A grid-iron incision in the loin could expose the ureter, allowing a characteristic, pipe-stem change to be seen; the ureter could then be incised. Tuberculous glands occasionally caused ureteric constriction. An ureteral orifice might be reddened, swollen and congested, the appearances of 'golf-hole' ureter. Many cases had tuberculous ulcers on the vesical wall. Ultimately, a whole infected kidney would be destroyed by local reinfection.

The treatment of renal disease could only be by nephrectomy:[23] Wade had never seen a healed lesion. He described his experiences retrospectively.[10] He had performed nephrectomy in 200 cases.[23] Between 2nd August 1922 and 5th June 1928, he operated on 53 patients. The mean duration of the symptoms was 18.8 months. Where the date of the operation was noted, five operations of nephrectomy were undertaken in 1922 and 1923; seven in each of the years 1924 and 1925, six in 1926 and two in 1928. No operations were recorded in 1927. The patients were aged 11–64 years.[24] The mean age, stated in 23 cases, was 28.7 years. In the 37 cases in which the sex was recorded in the laboratory notes, there were 20 men and 17 women.

Thirty-four cases healed by primary union. Twelve had a small residual sinus and five a larger sinus, but in only one did the wound break down completely. It was directly infected and required excision. Nearly one-third of those who were not operated upon died within two years.[25] Even if the disease was not eradicated, removal of the tuberculous kidney reduced inflammation of the lower ureter and urinary bladder. A residual complication was bladder involvement with

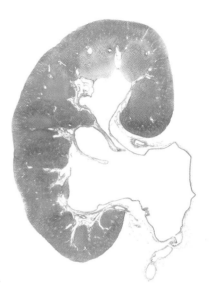

Figure 12.3 Tuberculous kidney. *The kidney was removed surgically in 1925 from a man aged 20 years. Subsequently, the patient developed tuberculous prostatitis. He died three months later. Sections of 46 kidneys from Wade's operations of nephrectomy were made and 14 were exhibited in Edinburgh to the 1927 annual meeting of the British Medical Association, the Lister Centenary meeting*

Figure 12.4 Kidney: hydronephrosis *(for comparison with Figure 12.3). The pelvis of the kidney is dilated greatly. Although infection may become a secondary complication, the margins of the pelvis are altered little by comparison with the destruction wrought by tuberculosis*

dilatation of the ureter and renal pelvis. In one case, a vesicovaginal fistula developed. The uncured patient, he believed, should not be allowed back to duty too soon: 'the surgical treatment was but a milestone in a long and weary journey'.

The average stay in hospital after nephrectomy was 21 days. Prolonged sanatorium care was necessary before, and almost always after, surgery. The immediate post-nephrectomy mortality was less than 2%, the ultimate mortality 6%. Postoperative deaths were attributable to persistent infection and a 'decline' of the patient, generalized tuberculosis or renal insufficiency. Thirty-five of Wade's cases from 1922–28 seemed cured but two died subsequently from disseminated tuberculosis, two from the activity of unremoved tissue and one from extensive disease detected before surgery. A sixth patient had an inoperable liver carcinoma. Wade's results may be compared with the series collected by Thomson-Walker:[26] of the 1,149 patients of five surgeons operating during the period 1923–27, an average of 22.9% were dead and 53.3% ultimately 'entirely well' but 19.7% only 'improved'.

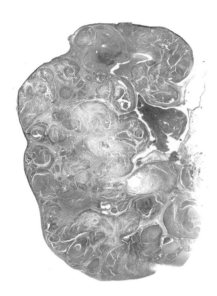

Figure 12.5 Renal carcinoma from a patient of Henry Wade. *The patient was subjected to operation on 11th September 1926. There was a recent history of painless haematuria. At that time, the histological diagnosis was 'papillary carcinoma'*

Renal tumours

The cardinal symptoms and signs of a primary malignant renal tumour were: painless intermittent haematuria, loin discomfort, pencil-like urinary blood clots, renal enlargement and an altered pyelographic contour.[27] Cystoscopy revealed the nature and origin of the bleeding. Infusion (retrograde) pyelography, Wade claimed, should not be used by itself but always with excretion (intravenous) urography: the former identified the tumour and the latter defined its effects on renal function. Excretion urography might enable an estimation of the degree of malignancy. Biopsy (Chapter 3) was seldom practiced.

The only possible cure for renal cancer was nephrectomy.[27] It remained the mainstay of treatment but might be supplemented by radiotherapy. When a tumour had invaded the renal vein, 'the surgical skill of the operator was tested admirably'. In Wade's hands, the operative mortality fell below the disastrous figures for 1885 (76%), 1888 (65.2%) and 1902 (22%),[26] although haemorrhage, pulmonary embolism, anuria and cardiac failure remained threats to survival.[26] Recurrence was likely in 70% of instances within one year. It is of interest to compare these figures with those recorded for the years 1989–99, when the frequency of renal cancer had increased both in men and women. In men 39.5% of patients survived five years, in women 37.0%.

Surgery of the ureter

Calculus

Lithotomy is recognized as one of the very earliest forms of surgery, but the safe surgical removal of ureteric calculi by open surgery demanded antisepsis. 'Bouncing' stones, or stones immobilized outside the bladder, at the lower end of the ureter, could offer difficulty. The size of the stone, its nature and the degree of obstruction were factors influencing a decision. High stones might slip back into the renal pelvis. When a kidney was destroyed, nephrectomy and ureterectomy might prove necessary.

Wade emphasized the problems encountered during his army service (1915–19).[15] The passage of an X-ray catheter was the most certain means of recognizing a stone. Pelvic phleboliths gave misleading appearances. Diagnosis was difficult if a ureter divided just above the bladder and a stone lay within one channel. Six of Wade's 50 military patients were operated on: two stones were extracted by intravesical forceps, two impacted in the ureteral orifice were removed by suprapubic cystotomy, and two by suprapubic opening of the ureter, a major operation with mortality of 2%.

Wade later described two cases where calculus culminated in renal failure.[28] In one, a woman aged 45 years had suffered from tuberculosis of the hip joint. Some weeks after returning home, she developed complete anuria. The left kidney had been destroyed by an impacted ureteric calculus. The outlet from the right kidney had been blocked by a second calculus. However, this stone was removed surgically and renal function recovered.

Stricture

Wade referred to Hunner's operation for stricture but 'did not fall for it'.[10] Outspoken, and with firm individual opinions, Wade classed the relief of ureteric stricture, operations for floating kidney and promiscuous gastro-enterostomy as 'surgical fashions'.[29]

Surgery of the urinary bladder

Tumours

Wade developed a special interest in urinary bladder cancer.[30,31] Before 1939, understanding of the behaviour of vesical neoplasms was very limited. Wade's papers demonstrate an intense dedication to the welfare of his patients and a preoccupation with new techniques for dealing with this potentially fatal affliction.

The first sign of a primary bladder tumour was sudden, unexpected, painless haematuria in a healthy person, although, occasionally, bleeding might come from an extravesical invasive carcinoma. Seventy-five percent of people who complained of haematuria suffered from tumours of the bladder, although sometimes a renal pelvic papilloma could account for the bleeding. With primary vesical neoplasms, a relation was seen between the degree of malignancy and the age of the patient. Cystoscopy was crucial to diagnosis and biopsy increasingly important. Ninety percent of bladder tumours were papilliform. Multiple tumours were frequent. The rough area around the base of a papilloma had a 'brushwood' character distinct from primary epithelioma and adenocarcinoma.

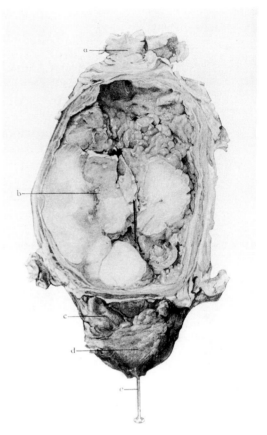

Figure 12.6 Urinary bladder: carcinoma. *The insidious, intractable and painful condition of cancer of the urinary bladder was one of the most difficult to treat surgically. During Wade's years as urological surgeon, there was no alternative therapy. He developed the operation of vesical exclusion, which offered relief to many sufferers. His reputation in this field of surgery was one reason he was elected to the Presidency of the Section of Urology of the Royal Society of Medicine in 1937*

Conservative treatment

Benign villous papillomas were treated by repeated fulguration. There was a special place for diathermy, a technique introduced by Beer.[10,31] However, there was a risk of implanting tumour cells, perforation of the bladder wall and the need for repeated cystoscopy.

Partial cystectomy

Early malignant tumours were treated by suprapubic cystostomy. Silver nitrate was infused to prevent the implantation of daughter tumours. Many surgeons preferred cystotomy and hemicystectomy to a more hazardous radical operation. Preliminary laparotomy was followed by excision of the primary growth and the portion of the bladder that was invaded. Wade chose to leave a divided ureter *in situ*, so that it underwent a process of 'natural re-implantation' into what had come to be a diverticulum.[31]

Total cystectomy

Inoperable vesical cancers, such as those in which both ureters were implicated, could be treated conservatively by the unreliable methods of radium implantation, X-irradiation or Coley's fluid. However, Wade favoured total cystectomy. This radical procedure was hazardous.[32] Wade had experience of eight cases. He accepted partial cystectomy when there were only multiple benign tumours, but, even in such cases, he advised total cystectomy if symptoms persisted for as long as two years.

As a preliminary to total cystectomy, Wade implanted the ureters into the pelvic colon at independent operations. Debility was a contraindication. Alternatively, therefore, the individual ureters could be implanted on to the lateral aspect of the abdominal wall. However, there remained a problem of obstruction and the apparatus worn for the collection of urine was cumbersome and unreliable. Cystectomy followed three weeks after ureteric transplantation. Suffering could be reduced by sympathectomy.

Vesical exclusion

In selected cases, and for the relief of pain, vesical exclusion was an alternative to total cystectomy. Wade chose this subject when he delivered his Presidential address to the Section of Urology of the Royal Society of Medicine on 28th October 1937.[33] He returned to this topic in the following year and in his last address to the Section.[29,34] By that time, he had operated on 60 cases.

The indication for vesical exclusion arose when the urinary bladder had lost its capacity to retain urine or when there was irreversible disease or destruction of bladder tissue. Wade conducted the operation under spinal anaesthesia induced by spignocaine.[31] He invariably recommended bilateral ureteric transplantation, with the formation of a 'urodaeum' and 'proctodaeum' with differential functions, so that the urinary and intestinal contents were voided separately.

A high standard of nursing care was demanded, day and night, for 10 days. The immediate postoperative mortality was high. The greatest hazards of vesical exclusion were in those treated for vesical carcinoma, among whom the mortality was 51.6% for the earlier cases and 43% after January 1936. The dangers to patients who suffered from non-malignant conditions were much less: the mortality was 25.5% for the earlier series and 9% after January 1936.

Surgery of the prostate gland

Wade made his surgical name through his pioneering studies of prostate disease – a field of work that has grown inexorably as the expectation of life has increased in the western world. His archives give a clear indication of his continual activity in this field of research.[C]

In the early years of the twentieth century, the surgery of prostatic disease was in its infancy, the mortality very high. Much effort was therefore devoted to modifying and improving surgical techniques. Wade defined 'prostatism' in very broad terms.[35] He regarded the condition as a syndrome in which there was hypertrophy of the gland – chronic lobular prostatitis (110 cases), fibrosis without hypertrophy (10 cases) and carcinoma (14 cases). In untreated disease, death resulted from obstruction to urinary flow, hydroureter, hydronephrosis, uraemia and secondary ascending infection.

Wade's skills were catalyzed by his early studies of pathological anatomy (Chapter 3), during which he dissected 134 glands. Fifty had been removed by suprapubic or perineal prostatectomy.[36] Histological sections of whole glands were made. His expertise was recognized when he addressed the 81st Meeting of the British Medical Association in Brighton in 1913, where he encountered Hugh Hampton Young of Baltimore and Cunningham of Boston. Young invited Wade to the Buchanan-Brady Institute about to be opened in the Johns Hopkins Hospital as a urological department. However, the war intervened to delay acceptance of the invitation, which could not be implemented until 1920 (p 186). With the support of the distinguished Americans, Wade published a definitive paper in 1914[36,D] – work that soon attracted further publicity.[37] David Band, Wade's close colleague, commented:[3]

Figure 12.7 Wade's 1914 paper on prostatitis. *With the publication of this paper in the Annals of Surgery, Wade ensured that his pioneering studies of prostatic disease would be known widely. It was on the basis of this work that he received an invitation to visit Hugh Young in the United States. The invitation could not be accepted until after the end of the First World War*

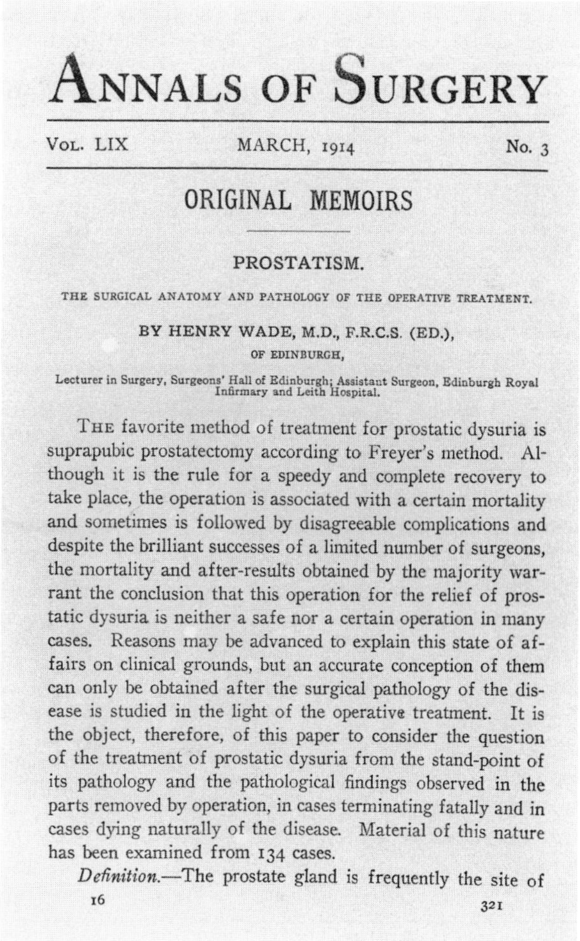

ANNALS OF SURGERY

VOL. LIX   MARCH, 1914   No. 3

ORIGINAL MEMOIRS

PROSTATISM.

THE SURGICAL ANATOMY AND PATHOLOGY OF THE OPERATIVE TREATMENT.

BY HENRY WADE, M.D., F.R.C.S. (ED.),

OF EDINBURGH,

Lecturer in Surgery, Surgeons' Hall of Edinburgh; Assistant Surgeon, Edinburgh Royal Infirmary and Leith Hospital.

THE favorite method of treatment for prostatic dysuria is suprapubic prostatectomy according to Freyer's method. Although it is the rule for a speedy and complete recovery to take place, the operation is associated with a certain mortality and sometimes is followed by disagreeable complications and despite the brilliant successes of a limited number of surgeons, the mortality and after-results obtained by the majority warrant the conclusion that this operation for the relief of prostatic dysuria is neither a safe nor a certain operation in many cases. Reasons may be advanced to explain this state of affairs on clinical grounds, but an accurate conception of them can only be obtained after the surgical pathology of the disease is studied in the light of the operative treatment. It is the object, therefore, of this paper to consider the question of the treatment of prostatic dysuria from the stand-point of its pathology and the pathological findings observed in the parts removed by operation, in cases terminating fatally and in cases dying naturally of the disease. Material of this nature has been examined from 134 cases.

Definition.—The prostate gland is frequently the site of

16   321

'The drawings [in the 1914 paper] in black and white and in colour of the entire urinary tract in prostatism demonstrated more perfectly than had before been done the effects of backward pressure on the upper urinary tract. The whole sections clearly showed that in the operation of prostatectomy, enucleation of the gland had not been complete, but that the adenomatous part alone had been enucleated through a line of cleavage between it and a false capsule produced by compression of the more peripheral gland elements. These lie within the true gland capsule and, with the latter, must remain intact if the operation of enucleation of the prostate is to be performed with success.'

Among Wade's papers is a table compiled from the records of the RIE for the years 1899–1911.[E] Table 12.2 shows the frequency with which prostatic disease was recognized. Four categories were described: enlarged prostate, sarcoma, malignant disease and abscess. The diagnosis of sarcoma was made only in 1899, when a single case was recorded. There were 10 cases of prostatic abscess.

Simple enlargement of the prostate

Wade fully understood the importance of chronic lobular prostatitis – 'simple enlargement of the prostate'.[26] Both Wade and Thomson-Walker found prostatic enlargement in 34% of men over the age of

Table 12.2 Prostatic disease in Edinburgh. Diseases of the prostate gland recorded in the Royal Infirmary of Edinburgh, 1899–1911

Year	Enlarged prostate			Malignant disease			Prostatectomy – suprapubic			Prostatectomy – perineal		
	Number of cases	Died	Mortality (%)	Number of cases	Died	Mortality (%)	Number of cases	Died	Mortality (%)	Number of cases	Died	Mortality (%)
1899–1900	13	1	?	–	–	–	0	–	–	0	–	–
1900–01	11	?	?	–	–	–	0	–	–	0	–	–
1901–02	28	?	?	–	–	–	4 suprapubic and perineal	–	50	–	–	–
1902–03	23	?	?	1	–	–	5	4 suprapubic and perineal	50	3	–	–
1903–04	16	?	?	–	–	–	5	3	60	2	1	
1904–05	34	10	30	–	–	–	11	5	45	–	–	–
1905–06	36	8	22	3	–	–	16	5	30	–	–	–
1906–07	30	11	36	5	–	–	21	11	52	–	–	–
1907–08	41	9	22	2	–	–	19	5	25	1	–	–
1908–09	37	9	24	8	2	25	18	5	28	1	–	–
1909–10	40	11	27.5	5	1	25	21	5	22.76	2	–	–
1910–11	53	12	22.6	12	?4	33.3	29	8	27.6	6	3	–
Total	362	71	26.3	36	?7	44	145	47	39	15	4	–

?, not known: –, not recorded

60 years. Its high frequency and significance contrasted with that of malignant disease of the prostate. Untreated, prostatic obstruction was followed by chronic ill health and death.

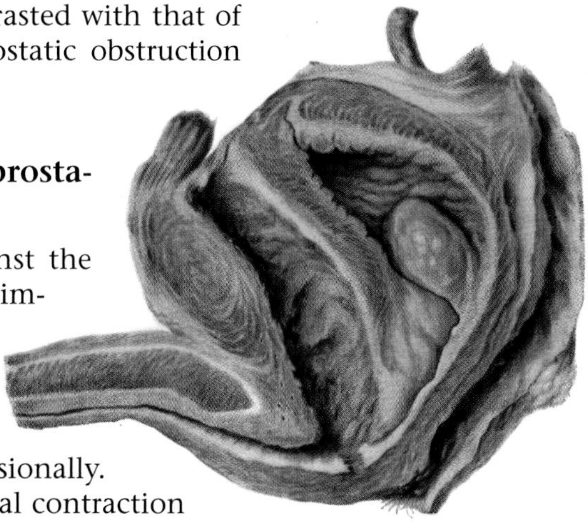

Conservative treatment of chronic lobular prostatitis

Wade always balanced the risk of operation against the increasing hazards of palliation. The treatment of simple prostatic enlargement stressed the avoidance of urinary retention and sepsis. Ergot or strychnine could be given. Castration or vasectomy had been abandoned but X-irradiation and the implantation of radium were still advocated occasionally. There was a choice between forced voluntary vesical contraction and catheter-dependent life, a measure adopted only when operation was not possible.[26] Survival was for no more than 2–4 years. Occasionally, preliminary suprapubic cystotomy was recommended.

Figure 12.8 Hypertrophy of middle lobe of prostate. *The original caption reads: 'Median sagittal section of pelvic contents of man aged seventy-three, who died from rupture of urethra with extravasation of urine into space of Retzius, showing hypertrophy of middle lobe of prostate which projects into bladder. Water colour drawing'. The illustration is a reproduction of Figure 27 from Wade.[36] The artist has not been identified*

Operative treatment of simple enlargement of the prostate[38]

When Wade began prostatic surgery, this subject had passed through a first phase of innovation. Extraperitoneal suprapubic prostatectomy – blind or through an open incision – was preferred to a transperitoneal approach. Perineal prostatectomy had been developed but open dissection had replaced blind dissection and transurethral prostatectomy by punch was being tested. When the urinary bladder was already open and infected, a two-stage operation could be attempted. Retropubic prostatectomy was not introduced until 1945.[39]

Suprapubic prostatectomy

After early attempts by McGill and Fuller,[40,41] the method of blind suprapubic prostatectomy used by Freyer earned widespread respect.[42–44] Wade attended some of Freyer's operations at St Peter's Hospital, London.[29] The local complications included urinary incontinence, return of the obstruction, loss of sexual power, persistence of vesical fistulae, epididymitis and the formation of calculi.[35] The systemic complications were haemorrhage, pain, shock, cardiac failure, uraemia, sepsis and epididymitis. Prognosis was influenced by age, the dangers of sudden relief of retention, sepsis, circulatory failure, mental and nervous disorders, and alimentary disturbances.

Although recommended in an ideal case, suprapubic prostatectomy remained hazardous.[37] Before 1913, the Edinburgh mortality was 25%. It stayed at that level until at least 1920. Of 164 cases operated on by Wade during his early years, 54 died – a mortality of 35.4%.

Walker quoted figures of 20.3% from St. Thomas's Hospital,[38] and Wade recorded 21.5% from four other London hospitals. By the late 1930s, the mortality in expert hands ranged from 3.4% to 5%. In general hospital practice, however, it was approximately 8%.[36]

Transurethral prostatectomy

The results of blind division of the bladder neck with a urethrotome had proved disastrous. The galvanocautery had also given poor results. The illuminated cystoscope offered the opportunity for change.[45] HH Young took advantage of this development, using a punch to excise tissue from the bladder neck.[46] Haemorrhage often followed, but this danger was overcome when Caulk introduced his cautery punch.[47] In 1925, Walker substituted diathermy for the cautery.[48] Wade remained sceptical and observed that '[in 1913], the practice of transurethral prostatectomy had swept through the United States'.[29] He 'did not take kindly to a prostatic gamble'.

Perineal prostatectomy

Perineal prostatectomy had been promoted by Proust.[49,50] A transverse, prerectal incision was used. The technique was employed extensively by Young.[51] Wade accepted this perineal procedure but recognized that it required accurate anatomical knowledge, experience, special instruments and a well-trained team. The operative mortality was relatively low (2.2–6.2%) but serious complications included urinary fistula, incontinence, poor control of bladder function, loss of sexual powers, epididymitis and postoperative stricture.

Malignant disease of the prostate

Wade devoted little space to the discussion of the surgery of this condition. During the years of Wade's practice, life expectancy and the prevalence of disease changed significantly. In 1905, prostate cancer comprised no more than 2.3 per 1,000 of the cases of cancer seen at the Middlesex Hospital.[26] In the 1920s and 1930s, benign prostatic hyperplasia was approximately six times as common as prostatic cancer. The palliative treatment of prostatic cancer in the period 1909–39 could be no more than the relief of symptoms by analgesic and other compounds, the passage of catheters and suprapubic cystotomy. Perurethral resection could be used to relieve obstruction. Radical operations were rare, as it was accepted that in few instances was it possible to enucleate a 'malignant prostate'. The operative mortality for radical prostatectomy was exceedingly high.

The first claim of surgical cure had been made by Young.[52] Two forms of perineal operation were described by Thomson-Walker.[26] In the first, the procedure was identical with that used for benign prostatic enlargement. In the second – Young's operation – the prostate and its sheath, the prostatic urethra, the adjacent portion of the bladder wall, the seminal vesicles and the lower ends of the vasa deferentia were excised. In 27 cases reported by Muir, the mean duration of life after prostatectomy alone was seven months and after prostatectomy with deep X-ray therapy, 22 months.[53]

Royal Society of Medicine

By 1937, Henry Wade's work had attracted national and international interest. In comparison with the literary output of some of his contemporaries, his papers on urinary disease were comparatively few; however, they carried great weight and convinced his colleagues not only of his superlative surgical skill but of the breadth and perception of his views. It came as no surprise therefore when, in 1937, he was elected President of the Section of Urology of the Royal Society of Medicine. He was recognized as a pioneer in a rapidly growing surgical speciality.[54–56]

For much of human history, peacetime urological surgery had been synonymous with lithotomy.[5] Following the Listerian revolution, there was an extraordinary burgeoning of many aspects of the subject.[4] It has been claimed that Guyon and Nitze founded modern urology.[45,57,58] In Britain, urology was advanced significantly by Thompson and Thomson-Walker.[26,59] In the United States, Young made many important contributions.[32] The first surgical hospital devoted solely to urological surgery in London was St Peter's, which opened in 1860. Although the first urological department in a general hospital in Scotland is believed to have been that of Jacobs in the Glasgow Royal Infirmary of 1936,[60] Wade had established such a unit in the RIE by 1924.

During the period 1924–39, when Wade was in charge first of Wards 5 and 6 and then of Wards 15 and 16 of the RIE, he was responsible for numerous advances in the practice of urology. The key to his surgical success lay in his grasp of renal physiology and pathology, his use of new techniques of investigation and his manual dexterity. The development and skilled practice of urological surgery and progress in the diagnosis, treatment and relief of many sufferers from some of the most distressing and intractable disorders in the whole of medicine stand as a monument to Wade's life's work.

CHAPTER 13

Teacher and examiner

1906–46

Let such teach others who themselves excel,
And censure freely who have written well.

(Alexander Pope, *An essay on criticism*, 1711)

Henry Wade was a clear, incisive public speaker – his unaffected, slight but pronounced Scottish brogue popular both in undergraduate and postgraduate education. Much in demand for formal and informal classes, he taught in the University of Edinburgh Medical School and in the Royal Infirmary of Edinburgh, the RIE. Above all, he flourished in the educational activities of the Royal College of Surgeons of Edinburgh, the RCSEd, and in those of the associated Extramural School of Medicine of the Royal Colleges, the SMRC.

Wade's first teaching appointments were in the University Faculty of Medicine. Initially a Demonstrator in Anatomy (1902), he became a Demonstrator in Pathology in the following year and, simultaneously, a Clinical Assistant in the RIE, where he took part in the bedside and operating theatre instruction given by Francis Caird[A] – his 'Chief' (p 41). From 1906 until 1908, when he was appointed an Assistant Surgeon to the Leith Hospital, much of Wade's time was given to the pathology service of the RIE. Then, in 1909, he was promoted to the position of Assistant Surgeon to the RIE, an appointment that gave him the status of Honorary University Lecturer in Clinical Surgery with the occasional but formal teaching responsibilities that this entailed.

To understand the teaching appointments that Wade came to occupy in the SMRC, it may be of help to examine the way in which Edinburgh had come to have two substantial Medical Schools. The first was that of the University, in which a Faculty of Medicine had been established in 1726, the second that of the Royal Colleges of Physicians and Surgeons, incorporated as a School of Medicine in 1892. In the latter part of the nineteenth century, the demand for medical education in Edinburgh grew dramatically, favouring the long-established practice of medical and surgical teaching outside the University.[1-6] In his account of 'The Edinburgh Medical School after 1870', Comrie placed the matter in perspective when he wrote:[1]

> 'The last quarter of the 19th century was, in regard to teaching in the University, rather a period of decline.'

Comrie was careful to separate this comment from his praise for the individual brilliance of many Edinburgh teachers – Joseph Lister, Henry Duncan Littlejohn and William Turner among them. He continued:

> 'Partly in consequence of the fact that practical classes were not so highly organised as at the present day [1932], and partly owing to the arrangement of the curriculum, it was a practice commonly followed by students to take out a class of lectures on the same subject twice over, usually from different teachers on the two occasions. As a result, the number of extra-academic teachers increased and they lectured to large classes, often greatly in excess of the numbers attending the corresponding classes of the professors.'

He added:

> 'About the same time, the accommodation for medical classes in the Old University was becoming insufficient. In 1869, the number of [undergraduate] students in the University had risen to 1,500, and that of the professors to 33, while there were only 17 classrooms for their use.'

Comrie and other writers referred to the SMRC only when detailing the activities of the best known lecturers.[1,6] Yet the contributions of the Edinburgh Colleges to world medical education in the 53 years before the advent of the Scottish National Health Service in 1947 were of the greatest importance. Not only did many students of brilliance emerge from their classes and laboratories but 35 of their lecturers advanced to chairs in the University of Edinburgh or other universities. Theodor Shennan (p 91), for example, became Professor of Pathology in Aberdeen, Peter McCallum in Melbourne.

Origins of the Extramural School of Medicine

The scene of Wade's main teaching activities is best set by outlining the origins, buildings and activities of the SMRC. The long history of extramural teaching in Edinburgh extended back to the early years of the nineteenth century and the opening of the new 1832 building of Surgeons' Hall.[B] An Edinburgh medical calendar, published from

J. S.

Figure 13.1 School of Medicine of the Edinburgh Royal Colleges. *The east-facing wing is all that remains of the three-storey building that housed the School of Medicine of the Edinburgh Royal Colleges. The remainder of the building, facing Roxburgh Place, was demolished in the early 1960s, to make way for the Lister and Pfizer buildings*

1833, gave details of all medical classes in Edinburgh, within or outside the University.[4] Among the numerous independent 'Schools' that contributed to medical teaching for limited periods were a short-lived Queen's College (1840), the New School (Bristo Street), Minto House School,[c] Park Place School, Nicolson Square School and the School of Medicine, Argyle Square (1838–39)[D], with which Robert Knox (p 91) was briefly associated.[7] Queen's College taught subjects as varied as Botany, Anatomy, Operative surgery, Midwifery, Practical chemistry, Natural philosophy, Practical mechanics, Mathematics, Mineralogy and Geology. The Argyle Square School offered in addition Practical physic, Medical jurisprudence, *Materia medica* and Modern languages. Many of the buildings occupied by these private establishments no longer exist. For example, 23 Nicholson Square, acquired by John Chiene (p 23) for his classes, is now a car park sandwiched between a commercial bank and a Methodist hall.

Teaching was one matter, acceptance of a 'School' for the purposes of legitimate medical practice another. This was not a barrier to medicine and surgery in the 1830s and 1840s, as these professions were not yet licensed and formal recognition by the State of extramural teaching not yet agreed. In 1855, however, a letter from Professor James Syme brought the issue to a head. Extramural teachers were then recognized by the University, and students could choose to attend classes within the University Medical School, within an extramural School or in both.

In 1858, the Medical Act created a General Medical Council, the GMC, and ratified the licentiateships granted by the Royal Colleges of Medicine and Surgery of Edinburgh. Recognition of the Faculty of Physicians and Surgeons of Glasgow came in 1884. Possession of a College Diploma granted permission for the legitimate practice of medicine. As the practice of teaching outside the University prospered, the extramural teachers drew together and on 1st May 1883, a committee of the RCPEd 'prayed' to be incorporated as a formal academic body. The key figures in the negotiations were Henry Duncan Littlejohn and George Alexander Gibson. With the passage of the years, their object was achieved. The first minutes of the incorporated School were taken on 8th July 1892. In 1894, a petition for a charter was submitted to the Queen. With the spread of Empire, the activities of the surgeons began to be enacted upon a larger stage.[E]

Fellows and Licentiates of the RCSEd followed the trade routes to the colonies and dominions, tracing imperial, commercial paths to India, China, Burma, Hong Kong, Nepal and Singapore, as well as to countries of Africa and the Middle East. Aspiring students from these many countries and from Canada, South Africa, Australia and New Zealand sought the prestige offered by a qualification from the Colleges' School of Medicine and Surgery. At the same time, Fellows and Licenciates, in whatever part of the world, were bound by the statutes of the GMC, which reported misdemeanours and felonies to the licensing Royal Colleges. In turn, the Colleges could exercise their authority by striking an offender from their records and requesting a return of their licence (p 271). In 1928, the cases of Dr Deane in the Falkland Islands and Dr Glucksman in South Africa exemplify the regulatory influence of the long disciplinary arm of the College.[8]

A decline in imperial ties and a growing sense of national independence in the period from 1919–39 encouraged ambitious dominions to found their own Colleges of Surgery. Nevertheless, recruitment to the Edinburgh Extramural School waned only slightly, although there were complaints from Canada about the lack of interest in the welfare of professional brethren in the colonies.[9] The Council of the RCSEd was told of the formation of a College of Surgeons of Australasia on 11th October 1928.[10] In spite of this understandable act of independence, the Australians and New Zealanders kept, and keep, very close links with Edinburgh, the first manifestation of which was an invitation to send a delegate to the opening of the new Australian building in Melbourne in 1935. The South Africans also requested a representative from the RCSEd at the centenary of the formation of the South African College of Medicine, although the College of Surgeons of South Africa was not formed until 1955. In the years 1936–40, a small influx of German students was noted in Edinburgh, coinciding with the rise to power of Adolf Hitler's National Socialist party. Many already possessed medical qualifications from their own country. During these years, considerable numbers of North American students also came to the Edinburgh Royal Colleges. Their numbers ranged from 148 in 1935 to 219 in 1939. With the outbreak of war, it was not surprising that fewer and fewer Americans could travel to Scotland, and, by 1944, only five remained in the SMRC.

The Extramural School of Medicine came to an end in 1948 after the recommendations of the 1942 Goodenough Report on *The future of non-university medical schools* (p 278). A concise analysis of 'Goodenough' was conveyed to Professor WS Craig in 1972 by Professor Derrick Dunlop. In his *History of the Royal College of Physicians of Edinburgh*, Craig quoted Dunlop's characteristically sardonic words. He referred to the period in the late nineteenth century when the College of Physicians was part of an important undergraduate teaching School, competing with the University and possessing their own research laboratory. He said:

> 'The systematic teaching of Medicine demanded no more than a lecture room, some wall diagrams and bottled specimens, a skeleton and a teaching personality.'

By 1948, these days were ended and Goodenough wrote:

> 'We have no doubt that the buildings of the Extramural School could be put to other uses.'

School of Medicine buildings

The single main factor that enabled the Royal Colleges of Edinburgh to sustain an integrated School of Medicine was the availability of a large and commodious building. It originated when William Playfair was chosen in 1828 to design a new Surgeons' Hall, the Playfair Hall, which opened in Nicolson Street in 1832. He had been asked to incorporate a class room capable of accommodating 250 students and to include a dissecting room. In the event, the classroom was omitted from his final plan, perhaps because of cost. The School building, adjacent to and coextensive with the Playfair Hall, came about in 1832 when a Dr DB Reid expressed a wish to lease the ground behind the new (Playfair) Hall so that he could build rooms to teach chemistry. The building constructed for these reasons faced east, to Roxburgh Place. Some years later, in order to promote the cause of the extramural teachers, the College's authorities bought these rooms

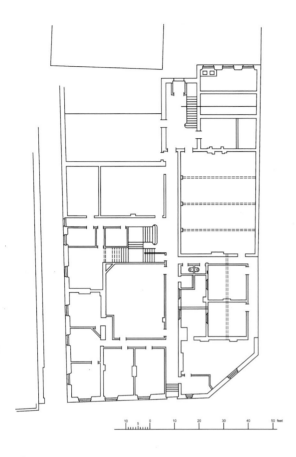

from Dr Reid, who was in debt to them. The structure was rebuilt and extended at a total cost of nearly £1,600. The new development, which included two lecture theatres, a dissecting room, a laboratory and a small museum, was made available to the extramural lecturers, who, collectively, paid the College a composite annual fee of £180 for its use.

The structure of the School building gradually altered. In 1884, additional classrooms, including an anatomical room, were added to a first floor. Two staircases and windows facing east were among further alterations, and three years later further minor changes included a cloakroom and heating for the anatomical room. Significant additions to the structure were undertaken in 1890,[11] in particular, a second floor. In 1895, electric lighting took the place of the older gas illumination. The result of these developments was the completion of a building large enough and of sufficient versatility to deal with the great numbers of students who began flooding into the programmes of the School of Medicine when systematic, integrated undergraduate teaching began in 1896. Later, smaller modifications took place in 1913 and 1923 although the costs of maintaining the building remained high.[F]

Figure 13.2 Floor plan of the School of Medicine of the Edinburgh Royal Colleges. *Initially of one floor, the nineteenth-century extensions converted the building into an impressive structure, with a lecture theatre for 250 students, a dissecting room, laboratories and supporting facilities*

Lister Institute of Postgraduate Medicine and Research

Because of his growing seniority, influence and involvement with the RCSEd, Wade was closely implicated in the long drawn-out plans to erect a memorial to Joseph Lister. The shadow of Lister hung like a beneficent cloud over the RCSEd from 1912 until 1967, when a fitting memorial, a Lister Institute, was at last completed in Edinburgh (p 252). The building marked the renaissance of Edinburgh postgraduate medical teaching and coincided with the construction of the adjacent Pfizer building. The history of the Lister Institute exemplifies the immense difficulties faced by large academic organizations attempting to implement costly architectural plans.

Following the death of Joseph, Lord Lister in 1912, worldwide concern, exemplified by a letter of condolence received from the German ambassador, Count Metternich, was recorded in the College's minutes.[12] Lister's death engaged international and national, as well as local, sympathies. In the RCSEd, a Lister

Memorial Committee was formed, with Francis Caird, the forth-coming President, as Convener. There was close collaboration with the University of Edinburgh. Because of his intimate association with the affairs of the RCSEd, it was inevitable that Wade should be drawn into the discussions regarding a Lister Memorial that began shortly before the outbreak of the First World War. On 25th July 1912, Wade reminded the Committee of the urgent need to plan constructively because of the speed with which a memorial in Westminster Abbey, a statue and an international fund had been set up in London. Those in London and Glasgow had moved swiftly to commemorate Lister's work.[13]

The idea of a memorial building in Edinburgh was initiated in 1913. The aim was to create an Institute of Pathology and Cancer Research. A Lister Memorial Fund was promoted by the cancellation of an ear-lier agreement that required the repayment of £10,000 to the Carnegie Trust whose 10-year commitment to the Laboratory of the RCPEd had expired.

The College believed there should be a marble bust and an Institute created by means of collaboration between the Royal Medical and Surgical Colleges of Edinburgh and the University of Edinburgh. The cost might amount to £50,000, ten times the annual income of the RCSEd. Whether significant or not, the page recording the report pre-sented by Wade to the RCSEd on 16th October is blank. By May 1913, it had been agreed that the most fitting tribute to Lister would be a building to be entitled the *Edinburgh Lister Institute of Pathology*. Ten pages of discussion followed, with agreement on the need to name an architect and an offer by the College of an early £5,000 towards the costs of the ambitious project. The President's Council devoted much time to the plans.[14]

Then war intervened. All Lister negotiations were suspended, although a sum of £3,000 was held in readiness for the completion of the memorial.[15] Very reasonably, the College decided that the £500 cost of a Lister bust 'would be better spent on the sick and wounded'. However, the site in Edinburgh of the Lister building had already been agreed. It would be between Heriot Place to the east, Graham Street to the west, Lauriston Place to the south and Keir Street to the north. But it was not until December 1922, when Wade was assuming an influ-ential position in the Edinburgh surgical world, that further serious consideration was given to the memorial. Wade had become a war hero and an international authority on urological surgery. In the same minutes in which the College Treasurer called for economy, there was evidence that £2,000 was required for the Lister memorial 'but not in the immediate future'. In October 1923, a Fellow asked: 'What progress has been made with the Lister Memorial?' Nothing more is heard of the proposals until 17th December 1937, when a new com-mittee under Lord Keith was constituted 'in regard to the funds col-lected before 1914'. Wade and his colleague and friend Arthur Henry Havens Sinclair represented the RCSEd. Another friend, Dr William

Ritchie, represented the RCPEd. The committee reported on 7th February 1939.[G]

For understandable reasons, negotiations did not resume until the end of the Second World War. The destruction of the greater part of the original buildings of the SMRC was followed by a lengthy period of new construction. Finally, a plaque at the entrance declared: *'Opened by Nina, Lady Fraser on 11th November 1967'.* Lady Fraser was the widow of the former Principal of the University of Edinburgh, Sir John Fraser. He had been Regius Professor of Clinical Surgery (p 188). The adjoining Pfizer building had been inaugurated four years previously.

Lecturer in the Extramural School of Medicine

In Wade's day, teaching in the School of Medicine was traditional, based on didactic lectures. The 'tools of the trade' were the blackboard and chalk. There were lecture programmes in Anatomy, Chemistry, Pharmacology (*Materia medica*) and Pathology, while the practical laboratory classes incorporated relevant parts of these disciplines. Anatomical dissection was as important as it was in the University. In an old tradition, students paid teachers directly, and the teachers, in turn, funded the RCSEd for the rent of classrooms. A matriculation fee was introduced in 1930. Many others in addition to matriculated students attended SMRC classes. In 1937, for example, 14 'occasional' undergraduates, 23 graduates attending a course for the Diploma in Public Health and 19 'occasional' graduates, as well as 148 dental students, subscribed to the educational programmes.

University students frequently chose to take classes in their own departments as well as in those of the SMRC. Undergraduates could benefit from the skills and knowledge of two or more teachers in the different institutions, both covering the same ground. The many students who exercised this option selected the additional SMRC classes during the winter months. Consequently, the average number attending the SMRC summer sessions was almost always considerably smaller than for the winter sessions. In the five years before the First World War, the average number of students enrolled for the classes of each winter session was 991, for each summer session 807 (Table 13.1). However, the numbers varied greatly – the largest being 1,023 in the winter of 1913 and the smallest 790 in the summer of 1911. During the First World War, numbers fell dramatically and some classes were in abeyance.

Recognized teachers within the undergraduate courses were Ordinary Lecturers. In 1909, there were 12. They were assisted by others not formally recognized, and at the time of Wade's graduation in 1898, the total number was 44. The average number of lecturers was 35, the largest 50. During the war years 1914–19, classes continued under austere conditions, but in the 1920s their frequency and size returned to pre-war levels.

Table 13.1 Numbers of students who attended the School of Medicine of the Royal Colleges of Edinburgh, 1908 to 1945. In 1930, a matriculation fee was levied, and the number of students for each year was given as a single figure, not broken down into winter and summer sessions. From 1934 onwards, the total number who attended the School each year is given in brackets after the number of matriculated students

Year	Students		Teachers	American students	German students
	Winter	**Summer**			
1908–09	965	808	–	NS	–
1909–10	1018	790	50	–	–
1910–11	1044	808	41	–	–
1911–12	–	–	39	–	–
1912–13	1023	837	38	–	–
1913–14	879	820	31	–	–
1914–15	–	–	–	–	–
1915–16	569	426	–	–	–
1916–17	249	235	26	–	–
1917–18	276	197	27	–	–
1918–19	394	540	20	–	–
1919–20	577	677	21	–	–
1920–21	730	612	24	–	–
1921–22	784	627	31	–	–
1922–23	653	529	25	–	–
1923–24	542	460	32	–	–
1924–25	442	300	32	–	–
1925–26	325	300	33	–	–
1926–27	–	–	29	–	–
1927–28	381	278	–	–	–
1928–29	408	309	35	–	–
1929–30	569	400	–	–	–
1930–31	462	–	–	–	–
1931–32	528	NS	–	–	–
1932–33	586	"	47	–	–
1933–34	638	"	NS	–	–
1934–35	558 (731)	"	"	–	–
1935–36	523 (727)	"	"	148	–
1936–37	543 (761)	"	"	159	6
1937–38	542 (761)	"	"	188	7
1938–39	524 (760)	"	"	212	7
1939–40	535 (760)	"	"	219	6
1940–41	270 (427)	"	"	58	5
1941–42	284 (401)	"	"	28	0
1942–43	324 (428)	"	"	11	0
1943–44	324 (428)	"	"	7	0
1944–45	454	"	"	5	0

NS = not stated; – = not recorded

Postgraduate lecturer

In 1906, the SMRC developed far-reaching and ambitious programmes of postgraduate medical and surgical education. Like the undergraduate classes, the teaching centred on didactic lectures. However, instruction was accompanied by practical demonstrations held in the Museum of the RCSEd and by clinical teaching in both the hospital wards and operating theatres.

Until 1905, the University of Edinburgh Medical School had offered no formal, structured, postgraduate medical teaching, although there had been periodic lectures, classes and courses on selected topics. In that year, a decade after the incorporation of the SMRC, Daniel J Cunningham, Professor of Anatomy, chaired a committee that outlined a long vacation course to be presented through the combined resources of the University, the Royal Colleges and the extra-academic lecturers.[1] The first course, for general practitioners, was facilitated by

Figure 13.3 Wade's ward class. *The class of clinical students who were taught by Wade and his colleagues in Wards 15 and 16 of the Royal Infirmary of Edinburgh in the spring term, 1937. The surgeon to Wade's left is RL Stewart; at his far left is TI 'Tammas' Wilson. The photograph includes the nursing sisters of both the wards and the operating theatre*

the Managers of the RIE and other hospitals but more specialized instruction soon began, both for physicians and surgeons. After the First World War, Obstetrics and Gynaecology and Paediatrics were added to the curriculum, and postgraduates were encouraged to attend outpatient clinics. In parallel with this new programme, the University established Diplomas in Tropical Medicine and Hygiene, in Psychiatry, in Public health and in Radiology.

From the point of view of the RCSEd, the quality of teaching for the Diploma of Fellowship was quite naturally the prime consideration. Surgeons were selected to teach within the courses designed to prepare graduates for the Fellowship examinations. To be appointed a Lecturer in the postgraduate programme was a considerable privilege. The choice of lecturers was approached very cautiously. In each case, a small selection panel was appointed. Their task was to interrogate an applicant and to decide whether he had the qualifications and skills necessary to teach adequately. In July 1910, the laws of the RCSEd were revised in their entirety. With regard to Lecturers, it was stated that:

> 'Lectures by Fellows are not recognised as qualifying for examinations for the College Diplomas unless the Lecturer shall have been specially recognised and admitted by the College as a Teacher of the particular subject which he professes.'

Initially, Wade was examined to determine whether he was qualified to lecture in Pathology. On 13th October 1906, he became a recognized Lecturer in Surgical Pathology and Operative Surgery. On 4th July 1907, Wade faced another ordeal. He already had been appointed as an Extra-Academical Lecturer in Surgery to the Medical College for Women, the classes for which were conducted in the SMRC: this position was confirmed by the University Court on 28th July 1908 and recognition granted him to teach the whole medical class. Now a Board of College examiners was convened to test his ability to lecture in Surgery on behalf of the RCSEd. The panel comprised Charles Watson MacGillivray, the President, in the Chair; Mr John Smith, Assessor; and Mr JM Cotterill, Special Examiner. The minutes of the Council record that:

> 'Mr Wade, having been called, underwent a full examination on his qualifications to lecture in Surgery as a branch of the curriculum in terms of the Laws [of the College] and was found duly qualified and the Board, having also nominated his [sic] Museum and teaching appliances found the same sufficient for the illustration of lectures on the above branch and beg leave to report to the College accordingly.'

An excerpt from these minutes was forwarded to Mr Wade. His reputation as a teacher pursued him, and, on 27th October 1919, Wade received a cheque from an appreciative RA Cooper for the course in surgery he had attended in 1912–13. Cooper said:

> 'I shall take my Finals next April and would appreciate a Certificate for attending the course.'[16]

Wade remained a Lecturer in Surgery to the SMRC until 1923. He collaborated with many of the most eminent teachers of his time.[H]

Museum demonstrations

Among the most important of the postgraduate classes were those given by the Conservators of the Museum of the RCSEd (Chapter 6). During his years as Conservator, Wade played a vigorous part in these programmes, many of which were entitled Demonstrations. At first, his College Demonstrations were held three, four or five times each term, but their frequency increased until they became weekly. At the end of the First World War, a demand for such teaching arose again, and, in 1919, an aspiring female candidate for the FRCSEd examinations wrote to ask when Wade's Demonstrations would resume. The number varied from three to 15 per session. They were concentrated in the winter and summer terms.

Records of attendance were not always taken. In the winter of 1907, the class size varied from 62 to 103. By 1910, the numbers attending the Demonstrations had become so large that two simultaneous groups were needed. The sessions were held in the Playfair Hall of the College, but, in 1910, with the construction of the New Museum Hall, this theatre was found to offer an even better place for the presentations.[17] The classes continued after the war, and Wade conducted his courses in Surgical Pathology in collaboration with David Wilkie. On 21st February 1923, Wade sent his friend £38/5/6d, reminding him that this was the sum to be declared to the Inland Revenue. It was his share of the course fees, taking into account £6 paid to Ryland Whittaker[I] as a contribution to the rent of the lecture room and three guineas given to Waldie (p 108) as a gratuity for his help in the Museum.

Teaching after the First World War

Change was afoot, accelerated in response to the rising demands that followed the end of the War.

The first proposal was for the clinical teaching of undergraduates. In undated letters addressed to James Lorrain Smith, Dean of the Faculty of Medicine of the University of Edinburgh, written after the end of the war on behalf of his colleagues at Leith, Wade set out proposed arrangements for teaching at a surgical clinique at the Leith Hospital.[18] He wrote on behalf of JW Struthers, Senior Surgeon and Chief of the Clinique; H Wade, Surgeon; DPD Wilkie, Senior Assistant

Surgeon with beds; and Dr Torrance Thomson, Anaesthetist. It was agreed that 'each man must pull his weight'.[19] A tutor would be appointed.[20] The number of students was to be limited to 50. The programme was to run from 10 am to 1 pm each day. Transport would be needed for the students. It was planned to make use of the facilities of the SMRC. The initiative would be pursued in spite of the inadequacy of the available funds, which would be divided between the teachers. A similar document was circulated on behalf of the physicians headed by a slightly reluctant Dr Edwin Matthew, soon to be Professor of Medicine in the University Faculty of Medicine.

The proposed plans, coming from teachers of the SMRC, were not immediately acceptable to the University. On 12th February 1920, it proved necessary to ask the Dean of the Faculty of Medicine, Professor Lorrain Smith, for a response.[21] There is no record of Lorrain Smith's reply.

An important second set of proposals related to the needs of young postgraduates who had served in the armed forces during the war. In October 1919, RW Johnstone, Secretary of the Edinburgh Postgraduate Courses in Medicine, asked Wade if he could give two lecture demonstrations, on 19th November and 8th December. Characteristically, Wade spoke from experience when he replied:

'The summer course disappointed the more senior post-war surgeons who want demonstrations of the latest procedures, not lectures.'

Wade suggested that demonstrations be given at Leith. Johnstone replied:

'The Committee would also be happy for the Demonstrations to be given there. The Demonstrations should keep to what was planned, i.e., a general course to enable young graduates who had been hurried into the army to brush up their general knowledge of Surgery. Specialised teaching can come later.'[22]

The subjects of Wade's own contributions would be 'Treatment of industrial accidents in the hospital' and 'Estimation of renal functional activity in surgical cases, parts 1 and 2'. Sadly, few ex-servicemen and women applied for the proposed post-war course, and on 5th January 1920, RW Johnstone was obliged to write to Wade to say:

'There have been so few applicants for the postgraduate course that it will not be held.'[23]

The response was surprising: the popularity of the classes of the SMRC had always been high. Nonetheless, Wade received four guineas for his efforts.

Clinical teaching

Wade's personality made him a formidable clinical teacher. Ross describes his style in the following words:[24]

> 'Mr Wade would stride in to the clinic, a tall figure with thick, greying hair tending to sweep down over the right of his forehead. He would interview his out-patients in his loud voice with its strong Scottish accent, with many a colloquial and homely phrase, driving his points home with great emphasis as he taught. He did not patronise anyone but spoke to patients in their own vernacular, often with a spice of pawky humour. Thus he instilled immense confidence, well borne out by the results obtained from his superlative skills.'

Clinical instruction in the hospital, at the patient's bedside or in the operating theatre was a corner stone of Edinburgh medical education that could be traced back to the School of Medicine of Leiden.[J] Teaching was conducted in the outpatient clinic, in the wards and in the operating theatres themselves.[K] As the years passed, many of Wade's postgraduates were especially anxious to observe the surgical techniques, such as nephrectomy, prostatectomy and vesical exclusion, in which he had become a master craftsman (Chapter 12). However, there were no retrospective 'death rounds' of the kind promoted some years later by Professor Sir James R Learmonth, staff meetings at which the case of every surgical patient who had died in hospital was reviewed and analysed.

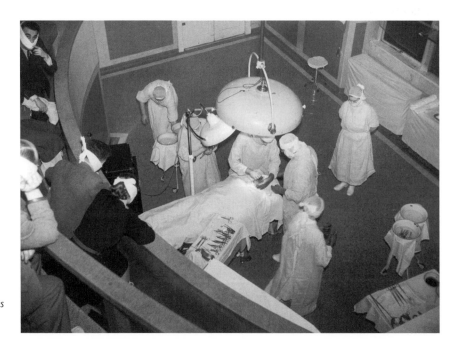

Figure 13.4 Operating theatre instruction.
Students in an operating theatre gallery of the Royal Infirmary of Edinburgh. Gauze masks cover their faces, but they are dressed in their daily clothes and no screen separates them from the floor of the operating theatre

Since the RIE was a voluntary organization, the consultant staff honorary, the task of teaching undergraduate medical students was presumed rather than obligatory. Writing of the RIE, Logan Turner[L] did not index either 'teaching' or 'lecture theatre'.[5] Nevertheless, there was provision for undergraduate instruction in lecture theatres constructed in the corridors of the hospital.

To provide for teaching in the course of surgical operations, operating theatres (p 192) were built to include galleries where rows of seats, raised some feet above the theatre floor, enabled undergraduate and postgraduate students and visitors to watch the surgeons at work. There were no glass panels or screens between the operating table and the onlookers. Students did not wear masks or gowns and did not pass through any kind of disinfectant procedure before entering the gallery. The arrangements, therefore, did not differ significantly from those that were commonplace in the later years of the nineteenth century. Occasionally, accidents occurred. One day, an enquiring individual, intent on the surgery, fell to the theatre floor and sustained a fractured skull. The theatres were also used for systematic and didactic teaching when they were not required for operative surgery and served a purpose when small seminars or short lectures were to be given. The Surgeon, his Assistant Surgeon or the Clinical Tutor could speak to students from the floor. It was a practice that continued until modern times.

In his fine history of the RIE, Dr Logan Turner[5] described the complex relationship that evolved between the University's clinical teachers and the honorary staff of the hospital.[11] Surgeons-in-Ordinary were granted the University status of Honorary Senior Lecturers and Assistant Surgeons that of Honorary Lecturer. A converse relationship developed, so that the University's professors, readers and lecturers might hold recognized appointments within the voluntary hospital, allowing them access to patients, the hospital laboratories and other facilities.

The surgical units of the RIE were largely autonomous. Each undertook clinical teaching and, for this purpose, accumulated pathological specimens and other artefacts in small museums. Professor John Fraser's museum was behind the operating theatre of Ward 7, beside his ward laboratory. In this context, the generous offer by Logan Turner in 1926 to sponsor three teaching and museum rooms in the Ear, Nose and Throat Department of the hospital was welcomed. His offer was conditional on the agreement that if the rooms were required for another purpose the contents of his museum would be passed to the RCSEd.

On his return to Scotland from Egypt in 1919, Wade began highly popular hospital ward classes for postgraduate students on Saturday mornings. The teaching was under the auspices of the Postgraduate Committee. One obituarist described his 'round' as the 'first regular clinical instruction, apart from vacation courses, provided [in Edinburgh] for [surgical] postgraduates'. He continued much of this teaching throughout the 1920s and 1930s. The 'rounds' attracted large numbers of those who were studying for the Fellowship examinations. They came not only from Scotland but from those countries with which Edinburgh had particularly close associations, including Australia, New Zealand, South Africa and India.

Examinations

Undergraduate examinations

Undergraduate students attending the courses of instruction of the SMRC completed their education by sitting examinations for the Triple Qualification, the TQ, the LRCSEd, LRCPEd, LRCPSG. Wade was closely involved with these examinations, to the extent that in April 1920, he was compelled to write to Mr DL Eadie, Clerk of the College, to ask him to arrange for someone else to conduct the TQ orals, as he, Wade, was leaving for America.[25]

Large numbers of students sat these examinations. In 1897, 205 of 466 candidates for the Licentiateship, passed. The corresponding figures for Dental Surgery were 59 and 45. Thirty years later, the content of the examinations of the Conjoint Board was still being discussed.[26] The subjects in the 1920s were very similar to those examined in the 1890s: Chemistry; Physics; Biology; Botany; Zoology; Anatomy; Physiology/histology; *Materia Medica* and pharmacology; Pharmacology/therapeutics; Pathology; and Medicine including Mental Diseases, Forensic Medicine, Public Health, Surgery and Surgical Anatomy, Midwifery and Gynaecology.

Postgraduate examinations

The postgraduate Fellowship examinations were central not only to the educational policies of the RCSEd but were the main determinant of the College's financial security and its livelihood. To become an examiner was a considerable distinction. The choice of examiners was carried out in the same meticulous way as the selection of undergraduate and postgraduate teachers. Examiners were required to be consultants in the fields of surgery in which they practised. Occasionally this led to difficulty. For example, in 1931, the Council decided that Miss Gertrude Herzfeld's name (p 280) should be withdrawn from the list of those licensed to examine in Gynaecology, as she held no consultant appointment in that subject.

Examiners were paid a modest sum for their time and effort. In 1921, the fee for an examination was two guineas for the first hour and one guinea for each succeeding hour. Examiners received first-class railway travelling expenses, an obligation that cost the College a great deal of money each year. In spite of this constraint, in 1930, Mr George Chiene had no hesitation in asking for examiners' fees to be raised.[27]

As an examiner for the Fellowship, Wade was something of an enigma. Hidden behind his taciturn, gruff exterior was a warm heart.

Dr John Loudon (personal communication) remembers being examined for the FRCSEd by Sir Henry Wade in 1954. The elderly surgeon was nearing the end of his life. It was unusual for examiners to be allowed to continue beyond the statutory age of 70 years, although, occasionally, a retired examiner was recalled when a colleague withdrew at short notice. Wade was kind, tolerant and understanding, qualities not always displayed under such circumstances when the conjunction of an ignorant candidate and an irascible examiner could be explosive.

Mr James Scott (personal communication) remembers that, like many examiners, Wade tended to ask questions about pathological specimens in which he had a personal interest. Thus, on one occasion, a brain, the site of a temporal lobe abscess, was placed before the candidate who gave an exemplary answer. Wade then recalled the kindly personality of the individual from whom the specimen had come, reminding his fellow examiner that he (the owner of the brain) had been a well-respected Edinburgh solicitor.

From time to time, the content of the examinations was reviewed critically. In 1902, for example, the question of specialization in surgery was confronted. It was unavoidable that the special branches of surgery, emerging quickly with the exploitation of Listerian antisepsis, anaesthesia and new laboratory methods, should be included in the examinations in General Surgery. In view of the slow reaction of the Managers of the Royal Infirmary to the growing pressure for a Department of Orthopaedic Surgery after the First World War, it is not surprising to learn that, in 1918, the College Council had still not decided to return this subject to the list of subjects for the Fellowship examination. Orthopaedic Surgery had been removed from the list in 1900.[28]

Nevertheless, the possibility of agreeing to improvements in the FRCSEd examinations continued to exercise the Council.[29] On 16th May 1938, proposals centred on creating a single examination shared with the other Surgical Colleges, but the committee was unable to agree to this apparently reasonable idea. Wade and his fellow members of the President's Council accepted that uniformity in examination standards and content throughout all Royal Surgical Colleges would be desirable but were faced with barriers of traditional rivalry that they could not overcome. On 17th December 1943, the Council returned to the subject of a single shared examination and expressed a 'general feeling' that the examinations for the higher Diplomas of the English, Edinburgh, Glasgow and Irish colleges 'might be brought more closely into line'.

There was also concern whether marking conformed to the style advised by the GMC.[30] Improved proposals were discussed for the FRCSEd examination. They recommended that, within a postgraduate course in Surgery, questions in allied subjects, together with Anatomy and Physiology, should be initiated; that the post of Conservator (p 91) be filled as soon as possible, combined with that of Director of Postgraduate Studies; and that suitable premises be provided for postgraduate teaching, in this way anticipating the building of the Lister Institute (p 250).

In the following year, on 19th December 1944, the committee considering the FRCSEd examinations presented a new report.[31] Major changes were afoot. The committee concluded that the content of the examination should be coordinated with postgraduate training; that a candidate should have not less than three years' postgraduate experience before admission to the examination; that this should include at least one year of pre-registration employment, one year of basic science and one year of further clinical experience; that the examination should comprise a first part, a Primary examination, in Anatomy, Physiology, Pathology and Bacteriology, all as applied to surgery, and a second part, a Final examination, in General Surgery and in special subjects that were detailed.

Candidates and cost

At the centre of the Fellowship examinations were the young surgeons whose careers were at stake. Many, if not all, were free to take the corresponding tests of other Colleges in Britain or abroad. If the RCSEd became unpopular, the Edinburgh College would be faced with serious financial consequences. For the College, more was at stake than simply a reputation as a respected academic institution. There had to be a balance between maintaining standards and moderating charges. The cost of entering for the Fellowship examination had risen steadily. In 1928, the year in which George Chiene and JW Struthers became members of the governing body of the SMRC, it was increased from £45 to £50. Subsequently, the President's Council relented.[32] Not wishing to press for excessive profit, they decided that £10 might be paid on entrance to the examination and the remaining £40 on passing.

Candidates had their own viewpoints. They did not always act predictably and their behaviour and actions became the source of many illuminating stories. In a quaint, possibly unique footnote to the question of the conduct of examinations, a wartime candidate was granted permission to use a typewriter 'as he is unable to write owing to writers' cramp'.[33] Candidates had additional stocks of anecdotes. Their tales ranged from the critical capacity of sleeping examiners to the effects on examiners of their, the examiners', not infrequent illnesses. There was even talk of corruption in the form of examination questions being sold by members of the College staff in advance of the tests.

The number of candidates for the Fellowship examinations had always been an accurate index of the academic health of the College. In 1897, 45 diplomates advanced to the Fellowship, while nine failed.[34] In December 1925, 105 passed the FRCSEd examinations and

133 failed. As the Fellowship prospered, with growing numbers achieving professional success worldwide, so did the number of new supplicants. In 1940, the depredations of war quickly became evident. The number of candidates for the Fellowship examinations fell, leading to a reduction in College income. In December 1940, there were nine successes, and, in February 1941, only seven. The numbers then fluctuated, so that in May 1941, 19 candidates passed the examination followed by 17 in October and 16 in December.

For many years, it had been necessary for a candidate approaching the examination to have a sponsor. The relaxed attitude of Dr Ryland Whitaker' created doubts about the number of candidates who might be supported by a single sponsor. In February 1927, Wade, now a member of the Council, 'raised the question of the signing of a large number of petitions by certain Fellows and asked if steps could not be taken to insist upon the proposers and seconders of the candidates complying exactly with the requirements as printed in the petition form. Could some other form of entrance for the exam not be put in force?'

Wade at St Andrews

Wade was both an Extra Academical Teacher and External Examiner for the University of St Andrews, where the Faculty of Medicine had no clinical hospital association of its own. However, 1920 was exceptionally busy, and occasionally the University Secretary had to write of examination papers, as he did on 17th May:

'Please send them to me by return.'[35]

This reminder was followed by an even less comfortable letter from William Wilkie, the Quaestor (Treasurer) and Factor (Property Manager) of St Andrews University, who told Wade that no returns had been received for 1918–19 and that:

'the University proposes to withdraw the recognition held by you as an Extra Academical Teacher in the subject of Surgery.'

An irritated Wade wrote back:

'No returns have been submitted by me since, in 1918–1919, I have not held a class in Surgery.'

Wilkie responded by saying:

'Provided you propose to give a qualifying course of instruction next winter, the grant of recognition will not be withdrawn.'[36]

This was not enough to convince Wade that he should continue with his commitments to St Andrews, and this obligation ended when he wrote on 22nd June:

'I regret that I do not intend to give a qualifying course of instruction next winter.'[37]

The exchange did not prevent Wade asking for his travelling expenses,[38] and, in July, Wilkie sent Wade £14/16/–d:

'being half the amount due to you as Additional Examiner.'

Wade's position as External Examiner did not end, however, and on 16th November 1922, the University of St Andrews was obliged to ask him for the papers for the 4th professional examination which:

'should have been in Mr Andrew Bennett's hands by yesterday.'[39]

Wade clearly fulfilled this obligation, as he received a cheque for £29/1/–d on 1st January 1923 in payment of further travel expenses.

These minor, incestuous disagreements, commonplace in closed University academic circles, did not deter Wade from devoting an increasing proportion of his time to the affairs of the RCSEd and its Council, the responsibilities and privileges of which are described in Chapter 14.

CHAPTER 14

College councillor and president

1925–48

Tis the sublime of man, our noontide Majesty, to know
ourselves parts and proportions of one wondrous whole!

(Samuel Taylor Coleridge, *Religious Musings*, 1794)

Through the passage of years and increased seniority rather than by any conscious intention, Henry Wade now became a committee man. The transition from young surgeon to mature statesman cannot have been easy: he was by his very nature a man of action, not a politician. But the breadth of his knowledge, his practical common sense and the pragmatism born of surgical practice soon made him one of the most sought after members of the committees of the ancient Royal College of Surgeons of Edinburgh, the RCSEd.

To convey a convincing picture of the inner workings, the debates, discussions, controversies, yes, and the bitter disagreements, the clashes of policy and the irreconcilable differences between members of the board of an international commercial company is almost certainly beyond the wit of man. Yet this is precisely what must be attempted if a clear idea is to be formed of the inner workings of a Royal surgical College. The antiquity of a College, its traditions and customs compound the problem, imposed as they are on the practical necessity of guiding wisely the profession of Surgery. The holding of honorary positions by 'Office Bearers'; committee practices and calendars; even the frequency of dinners and formal lectures, are bound by ancient traditions that greatly enlarge the challenge of organizing what is, in effect, a 'big business'.

For much of his life, Wade had spent his time caring for patients in a voluntary hospital, the Royal Infirmary of Edinburgh, the RIE, while earning his living in his Drumsheugh Gardens nursing home. He was a successful teacher, closely involved with the education of medical students and postgraduates in the wards of the RIE and in the classrooms of the School of Medicine of the Edinburgh Royal Colleges, the SMRC. In his few hours of free time he was also an antiquarian. However it was now his duty to turn from these daily rounds to the sanctuary of the committee rooms of the RCSEd, whose patronage he

Chapter Summary

- **The College**
- **President's Council**
- **Presidency**
- **Business of Council**
- **The College and national policies**
- **Health of the Nation**
- **National Health Service**
- **Beveridge paves the way**
- **The College and domestic policies**
- **Women in surgery**
- **College finances**
- **War**
- **Conclusion**

had enjoyed since 1903. The spark that lit this commitment was his long association with the College as Conservator (Chapter 6). The flame that leapt from this source was his election in 1925 to the Council of the College.[A]

Formerly the Incorporation of Barber Surgeons,[1,B] the RCSEd was the oldest of the four Royal surgical foundations of Great Britain and Ireland.[C] Over the centuries, the College had acquired and maintained a powerful influence in the world of surgery. Consulted by governments and respected by civic authorities,[D] the College had practised within the law of the land as an autonomous body. Since its separation from the Town of Edinburgh in 1851, the College had not been directly responsible to parliament, any civic body, the University of Edinburgh, the Scottish Health Board or any part of the health services. As one result, the College gradually and unconsciously assumed an air of dynastic dignity that kept its activities hidden from the public. This remoteness was wholly in accord with the traditional philosophy of medical and surgical practice, based on the Hippocratic Oath. Confidentiality was at the heart of responsible medicine. The 'public' should know only as much of surgery as might be expected to enhance a beneficial response in diagnosis and treatment. How the surgeons themselves were trained, how they were taught and tested and how they exercised their skills were rarely matters of public concern and were, in any event, almost certainly beyond the comprehension of the lay person.

The College

By statute, the College belonged to its Fellows. Each year, a report listed the Fellows, the Office Bearers, the committees and the annual subscription. The great majority of Fellows obtained their Diploma by examination as a necessary part of their surgical advancement and training. Fellowship granted many privileges. In October 1924, there were 1,813 Fellows worldwide. Many were in Scotland, with smaller numbers in England, Wales and the North of Ireland. By 18th October 1939, the numbers had reached 2,944 and by 1961 there were as many as 6,000. Relatively large numbers practised in the lands of the Empire, particularly in Australia, New Zealand, South Africa, India, Nepal, Singapore, Hong Kong and the countries of the Middle East. From 1919 until 1934, for example, when King Feisal and his government assumed power in Mesopotamia (Iraq), the medical services of that country, like the military, were educated in the British tradition. Many were Fellows of the RCSEd.

Over the years, an average of five corporate College meetings, meetings of the Fellows, took place annually. The meetings were held in the College, although, during and following the war years from 1914–19, the Council itself often met in private houses that included 6 Chester Street, 2 Drumsheugh Gardens or, in 1924, 9 Great Stuart Street. College meetings took place in January or

Figure 14.1 Wade as a member of the Council of the RCSEd. *Elected in 1925, Wade served until 1948*

February, May, July, October and December. Occasionally, a special meeting would be called, as was the case in 1934, when the memoranda prepared for the committee on the Scottish Health Services were debated. The College meetings discussed political, financial and individual business but also the reports of the Special finance, the School of Medicine of the Scottish Colleges (the SMRC) – the Museum – and the Library committees. The various minutes were considered, their decisions ratified or rejected and their members appointed or reappointed.

During much of Wade's time, the office work of the College was regulated by the College Clerk, Mr CL Eadie. His office was at 50 George Square whence it moved, in 1919, to 4 Lauriston Place. Because of irregularities in the books, his employment was ended in 1929. In 1933, the Council decided to transfer the office of the Clerk to the College itself. Before 1928, the minutes of the College, like those of the President's Council, were written longhand in copperplate script. From 1928 onwards, they were printed.[E] There was an immediate loss of detail and intimacy. It was not until 1956[2] that it was agreed that a shorthand typist be employed. In 1958, the College bought its first duplicating machine,[3] although the Fellows doubted whether an electric typewriter was necessary.

At the October meeting of Fellows, the annual statement of the President's Council was presented. It gave a list of Fellows and of Honorary Fellows, of whom the first had been the Lord Provost of Edinburgh, Sir Andrew Ramsay, elected in 1671. The statement continued with a list of Office Bearers and examiners and an abstract of the College's accounts. The annual meeting, like so many formal College occasions, was succeeded by a dinner.

President's Council

Wade was elected as a member of the Council of the RCSEd on 21st October 1925.[F] The election was the result of a ballot of Fellows. The President was Arthur Logan Turner,[G] the Council members AA Scot Skirving,[H] WJ Stuart,[I] JM Graham,[J] WA Cochrane[K] and JW Dowden.[L] Wade remained a member of Council until 1948.

In political terms, the President's Council was a 'cabinet', in the same way that the Fellows constituted the 'backbenchers'. Within this cabinet, the President, the Vice President, and the Secretary/Treasurer constituted the 'Office Bearers'. In parenthesis, it should be noted that, with the passage of time and the increase in work, there came to be two Vice Presidents while the offices of Secretary and Treasurer were separated. For very many years, the policies, direction, control and management of the College therefore lay in the hands of a small but influential group of senior Fellows. Membership of the Council was a matter of considerable prestige and influence. Each member knew, at the time of their election, that they had the opportunity of becoming an Office Bearer and, indeed, of becoming President. There was subtle competition for these roles. However, the minutes show that each President, at the time of taking office, relied on the loyal support of existing Council members.

Throughout the period 1929–34, meetings of the President's Council, convened in advance of those of the College by one or two weeks, were held 8–10 times each year. There were, in addition, a varying number of extraordinary meetings held to deal with matters of difficulty or delicacy. Council members were expected to be present at each meeting of both College and Council but this was an unrealistic ideal for practising surgeons. After his election in 1925, Wade attended College meetings assiduously, although not constantly: he was unable to attend one quarter of them.

In 1934, Wade was invited to Melbourne to represent the Edinburgh College at the opening of the new building, in April 1935, of the Royal Australasian College of Surgeons. The Australasian College had been founded in 1927. In his invited lecture, Wade chose the subject of 'Renal Tumours'.[M] Before the visit, the President of the Australasian

College, Sir Henry Simpson Newland, had been proposed for the Honorary Fellowship of the RCSEd.[4] The Australian visit was doubly successful. It allowed Wade to visit his relatives in New South Wales (Chapter 1) and to meet old comrades from the days of the First World War. On his return to Edinburgh, he spoke warmly to the Council of the cordial welcome he had received.

Presidency

It was almost inevitable that Wade's devotion to Scottish surgery and his international distinction, should culminate in election to the Presidency of the College (Table 14.1).[N] Wade assumed this office on 16th October 1935.[5] The concept that the Presidency of a Royal College was a form of political sinecure, chosen to advance ambitious careers, was highly misleading. For a senior surgeon to devote the time required to properly discharge the duties of a President was a decision not to be taken lightly. Conscientious and hard-working, Wade would 'burn much midnight oil' in the execution of his responsibilities. Moreover, there were financial sacrifices. Despite receiving an honorarium, the Presidency deprived a surgeon of much of the time normally devoted to his patients. He depended for his income on the successful practice that centred on his busy Private Clinic (Chapter 9). As President, Wade could not expect to respond to calls for consultation as often as usual. However, he remained dedicated to his wards in the RIE.

Figure 14.2 Wade as President of the RCSEd. *Wade was elected to this position on 16th October 1935*

For the President and the Office Bearers there had always been professional responsibilities towards the Royal family. Over the centuries, the relationship between the Royal household and the RCSEd had been close. In 1871, Joseph Lister drained Queen Victoria's axillary abscess under chloroform anaesthesia – Sir Edward Jenner manipulated the carbolic acid spray – while in 1902, Frederick Treves saved the life of the new but uncrowned Edward VII when he developed appendicitis shortly before his coronation. There were also duties arising from events within the Royal family. The Presidents of Royal Colleges or their representatives were invited to coronation ceremonies, Royal weddings and funerals. Queen Alexandra died in November 1925,[6] and the College wrote appropriately. Almost at the moment of his election, Wade himself was expected to follow the same ritual when King George V died early in 1936.[7] Subsequently, he attended the 1937 Coronation of King George VI (p 319).

Business of Council

The subjects that engaged Wade's attention during his years on the Council of the College included many of far-reaching significance. They represented a large range of topics. Some recurred annually.[o] The most important were the annual election or re-election of the President, the Office Bearers, the Librarian and the Conservator.

Table 14.1 Presidents of the Royal College of Surgeons of Edinburgh during Wade's lifetime

Year	President
1875	Sir Henry Duncan Littlejohn
1877	Patrick Heron Watson
1879	Francis Brodie Imlach
.1882	Sir William Turner, KCB
1883	John Smith
1885	Douglas Moray Cooper Lamb Argyll Robertson
1887	Joseph Bell
1889	John Duncan
1891	Robert James Blair Cunynghame
1893	Peter Hume Maclaren
1895	Sir John Struthers
1897	John Chiene, CB
1899	James Dunsmure
1901	Sir John Halliday Croom
1903	Sir Patrick Heron Watson
1905	Charles Watson MacGillivray
1907	Sir Joseph Montague Cotterill, CMG
1910	Sir George Andreas Berry
1912	Francis Mitchell Caird
1914	Sir James William Beeman Hodsdon, KBE
1917	Robert McKenzie Johnston
1919	George Mackay
1921	Sir David Wallace, KBE, CMG
1923	Sir Harold Jalland Stiles, KBE
1925	Arthur Logan Turner
1927	Alexander Miles
1929	James Haig Ferguson
1931	John Wheeler Dowden
1933	Arthur Henry Havens Sinclair
1935	Sir Henry Wade, CMG, DSO
1937	William James Stuart
1939	Harry Moss Traquair
1941	John William Struthers, LLD
1943	Robert William Johnstone, CBE
1945	James Methuen Graham, LLD
1947	Francis Evelyn Jardine
1949	Walter Quarry Wood
1951	Sir Walter Mercer

Following closely on these necessary tasks were the challenges of finance, education, conduct of examinations, disciplinary proceedings and property. The finances of the College are outlined below, while those of the SMRC and its undergraduate and postgraduate classes and examinations are discussed in Chapter 13.

Wade served as College representative on the General Medical Council (GMC) from 1943 until 1953. The GMC bore the statutory responsibility for the licensing of doctors to practise and for the maintenance of acceptable standards not only of professional work but of ethics and morality. The GMC were also empowered to ensure proper levels of medical education. They had, for example, inspected the College's examination system early in 1921.

The ethical regulation of the surgical profession concerned the College greatly. The College Council monitored the standards of education and training of their candidates and the morality, legality and responsibility of those who became Licentiates or Fellows. In whatever part of the world, Fellows were bound by the statutes of the GMC, which reported misdemeanours to the licensing Royal Colleges, each of which had the authority to strike an offender from their records by requesting a return of their licence (p 248). Every year, one or more surgeons appeared before the disciplinary committee of the GMC. They were asked to account for their behaviour, to justify actions that had led to fines or imprisonment or to explain advertising and other claims that were not acceptable to their profession. The names of these individuals were passed to the College. An investigation of the utmost rigour was then instigated. Although disciplinary proceedings were pursued only after very full evidence had been considered and every proper legal avenue explored, those proven to be miscreants were deprived of their diplomas. When a charge was sustained, the outcome was for the Licentiateship or Fellowship to be withdrawn: the individual could no longer enjoy the prestige of Fellowship, although the legal right to practice in the UK remained a matter for the GMC to decide.

The same College statutes applied in whichever part of the world a Fellow might be practising, although the consequences of erasure were not necessarily the same. After Wade's death, the Lancet recorded how, on his retirement, the President of the GMC wrote:[8]

'Sir Henry Wade rendered notable services on the Education Committee [of the General Medical Council] when the revision of the curriculum was under debate; and on the Executive Committee and in the disciplinary business of the Council his cautious judgement was of great assistance. His colleagues will long remember his shrewd comments on matters both educational and moral, his happy social interests and attractions, and his unfailing sense of humour.'

Figure 14.3 Wade and colleagues welcome Lord Moynihan. *The occasion was the visit to Edinburgh in 1932 of Lord Moynihan on whom the Honorary Fellowship of the College was being bestowed. In the front row, left to right, are: Dr George Crile, the distinguished American surgeon; Berkley George Andrew, Lord Moynihan; Professor Sir David Percival Dalbreck Wilkie and Mr Henry Wade. In the back row are Mr John James McIntosh Shaw; two Fellows who have not been identified; Mr David Band and Mr Charles Illingworth*

From time to time, the rare distinction of Honorary Fellowship was bestowed on persons of surgical, scientific, military or political distinction. The decision to award such an honour invariably evoked debate. After careful consideration, 36 Honorary Fellowships were granted at the time of the celebrations of the 400th anniversary of the College in 1905. The Honorary Fellows were selected from 12 countries. They included Lord Lister, the Presidents of the other Royal Colleges and the Director Generals of the Army and Navy Medical Services. In 1919, Honorary Fellowships were offered to the leaders of the victorious British and Allied forces. In 1927, Sir Robert Philip, Chairman of the BMA Edinburgh Congress, and an internationally recognized authority on tuberculosis, was designated as an Honorary

Fellow, as was Sir W Watson Cheyne (p 74). A similar honour was accorded in 1930 to the first President of the young Royal College of Physicians and Surgeons of Canada; in 1932 to Lord Moynihan, President of the Royal College of Surgeons of England; and in 1934 to the President of the Royal Australasian College of Surgeons.[9,10] During the Second World War, a Polish Medical Faculty was accommodated in Edinburgh. An Honorary Fellowship was bestowed on the Dean, Professor Jurasz.

Expressions of mutual regard among the Royal medical and surgical Colleges continued to be frequent. In 1926, a lunch to commemorate the 250th anniversary of the foundation of the Royal College of Physicians of Edinburgh, the RCPEd, cost the attending surgical Fellows £60.[11] Although a proposal to finance the manufacture of a mace to be given to the Americans who had taken part in the military campaigns of 1917–18 met with a mixed reception (p 182), an offer of a plaque to honour the memory of Crawford Williamson Long (1815–78) was warmly welcomed. He had been the first to use ether, in 1842. The plaque was presented by an American delegation from

Figure 14.4 Crawford Williamson Long plaque.
The occasion was the presentation on 30th March 1937 by the Southern Society of Clinical Surgery, USA, of a plaque commemorating the contribution made by Crawford Williamson Long to the adoption of ether anaesthesia. In the group, left to right, are Mr John William Struthers, Secretary and Treasurer of the RCSEd; Dr Wavell, representing the Southern Society of Clinical Surgery; Mr CR Naismith, the American Consul; Mr Arthur Henry Havens Sinclair, past-President of the College; and Mr Henry Wade, the College's President.

the Southern Society of Clinical Surgery, which visited Edinburgh on 30th October 1936. Wade presided over the simple ceremony.

Each year there were prizes to be awarded and commemorative lectureships to be filled. The Francis Caird memorial fund, for example, had attracted £198/5/2d by 1928,[12] and nominations for the Struthers lecture were necessarily considered. In 1926, the name of David Waterston, Conservator of the Museum in 1902, was proposed for this honour.[13]

The RCSEd worked closely with the RIE[14] and designated two Fellows to be members of the Board of Management of the hospital (Chapters 10 and 11). In 1921, for example, Mr CM Cathcart and Mr George Mackay were chosen by the College to represent their interests.[15] In spite of his close working relationship with the RIE and his membership of the College Council, there is no evidence that Wade assumed this responsible position.

The Museum of the RCSEd occupied a considerable proportion of the Council's time (Chapter 6), and, in 1938, when the morale of the Museum was low, serious consideration was given to combining the post of Conservator with that of Director of Postgraduate Studies.[16] This proposal, the brainchild of the President, Mr WJ Stuart, was not pursued, but, meanwhile, the Council's minutes recorded a series of comments from the Acting Conservator, Mr Charles Illingworth.[17] The Council was equally concerned with the quality and work of the College's Library, a centre of international surgical and historical significance.

Occasionally, the President's Council seemed to concentrate on matters of ritual rather than of practicality. Thus, the question of whether those who received Honorary Fellowships at the time of the Quartcentenary should be given their robes, exercised the Council greatly. Less serious matters also found their way on to the agenda. Early in 1923, for example, the cleaning of the College's blinds occupied Council's time and attention,[18] and the results of the annual curling and golf matches against the RCPEd were recorded with zest.[19,20]

The College and national policies

The nature of Wade's Presidential appointment and the role of the Royal Colleges in regulating surgical training and standards meant that he was frequently involved in discussions of national significance. In one instance, the subject was to have far-reaching implications for many years to come: it was the continuing debate on the proposed formation of a Ministry of Health[21], a concept that preceded discussions on a putative National Health Service.[22] It is not surprising that the reports of the College's representatives on the committee considering the Scottish Health Service were discussed in detail.[23,24]

A considerable proportion of the work of the College was directed towards furthering skill and responsibility in Dental Surgery. In 1917, for example, the College was aware that the Privy Council was considering the evils of unqualified dental practice. Soon after the First World War ended, Parliament began to debate a bill for the regulation of dentistry. In 1922, a register of dental practitioners was at last initiated. Discussions continued over the years and on 23rd April 1944, an Extraordinary College meeting was held to re-consider the work of the Interdepartmental Committee on Dentistry, which had been convened under Lord Teviot. Its aim was to review whether the present arrangements provided an adequate dental service for the population; steps to ensure an adequate number of entrants to the profession; the regulation of the practice and governance of the profession; and moves to encourage research on the causes, prevention and treatment of dental disease.

The relationships between the Royal Edinburgh Colleges and the British Medical Association (BMA) were not always easy. One reason was the need for each body to serve the interests of wholly distinct parts of the medical profession. A contentious historical issue was the charter sought eagerly by the BMA. Addressing a letter to the Privy Council, the College reminded this Council that 'your petitioners [the BMA] were incorporated into one body on March 3rd 1851. If granted, the petition would have a serious effect on the rights and duties of Fellows of this College'. In 1937, in a response to the BMA, the College offered a cautious reply to an invitation to nominate a representative on a Consultants' Board for Scotland. The exchanges could occasionally be lighter. Thus, on 3rd November 1919, Mr WE Warne, Financial Secretary of the BMA, London, WC2, had written to Wade:

> 'I now understood that you have been absent on Active Service for 5 years and would not have stopped your British Medical Journal had I known.[25] A 'Colonial' rate of subscription would be appropriate but the amounts for 1914, 1915 and 1916 have been paid on your behalf.'

With the outbreak of the Second World War, Wade became a member of the Specialists and Consultants Services Committee of the Scottish Central Medical War Committee, the SCMWC, of the BMA.[26] The SCMWC spawned a number of associated groups and subcommittees, among which were the Serving Young Practitioners Sub-Committee (SYP) and the Specialists and Consultants Services Committee. The meetings of the SCMWC were held at 7 Drumsheugh Gardens. In 1941, the Chairman was Professor Sydney Smith.[27]

Health of the Nation

The College Council had always been sensitive to the issue of the welfare of the Scottish people. In 1904, for example, the College considered carefully the health of Scottish school children. The Council commented:

'It was recommended that every aspect of children's mental and physical state should be recorded and that food, housing, cleanliness and clothing should be noted.'

It was decided to recommend that the age, weight, height and chest measurement of every child should be documented, together with their state of muscular development, a note of any disease and malformation, any mental impediment and the condition of the teeth. Among other matters, in 1914, the Government's Milk Bill attracted the College's concern. The Dogs Protection Bill also created anxiety. If enacted, its effect would be 'detrimental to surgery' [by preventing the experimental testing of surgical operations]. The supply of radium for the treatment of cancer, a development centred at the Beechmount Hospital, Edinburgh, was constantly under review. In 1928, the Council supported an appeal for donations of this radioactive element.[28] They were acutely aware of the success of the methods used in Stockholm.[29] In 1937, Sir John Fraser gave evidence on the Bill for the Rehabilitation of Persons Injured by Accident.[30] The following year, the College approved the private members' Nursing Homes Bill (Scotland) advanced by Sir Douglas Thomson. In 1939, they considered Workmans' Compensation.[31]

National Health Service

Wade's seniority and experience determined that he would play an important part in the social revolution that shook Britain after the conclusion of the Second World War. A Scottish Health Service was initiated in 1947 and the British National Health Service, the NHS, on 5th July 1948.[32] Wade was associated closely with discussions that presaged the NHS. His association with BMA committees was influential.

The origins of the NHS of England, Wales and the North of Ireland can be traced to Lloyd George's National Insurance Act of 1911.[33] In 1910 the College had already become concerned about the grave considerations posed by the preliminary Bill, for all medical practitioners. After this legislation was enacted, on 12th December 1912, the College agreed that its content was 'derogatory to the profession'. They believed the Act 'has the worst features of club practice'.[?]

Matters accelerated after the First World War, catalyzed by the Wall Street crash of 1929, when the Chancellor of the Exchequer, Neville Chamberlain, sought a means of reducing national expenditure. However, following the worldwide economic depression, unemployment, deprivation and ill health led to a growing demand for improved social conditions. Committees were set up for England and Wales and, separately, under Lord Lovat, for Scotland. After the latter, the conclusion was reached that:

'no real savings can be achieved…until they have been submitted to a comprehensive enquiry that would take into account modern medical knowledge and the prevailing financial conditions.'

In Scotland, the provision of health care was materially different from England and Wales.[22,Q] The 1911 National Insurance Act imposed burdens on poorer people. Even when individuals paid their weekly pennies, they could not be assured of medical care by 1913. There were insufficient general practitioners and an inadequate provision of hospital services. The Secretary of State for Scotland established a Committee on the Scottish Health Services in 1932. The chairman was Sir John Dove-Wilson. On his death in April 1935, the chair was assumed by Professor Edward Cathcart, Professor of Physiology at the University of Glasgow. The Royal Medical Corporations were represented by Alexander Miles, President of the RCSEd. The result was the 1936 Cathcart Report,[34] a blueprint for a Scottish National Health Service and the basis of the National Health Services (Scotland) Bill of 1947.

The College's role

In 1934, the Scottish Committee on Health Services asked the College to give evidence on the state medical services, including National Health Insurance; on hospitals, including waiting lists and payments; on voluntary public medical services; on consultant services; on nursing homes; on medical teaching, including the use of local authority hospitals; and on general health policy. The College responded by setting up four committees to prepare a memorandum. The first committee was of a general character – to coordinate all the evidence. The second was to consider the state of the medical services. The third was to review hospitals, nursing homes and contractual services, while the fourth was to debate teaching.

Wade was appointed a member of the first and third of these bodies. Soon afterwards, it was agreed that the individual memoranda by Douglas Miller and EC Fahmy on maternity services, by WG Sym on the supervision of child life and health, by WA Cochrane on orthopaedic surgery and by JS Fraser on a whole-time medical and surgical service, should be forwarded to the government. There was a proviso that these memoranda did not necessarily represent the views of the College as a whole. Wade supported a motion on consultative clinics with reference to cottage hospitals. He opposed the suggestion that patients' contributions towards the cost of their care should be in proportion to their financial position but supported the concept that there should be free treatment for the necessitous poor. The President – Arthur Sinclair, WJ Stewart, Henry Wade and George Chiene appeared before the Government's committee on 11th January 1935.

The organization of hospitals in Scotland, as well as the provision of care, was distinct from that in England, Wales and Ulster, and it has been argued cogently that there were not one but two distinct services: for Scotland and, separately, for England, Wales and the North of Ireland.[22] In England, there were four varieties of hospital: the 12 London teaching hospitals, other voluntary hospitals, the London

County Council hospitals and the provincial local authority hospitals. The position in Scotland, where more than 400 hospitals existed in 1934, was different. Among the 206 voluntary hospitals were the teaching hospitals of the medical schools of Aberdeen, Dundee, Edinburgh and Glasgow. The mean number of beds in each was 707, accounting for two-thirds of all the voluntary hospital beds. Medical school teaching centred on these large institutions. In 1926, it had been estimated that the voluntary hospitals could provide 3,000 of the additional 3,600 hospital beds required.[35] Seven years later, the Walker Report recommended a single hospital system in each region, with uniformity of equipment, staff, pay and charges.[36]

A flood of discussion erupted. The College was invited to give evidence on post-war hospital problems. Their evidence was complete by 9th July 1942. Two years later, as the implications of the Goodenough Report (p 249) were being considered, the College agreed to nominate the President, Secretary and three other Council members to join a committee proposed by the BMA to discuss and exchange views on the government's proposals for a National Health Service (p 276). The RCSEd did not react favourably to the suggestion by the Department of Health for Scotland that polyclinics be formed.

Beveridge paves the way

In 1941, Sir Arthur Greenwood commissioned Sir William Beveridge to prepare a plan for universal social security. Superseding the 1911 Pensions Scheme of Lloyd George, the remit was to outline ways in which a national minimum wage, unemployment benefit, health insurance, childrens' and widows' allowances and other benefits could be enabled by a new form of compulsory insurance.

The Beveridge Report was published in 1942.[37] At once it became the focus of intense interest in a war-riven Britain. Beveridge's plan for a National Health Service included not only a minimum national wage, but also compulsory insurance, unemployment benefit, a child allowance, and maternity and widows' benefit. This was wartime Britain. The plan was the immediate object of ridicule by the enemy. The Germans and Italians suspected that the purpose was to undercut the aims of their national socialism that was to be imposed on Britain once she had been subjugated. By 1943, the Beveridge Report had become an almost obligatory subject for discussion, taking minds away from wartime news that included the Battle of the Atlantic, submarine warfare and the loss of Singapore. The British Government's response to Beveridge was cool. In the House of Commons, 121 Members of Parliament asked for stronger government approval before giving their own support. However, the people were sustained by widespread hope for a better future. In their thoughts and desires, they were ahead of their parliamentary representatives. Responding, as a first step towards post-war revival, a Ministry of Reconstruction was created.

The main objection to the Beveridge plan was financial.[Q] Could the country afford to adopt Beveridge's proposals without imposing such a burden of cost on the markets that exports would no longer be competitive? The charge for complying with Beveridge's proposals, it was calculated, would impose a 2% burden on the national income. Opponents of the Report adopted tactics that recalled those used in the previous century to contest the Poor Laws. They included the large insurance companies, worried about their future.

In spite of these difficulties and anxieties, the new government adopted many of Beveridge's proposals, and, in particular, those for a National Health Service. Surveys of popular opinion showed that 55% of the public, 60% of doctors and 72% of students wanted a free health service. Moreover, 69% of the public and 89% of students approved of the idea of health centres. In 1946, Aneurin Bevan, the Minister of Health, published a white paper outlining plans for a Health Services Act. By this bold stroke, he paved the way for the greatest revolution in medical care ever known in this country. Wade was closely involved in translating the political concepts of the Act into the practical realities of care.

The College and domestic policies

Throughout the years of Wade's Council membership and Presidency, many other matters of a domestic character were debated. Thus, a broad picture of the future of medical education emerged at an extraordinary meeting convened on 21st October 1942. Wade was also appointed to a committee to review relations between the Carnegie Trust and the Board of the Laboratory of the RCPEd. Earlier in the century, Sir John Halliday Croom had reminded the College that examinations in Obstetrics had become more stringent and that the College's collection of relevant specimens was 'of no value for teaching'. In 1943, an agreed report emerged from a joint committee formed by the three Scottish medical corporations and the Royal College of Obstetricians and Gynaecologists, which analysed all aspects of consultant/specialist work in relation to post-war needs. There was widespread anxiety about the safety of cocaine in anaesthesia,[38] a local anaesthetic the addictive properties of which came into prominence in the 1890s.[R] In 1924, a letter from the Health Department suggested a total ban on the manufacture of heroin, an analgesic drug of value for the relief of severe and persistent pain.[39,40] The RCSEd Council did not accept this proposal. A Diploma in Tuberculosis had been suggested in 1923 but again this idea did not gain Council's support.[41]

Women in surgery

It was to be expected that the admission of women to the study of medicine would, sooner or later, lead to a demand that they be permitted to enter the profession of Surgery. To accomplish this, properly qualified female doctors would have to sit the examinations for the surgical Fellowship.

The history of this challenge was intimidating. The University of Edinburgh had admitted the first woman medical student in 1869. The Edinburgh School of Medicine for Women was founded in 1886. The Royal Colleges were expected to respond. However, the political scene deteriorated. By May 1913, the Museum of the RCSEd had been closed because of the activity of the suffragettes. Steel windows were to be installed but by 22nd August of that year were not yet in place. In wartime Edinburgh, from 1914–18, the position of women continued to be a topic for discussion with the University.[42] In the College, a retiring room was considered for female students on condition that it was only used between 9 am and 5 pm and that there was neither smoking nor 'lunching'.[43] However, the offer was quickly withdrawn because such a use would interfere with examinations.[44] On 20th July 1916, at almost the moment when events on the Somme were engaging the world's attention, the Treasurer reported 'at length' on the discussions with the University about medical education for women.

Towards the end of the war, in 1918, the National Association for Supplying Female Medical Aid to the Women of India asked that women should be eligible for the Fellowship, but the President's Council stated that College laws, as they stood, did not permit this.[21] At the Council's meeting of 14th November, Mr Alexis Thomson made a formal proposal that women be admitted to the Fellowship on the same conditions as men. An alternative proposal advanced by Mr David Wallace was that women be admitted but with privileges curtailed on the lines of admission granted by the English College of Surgeons. Thomson's motion prevailed and was carried by five votes to three. By December 1919 there was yet another excuse for delay.[45] A Sex Discrimination Bill had been drafted by Parliament, and the College felt it could do no more until the Bill had been disposed. The Bill received its Royal assent on 23rd December. Cautiously, the College felt that there might still be disagreement among its Fellows. They advised taking Counsel's opinion. Finally, faced with the inevitable, the College at last agreed to admit women surgeons on the same conditions as men. The first woman to seek admission to the Fellowship examination was Miss Alice Mabel Headwards.[46] She applied in 1920 and was successful. After passing the examination but before election to the Fellowship, she married and moved to Calcutta, India. The first woman to take her seat in the College therefore was the second successful candidate, Miss Gertrude Herzfeld.[s] Her renown grew quickly.[47]

College finances

The history of the College's finances during the years in which Wade was Conservator, a member of the Council or President shed much light on the decisions taken in virtually every field of collegiate activity (Appendix 14.1). It is not surprising that the issue of money was central to almost every meeting of the College and of the President's Council attended by Wade during the years 1925–49. Unlike a manufacturing business or a commercial service, the financial stability of the RCSEd rested on a delicate balance between an income derived largely from examinations and the substantial costs incurred for the maintenance of old and inadequate buildings (Table 14.2). There was an unavoidable obligation to pay the travel and accommodation costs of an army of examiners, together with the modest salaries and wages of a small but growing number of College staff. Moreover, the College Office holders, the President, the Secretary/Treasurer, the Librarian and the Conservator received honoraria and payments for their unavoidable expenses.

The College's finances at this time do not make happy reading. The cost of the original 1697 Surgeons' Hall, together with separation from the Barbers, had been sufficient to send the Incorporation into insolvency. During the last years of the nineteenth century, the College's financial state once more became unstable. The average annual revenue was £4,136 and the average ordinary annual expenditure £5,084. On 16th May 1899, it was decided to create a Special Finance Committee.[48]

From this time, the books were balanced more carefully. Even the President was not always free to spend without consultation. On 23rd January 1909, the President, JM Cotterill, requested £300 for a particular purpose. The Finance Committee was quick to rebuke him and to say that, 'notice should be given to the Finance Committee of all

Table 14.2 Finances of the Royal College of Surgeons of Edinburgh for the years 1896–1937

Date	Income		Ordinary expenditure		Balance	
	Annual income	**Mean income**	**Annual expenditure**	**Mean expenditure over previous five years**	**Annual balance**	**Mean balance over previous five years**
1898	4,131	NK	6,817	NK	−2,686	[£4,195 overspent in three years]
1902	4,494	4,537	2,545	2,908	843	1,109
1907	4,736	5,120	2,629	3,079	1,842	1,883
1912	5,703	5,391	4,857	4,022	846	1,513
1917	2,696	3,480	2,514	2,712	181	777
1922	5,639	6,159	5,920	5,576	−301	699
1927	7,720	7,956	6,132	5,824	1,588	2,137
1932	9,275	9,680	6,905	6,673	2,369	2,969
1937	10,278	10,611	7,014	6,851	3,213	3,751

NK = not known.

financial matters appearing in the Billet'.[49] The Committee issued periodic warnings to Fellows and to the Council about profligate expenditure.[50] As an unintentional result, the College could seem mean, so that, in 1929, the Council had no choice but to refuse to contribute to a memorial to the world-famous parasitologist Sir Patrick Manson in spite of their longstanding interest in tropical surgery.

The First World War had the same disastrous effect on the College's financial stability as it had on so many other institutions and professions. By 1912, revenue had risen slightly to £5,703. However, by 1915, the ravages of war had reduced the RCSEd income to £2,645 and, during the years 1915, 1916 and 1917, it halved. The balances remaining after meeting ordinary and extraordinary expenditure for these three years were £33, £35 and £181. Nevertheless, the effects of inflation were hardly noticeable until the 1930s. The Revenue increased from £4,164 in 1901 to £7,268 in 1925. By 1931, however, it had reached a figure of more than £10,000 and in 1939 it was £12,000.

War

Throughout the twentieth century, war had created political and financial problems for the RCSEd (Table 14.2).

First World War

In 1914, the College was faced with financial setbacks, the closure of the Museum and a deterioration in the quantity and quality of teaching.

Many wartime meetings of the Council were held at 6 Chester Street.[51,52] By 1915, supplies such as the glass jars used in the Museum were unobtainable and the President's annual reports could not be published on time because of a national shortage of printing paper. The Council was faced with grave responsibilities and was preoccupied with the task of supporting the armed forces while securing the health and welfare of the anxious civilian population.

During the First World War, the recruitment of surgeons remained of very serious concern. The country was depleted of physicians and surgeons, and, by 1917, there were 12 times as many medical officers in the army as in peacetime. In 1916, the government, faced with the military and medical disasters described in Chapter 7, asked whether first- and second-year students should be recruited to the forces. The state of the RAMC had occupied the close attention of the College in 1900 (p 23) and it was no surprise that similar considerations should arise during the subsequent two world wars. The RCSEd Council was already engaged in advising the government on ways of improving the lot of army medical officers and thus of boosting recruitment in the Great War of 1914–18.

Together with the RCPEd, another of the Colleges' early acts as war began was to offer the troops inoculation against typhoid fever. The 5th South Lancashire Regiment was the first to accept. As the war progressed, attitudes towards the enemy hardened. There had been understandable antipathy towards the Boers in 1899 and a similar response to Germans in 1914. Wisely, however, the College decided not to remove from display portraits of Honorary Fellows of German origin and to take no action over reports of the maltreatment of British prisoners by the Prussians.[52]

Second World War

When the Second World War started, the President was Dr Harry Moss Traquair.[T] The amount of Fellows' time that could be given to College affairs diminished. Facilities deteriorated, and staff were called to military duties. For Wade, 1939 marked the end of his time as a Surgeon-in-Ordinary – a senior consultant – to the RIE. To his evident frustration, but on the completion of 15 years' service as Surgeon to the RIE, he was obliged to retire from the senior staff. It was 31st December 1939. Under a long-established rule, the period during which such a position could be held was restricted by the Managers of the voluntary hospital to 15 years. He was granted the title of Consulting Surgeon on 20th November.[U] Wade had been appointed in 1924 (p 227). He felt the loss of his hospital position keenly: he was in his 65th year. Although his private surgical practice continued, he was doubly frustrated: first by the loss of his amenities in his 'Alma Mater' and second by the outbreak of a war in which he felt instinctively that he had much to contribute.

Under the auspices of the BMA, a committee was responsible for managing the employment of medical staff during the war years and for ensuring that the civilian population, their hospitals and clinics retained an adequate cover of health care. The committee was well established by 1941. The Chair was taken by Professor Sydney Smith.[V] Wade was not among those chosen for this responsible task. The RCSEd was represented at first by FE Jardine, who was joined subsequently by JW Struthers and Professor JR Learmonth. However, Struthers resigned on 17th July 1945, shortly before the end of the war against Japan.

Among the challenges faced by the BMA committee were recommendations concerning who should be drafted to the armed forces and who could be spared. In the UK during the period September 1939 to September 1942, 10,636 doctors were called to military service. Of these, 1,647 came from Scotland. Special pleading was frequent. It was made first by employers who wished to retain individuals of particular skill. In this category, Dr (later Professor) JA Anderson and Dr AR (later Professor Sir Alastair) Currie, for example, were designated 'reserved'.[53] In a second category, hospital authorities often wished to recall specialists needed urgently for the maintenance of services to the civilian community. Lieutenant Colonel (later Professor) Ian Aird exemplified this class of consultant. He was denied a return to civilian life by the BMA committee in August 1943 but was released by the War Office shortly afterwards.[54]

With the advent of the war, careful government plans came into effect to prepare for the receipt of the wounded. The preparations were the responsibility of the Secretary of State for Scotland, Tom Johnston. He had acted with efficiency and speed. There were two reasons for this commendable activity. First, he predicted that, in the event of war, there would be a flood of casualties and that Bangour Asylum, West Lothian, would once more be an ideal Scottish venue for their receipt (Appendix 14.2).[55] Second, he bore in mind the underprivileged Scottish poor for whom adequate numbers of hospital beds had never been a priority. After the war, he predicted correctly that a military use for Bangour would decline quickly, allowing the extensive wartime facilities to be put to good civilian use.

Pursuing this plan for Bangour during the early months of the war, a first step was the removal of the psychiatric patients to other hospitals. A second step was the construction of an additional hutted, military base hospital with accommodation for 940 patients. The first casualties from the Dunkirk evacuation were admitted to Bangour

Figure 14.5 Bangour Hospital, West Lothian.
The imaginative design of the hospital ensured that convalescent patients could take advantage of the verandas and the many facilities for recuperation

Village Hospital in the summer of 1940. By October 1940, as the German campaign of aerial warfare turned to the nocturnal bombing of British cities, the new buildings were barely complete. By the spring of 1941, however, civilian casualties had been admitted along with an increasing number of British and Allied wounded as well as injured German prisoners.

Wade's instinctive desire to help the 'war effort' was met in part when he was appointed Director of Surgery for the Emergency Medical Service (EMS). The appointment recognized Wade's immense experience and skills and offered him a measure of compensation for the loss of his position at the RIE. It also carried with it the responsibility for surgery at the country's largest Emergency Service hospital (Appendix 14.2). Wade visited Bangour twice weekly. He acted in an advisory capacity and did not undertake surgical operations. His colleagues gave their time very freely. They included CW Cathcart (p 91), still busy with the Museum Committee of the RCSEd, NA Gray[W] and JC ('Jock') Milne. Cathcart also worked at the 2nd Scottish General Hospital at Edenhall, Edinburgh, but still found time to design a gas mask and to develop the use of sphagnum moss as an economical wound dressing. At Bangour, a neurosurgical unit under the direction of Norman Dott (p 339) took shape, and a unit for the surgery of

Figure 14.6 Bangour Hospital, West Lothian. *In the First World War, the hospital accommodated as many as 3,500 casualties. The illustration shows wounded recovering in one of the wards*

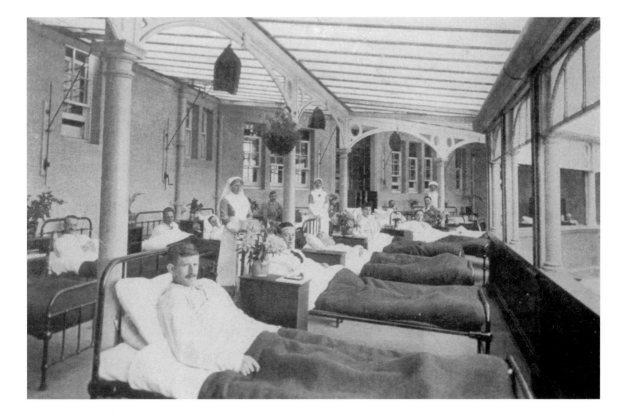

tuberculosis accepted patients from East Fortune and other sanatoria. As the war progressed, facilities for the treatment of burns and plastic surgery were established, laying the foundations for units that achieved public fame when the war ended.

From 1939–45, Wade's wide knowledge and experience proved of very great benefit not only to the EMS but to the Department of Health for Scotland and to the British Red Cross Society, with which he was associated closely. After the end of the Second World War, the hutted EMS hospital at Bangour reverted to civilian use, as Tom Johnston had predicted, providing much needed accommodation for civilian surgical specialities that included neurosurgery, plastic surgery and vascular surgery.

Conclusion

Henry Wade would have been the first to acknowledge that he had been privileged to play a central role in guiding the Royal College of Surgeons of Edinburgh, and thus the profession of surgery in Great Britain and the Empire, through some of the most difficult years in its long and turbulent history. It may be surmised that, with the passage of time, he was not entirely sorry to leave the committee room and the debating chamber and return to the solitary antiquarian pastimes that engaged him at Pilmuir House, East Lothian (Chapter 15). But the historian cannot see behind all the closed curtains of time and this must remain a matter of conjecture.

Figures 14.5 and 14.6 are from the Report on Bangour Hospital published in 1923.

CHAPTER **15**

Antiquarian at Pilmuir House

1925–55

Breathes there the man, with soul so dead,
Who never to himself hath said,
This is my own, my native land!
Whose heart hath ne'er within him burned,
As home his footsteps he hath turned
From wandering on a native strand!

(Walter Scott, *The lay of the last minstrel*, 1805)

The post-war decade of the 1920s was a crucible in which Henry Wade's life was transfigured by good but ravaged by ill. These were years of hope and reconstruction. The arts, literature and music thrived, and rejuvenated sciences entered a new period of growth and expansion. Scott Fitzgerald's *The Great Gatsby* enthralled an exhausted western world, while Eisenstein completed *The Battleship Potemkin*, Chagall *The Drinking Green Pig* and Noel Coward *Hay Fever*. In 1922, insulin was isolated, and in 1929 Fleming described penicillin. This was, sadly, also a time of cynical disillusionment. Depression and escapism were commonplace as men struggled to come to terms with the enormity of the destruction caused by war. Britain was no longer the greatest international power: the country had suffered dreadfully both during the conflict and in the influenza pandemic of 1918–19. In an impoverished Germany, still in part under military occupation, an ageing Hindenburg became President, while a malevolent Adolf Hitler reorganized the Nazi party, part of *Mein Kampf* already published.

Returning to Edinburgh from the army in May 1919, Wade reopened his house at 6 Manor Place, Edinburgh,[1,2] resumed his surgical practice and was re-elected Conservator of the Museum of the Royal College of Surgeons, the RCSEd. In 1922, in partnership with David Wilkie (p 166), Wade established the Private Clinic, the nursing home at 35 Drumsheugh Gardens, Edinburgh, which is described in Chapter 9. In 1924, he was appointed a senior surgeon to the Royal Infirmary of Edinburgh (the RIE). He was granted the enviable status of Surgeon-in-Ordinary. The position bestowed great authority but carried the immense responsibility for an entire surgical unit. In 1924, and again in 1925, the tantalizing possibility of a Chair of Surgery in the University of Edinburgh presented itself but his hopes and expectations were not to be fulfilled. It was a measure of compensation that in 1925 he was elected to the Council of the RCSEd (p 268).

Marriage

Wade's personal life was about to be transformed. On 15th September 1924, he married Christian Marjorie Mary Fraser-Tytler of Woodhouselee.[A] He was in his 49th year. She was 36 years of age.

Marjorie Fraser-Tytler was born on 25th May 1888. Educated at St Leonard's School, St Andrews, she came from an ancient artistic Scottish family of eminence and distinction. Her father was James William Fraser-Tytler of Woodhouselee, Midlothian, her mother Christian Alice Scott Fraser-Tytler Senior of Sunlaw, Roxburghshire.

> One of Marjorie Fraser-Tytler's ancestors was a cadet of the noble House of Seton in the time of King James IV of Scotland. Many years later, on the gentle slopes of the Pentland Hills, the estate of Woodhouselee became the home of William Tytler, Esquire. In 1792, his son, Alexander Tytler (1747–1813) succeeded to the estate, added the name Fraser to his own and 10 years later took his seat in the Court of Session as Lord Woodhouselee. Lord Woodhouselee was Senator of the College of Justice.[3] In 1823, a daughter married James Baillie Fraser (1747–1805). James Tytler, a scholar, traveller, scientist and eccentric, was nicknamed 'Balloon Tytler', as he is said to have made the first balloon ascent in Scotland. William Tytler's grandson, the historian Patrick Fraser-Tytler (1791–1849) was cofounder of the Bannatyne Club with Walter Scott and author of a monumental *History of Scotland* (1828–43). James Stuart Fraser-Tytler was Professor of Conveyancing in the University of Edinburgh from 1866 to 1891. Mrs Liddell, whose maiden name was Fraser-Tytler, was a prolific novelist who wrote during the years 1872–87. Christian Helen Fraser-Tytler lived from 1897 until 1995 and Edward Grant Fraser-Tytler from 1856 until 1918. There was a very strong military connection. General Sir James McLeod Fraser-Tytler (1821–1914), Lieutenant Colonel Sir William Kerr Fraser-Tytler (1886–1963) and Brevet Colonel Neil Fraser-Tytler (1889–1937) served the army at home and overseas.

The precise circumstances in which Henry Wade first met Marjorie Fraser-Tytler are not known. It is possible that their paths crossed during the First World War. It is more likely that their acquaintance was professional. Among correspondence about Wade's nursing home are letters relating to appointments for a C [Christian] Marjorie Fraser-Tytler of Aldourie Castle, Inverness; Humbie, East Lothian; and Braehead, Corstorphine, Midlothian. The exchanges describe consultations about a spinal problem that called for the attention of one of Edinburgh's leading surgeons. The letters tell us a little of the manner in which Wade conducted his practice from his rooms at 6 Manor Place, Edinburgh.[4]

Figure 15.1 Marjorie Wade. *Henry Wade married Christian Marjorie Mary Fraser-Tytler on 15th September 1924. This photograph, together with copies of it, were among his papers but there is no name inscribed on the portrait. Until now, no living person has been found who can confirm that the likeness is indeed that of Mrs Wade. Equally, there is no evidence to the contrary*

On 23rd August 1922, Miss Fraser-Tytler wrote to Wade from Inverness:

'Dr Campbell tells me that you think I should wear a support.'

Miss Fraser-Tytler enclosed an 'addressed wire [a telegraph] form'. On 25th September, Wade informed her:

'The support is now ready.'

She wrote again to say that she was not coming south before 27th October:

'My back is not aching much and I am managing 4–4½ hours rest daily in the shell.'

The exchange of letters continued. On 11th January 1923, Miss Fraser-Tytler emphasized:

'My back is ever so much better. I have just finished packing up at Woodhouselee.'

He responded:

'I would esteem it a 'favour' if you would come on Monday 15th January at 3.30.'

A month later, on 22nd February, Miss Tytler wrote from Braehead to say:

'I will be here till Monday March 5th.'

Henry Wade agreed with 'the late hour' of 6 pm on that day.

Their marriage took place on 15th September 1924 at Holy Trinity Church, Melrose. The bans were read 'after the manner of the Scottish Episcopal Church'. Marjorie Fraser-Tytler's address was recorded as The Priory, Melrose, and Henry Wade's as 6 Manor Place, Edinburgh. The marriage certificate was signed by JF Fraser-Tytler of 61 Lancaster Road, London NW, and by Henry Wade's old colleague, ANS Carmichael, of 2 Merchiston Drive, Edinburgh.

Searching for a home

After a short honeymoon, the Wades remained in Edinburgh. It was natural that Marjorie and Henry Wade should seek a settled home. The Edinburgh professions had always been attracted to the rich alluvial plain of East Lothian. Many owned houses in their city, located near offices, hospitals and consulting rooms. To escape, to seek relaxation in the country and to pursue the ancient game of golf, a property outside Edinburgh was desirable. Henry Wade himself had been a member of Gullane Golf Club since June 1904.[B] To the north, the river Forth offered a physical barrier. To the west, lay the industrial belt and Glasgow. To the south, the Borders were wildly attractive, but communication was not easy. The answer lay to the east. Travellers from England, approaching by train, enjoyed views of great beauty as they left Berwick-on-Tweed. Holy Island and Bamburgh Castle were silhouetted on the eastern horizon. The volcanic rock of Arthur's Seat came into view – a journey's end in sight. Wade wrote:[4]

'From the first, we decided to acquire a 'But and Ben'.[C] We explored the country around Edinburgh by car on many

Saturdays. On Middleton Moor, a mile beyond Carlops, we discovered a lone small cottage, called Carpet, from which a magnificent view of the surrounding country was obtained, without a single house to be seen. Here was the ideal 'Tree Top Nest' for two Love Birds. However, both of us were older in years and the fact that it lacked all modern amenities and the water supply had to be carried uphill for three hundred yards convinced us it was unsuitable.

The search continued. One Sunday in June [1925] we lunched at Keith Marischal with Marjorie's cousins, the Skene-Tytlers, and were sitting on the lawn in the sun after lunch when in the course of the conversation the 'But and Ben' question was mentioned, and Cha (Mrs Skene-Tytler) mentioned that there was a property called Pilmuir coming into the market which might be suitable. It was about three miles distant. Morris (Mr Skene-Tytler) drove us over to it, with Dr Frank Crombie, one of the party. The car stopped at the entrance to the private road and Marjorie and I walked along to the high stone wall surrounding the house and grounds and ultimately came to the entrance, tall central solid wooden gates, with a single gate for foot passengers at the side. This I opened and we both gasped as we saw a sight so fascinating as to appear almost unreal – a long straight drive leading up to a small, harled, yellow-wash house, nestling in the sun. On either side were broad grass lawns, a high stone wall surrounding the lawns, house, garden and dovecot.

It was Sunday afternoon at three o'clock, an hour of rest for many, and I hesitated to go further, but Marjorie seized me by the arm and we marched up and rang the door bell. After a short wait a lady arrived. She was Mrs Ogilvie. She advised us to consult Messrs Pringle and Clay, WS, of Rutland Square, Edinburgh. As soon as we returned to 6, Manor Place, we telephoned to my brother Callander (p 6), partner in the family firm of Russel and Aitken, Writers, Falkirk, and told him about our find. The following day, he contacted Messrs Pringle and Clay and got from them the Title Deeds of the property, and a copy of the advertisement of Knight, Frank and Rutley, who were entrusted with the sale.

We later inspected the house,[5] then tenanted by Commander McLeod and his sister, Mrs Ogilvie, and had it valued by Mr Watherston of Queensferry Street, Edinburgh, and agreed to an offer being made. In the autumn, we went by car to Skye and when travelling over the awful roads broke a spring and left the car for repair at Portree and were driven in a hired car to Dunvegan. A telegram arrived which we anticipated would tell us the new spring had arrived: it did not, but said: 'Successful in securing Pilmuir, Callander'. The telephone number of the house was Pencaitland 213.

In the autumn, after we had purchased the Residential and

Figure 15.2 Location of Pilmuir House, near Haddington. *In this 1825 Ordnance Survey map, Pilmuir and the adjoining Kirklands farmstead are seen (lower centre, right). The house is southwest of Haddington and within a few miles of the coast of the Firth of Forth. Copyright, see p 3)*

Agricultural Estate of Pilmuir and Kirklands, Messrs Pringle and Clay desired to know whether we would like to purchase Pilmuir Old Manse, Glebe and Church, which had been excluded from the original sale. We accepted this offer, and later the Manse was modernized and a private electricity supply installed (p 303). It was occupied by my wife's aunt, Miss Fraser-Tytler, and Miss Stewart, her companion. Mrs Ogilvie followed as tenant, and subsequently Dr Lewis Thatcher.

At the outbreak of war in 1939, the Manse was again vacant. As the sole, surviving proprietor of the Private Clinic, 35, Drumsheugh Gardens, with patients and staff of nearly one hundred, I had to consider the question of casualties occurring and an emergency arising in consequence. I therefore transformed the Church and made it into a building suitable for an emergency hospital, installing the County water supply, and putting in sanitary fittings and a small kitchen and cloak room.'

Marjorie Wade enjoyed travel. Her passport shows that she undertook an appreciable number of European journeys. Her passport, but not Wade's much later, renewed document, confirms that Marjorie Wade disembarked at Boulogne on 29th March 1925, passing through this same port again in April 1926 – the month in which she visited Modane in France. Marjorie Wade was in Calais and then Greece in the spring of 1927, Luxembourg and Germany on 27th July 1928 and Basel on 20th September of that year.

Pilmuir House

By instinct an antiquarian, Wade compiled *A short history of Pilmuir,*[6] a record not only of Pilmuir itself but of the early days of Wade's marriage. He also prepared the *Chronicles of Pilmuir.*[7,D] Neither the Chronicles nor the History was dated or published, but the contents suggest strongly that they were compiled after 1949. The following pages owe much to Wade's own writings and quote verbatim from both the Short History and the Chronicles.

The word Pilmuir means 'the tower or peel on the muir'. It is an ancient name originating in the 14th century or earlier, when the

Figure 15.3 Pilmuir House. *The evening sun cast long shadows on the house and its gardens. That the house was the home of a surgeon of the 17th century, William Borthwick, has always aroused particular interest*

Figure 15.4 Pilmuir House. *In another view, a watercolour depicts the house in summer*

grounds were ecclesiastical. The present house dates from the end of the sixteenth or the beginning of the seventeenth century. It was, and still is, regarded as an 'unspoiled example of early Scottish domestic architecture'. In addition to his fascination with Scottish houses, Wade had a strong interest in domestic design, which expressed itself in his collection of antique furniture and painting. It is not surprising to find, therefore, that Pilmuir house contains many fine pieces.

In an album of photographs taken by Henry Wade, views of the house from the north are recorded.[8,E] They show the original entrance. Above a moulded architrave is a panel bearing the initials WC for William Cairns and AB for Agnes Brown, his wife. Below, are the Cairns' crest on the right and the Brown's crest on the left. The date 1624 is inscribed below the shield. It follows that the year 1624 has been quoted as the date on which the house was created *de novo*.[F] The concluding words of the Sasine read:

'After the reading and publication of which Precept and Sasine the said Master Richard Maitland, Baillie for the said occasion, by virtue thereof and of his office of bailliary, gave, granted and delivered heritable sasine and real, actual and corporal possession of ALL and WHOLE the foresaid lands of Pilmuir with their pertinents, occupancies and adjuncts as above narrated to William Cairns there personally present and accepting for himself and also to Adam Sandson Attorney foresaid and in name of the said Agnes Brown by the handing over and delivery of earth and stone of the ground of the said lands in customary manner and according to the tenor of the said Charter and Precept above written: WHEREUPON and upon ALL and SUNDRY the premises the said William Cairns for himself and Adam Sandson Attorney foresaid asked that this present public Instrument one or more should be granted by me Notary Public subscribing.

These things were done upon the land and ground of the said Lands of Pilmuir about 10 am or thereby in the year day and month and reign of the King above written in the presence of James Knox (residing) in Bolton, John Brown there, John Gotray there and William Paterson (residing) in Pilmuir, servitors of the said William Cairns, witnesses of the premises called, asked and required (signed).'

There follows the formal docquet by the notary testifying that the above things were done in due form. It therefore seems that William Cairns and Agnes Brown occupied Pilmuir for an uncertain period before 1621, the year in which they acquired possession. They 'modernized' the house in 1624. The Privy Council's register recalls an adventure at the house:[9,G]

'Andro Lamb, indweller in Leith, purchased the lands of Palmore with its pertinents, lying within the sheriffdom of Edinburgh and constabulary of Haddington and conveyed it to his son, David Lamb. Together they cultivated it and it had been in their possession for several years and they had the heritable titles thereof. Nevertheless, Oliver Sinclair

Figure 15.5 Pilmuir House. *A perspective illustrates the corner of the house, which is believed to have been built towards the end of the sixteenth century*

Figure 15.6 The walled gardens of Pilmuir House. *The grounds offer seclusion and attract much wildlife*

of Petcarne and his servants came armed one day and attacked Alexander Lamb, Andro's son who was with the shearers in the field and wounded him with a spear. They returned later on the 21st day of September, Sunday, about midnight, looking for the said Andro or any of his bairns to slaughter them. Failing to gain admission, they went to the steading and drove away all the cattle and beasts.'

The Privy Council summoned Oliver Sinclair to appear before them, and, on his failing to appear, they denounced him as a rebel and 'put him to the horn'.[H]

Older history of Pilmuir

There is a much older history.[I] The Curator of Historical Records of Scotland was asked for his opinion.[J] He provided incontrovertible proof that Pilmuir had been inhabited long before 1624. The estate paid tribute to the ecclesiastical diocese of St Andrews. The Curator attached much importance to the fact that the General Register of Sasines gave the acquisition to be in 1621. The Privy Council's register explained how Andrew Lamb, indweller in Leith, at great expense and travail, conveyed (gave legally) to his son David Lamb the lands of Palmure with the pertinents lying within the Sheriffdom of Edinburgh and Constabulary of Haddington: he had 'cultivated' the same and been in possession there of diverse years, he had the heritable title thereof (thereafter there is recorded the incident of the assault).

Figure 15.7 Pilmuir House. *The house is of modest size and the rooms relatively small. When Wade first conceived the idea of offering the house to the Royal College of Surgeons of Edinburgh, he thought of it as a haven of rest for an exhausted President and a place where the Council could meet in secluded confidence rather than as a building that could accommodate a meeting or conference*

In the chronological record of Pilmuir, in the Barony of Bolton, in the Parish of Bolton, of the Constabulary of Haddington, the first reference is April 1366. The seventh reference is 31st August 1458.[10] It is a confirmation of the late William Bishop of St Andrews of charters and other documents that had belonged to the Nunnery of Hadingtoune relating to the foundation and gifts thereof and that had been destroyed in the English wars. An item mentions two oxgangs[K] of land and seven acres in the territory of Pilmure next Bagby, by gift of the late William de Vetere Ponte and of William of Vetere Ponte, the sons of William de Vetere Ponte, all called William and living at the same time. Thus, the record clearly shows that the Superiority of the Lands of Pilmuir resided in the Diocese of St Andrews.

Figure 15.8 Panel above a moulded architrave at the original doorway of Pilmuir House. *A date, 1624, corresponds with the occupancy of the house by William Cairns and Agnes Brown, his wife*

The Cairns' stone

In the Pilmuir book, Wade quoted extracts from *A history of the family of the Cairns*, giving particulars of the Cairns of Pilmuir.[11] It is mentioned that an old armorial stone is preserved at Kirklands[12]. The stone bears the initials JC but no date. It seems evident that this stone occupied a similar position in the family residence that was the predecessor of Pilmuir. Proprietors frequently transferred panels from their former residences to a new house (as at Keith Marischal), but it is difficult to account for the presence of the stone in Kirklands Farm Steading. A footnote is interesting:

> 'Pilmuir House remains today almost exactly as in William Cairn's time, and is one of the quaintest and most charming examples, in a diminutive scale, of the old Scottish baronial residences of about the date 1600. It might be described as a reproduction of the Shaws of Ballygelly, County Antrim, built almost exactly at the same time. The principal rooms are wainscoted with oak to the ceilings, one of which is richly decorated with ornamental plasterwork, in which the cinquefoil,[L] the crest of the Pilmuir family, is conspicuous.'

Wade continues:

> 'At the back of the House is an orchard of nearly four acres, enclosed by a massive wall. In the orchard is a great stone dovecot, of venerable age. In Scotland, no laird was

Figure 15.9 The Cairns' stone. *This old armorial stone was discovered at Kirklands farm, where it may have been taken from a building that was a family residence before Pilmuir House was built*

permitted to keep more doves, or properly speaking, pigeons, than could feed on his own estate; hence the size of the old dove-cotes indicated the approximate extent of an estate. The size of the Pilmuir dove-cote shows that its owner possessed a considerable property. A remarkable feature about Pilmuir is the fact that its builder must have been an artistic genius; because if viewed from a certain spot in the orchard, close to the dove-cote, every bit of the house is in peculiarly artistic perspective; to attain this, the windows have all actually been graduated in size to fit the view, and the dormer windows and roof sloped to correspond. One can understand a house making a pretty picture, but surely this example of a house being constructed to fit an artistic fancy, and actually being built to fit an imaginary picture, is unique.'[M]

The old windows

The majority of the windows in Pilmuir had deep sockets cut in the stone sills, above and below, to admit vertical iron stanchions. A small window leading into the dining room was revealed with the bars still *in situ*. Shallow grooves cut in the upright stones on either side were for the leaded glass and wooden shutters of the shot windows (below). The preface to Plate 51 of Small's book states:[13] 'Shutter Boards were in common use at this time'. They formed the lower part of the windows, generally occupying more than half of the space, and were made in two leaves to open inwards, 'the top part of the windows being filled with fixed glazing so that the shutter boards were the only means for regulating the entrance of fresh air'.

The presence of iron stanchions was common in 16th century and older houses. They could be taken as loot in time of war. Although primarily for protection from without, they were a means of preventing escape. In the *Story of our windows*,[14] the *Ballad of Frendraught* is referred to and quoted:[N]

'He did him to the wire window
As fast as he could gang
Says wae to the hands put in the Stanchions
For out we'll never win.'

The origin of this ballad is as follows:

'A skirmish took place in Banffshire on 1st January 1680 between Sir James Crichton, Laird of Frendraught and William Gordon of Rothiemay, in which the latter was killed. On a later occasion, John Gordon, Viscount of Aboyne and John Gordon of Rothiemay, when visiting Frendraught, were persuaded to stay overnight. They were entertained bountifully and went to bed joyfully in the old tower of Frendraught. A fire broke out and they were trapped in their bedroom and escape through the window was impossible owing to the window bars. They made piteous calls for help to Lady Frendraught who stood upon the green. The cause of the fire is disputed. The ballad makes it out to be the outcome of a deliberate plot.'

The shot window

Wade adds:[7]

'For a time, so precious was glass that windows were made portable and were carried about from house to house, as the owner changed his residence. The Scots had hitherto fitted their opening with a transome which permitted an upper and lower pair of shutter [sic]. The upper section was filled with tiny panes of glass and the lower part was fitted with fir boards on hinges so that one could readily put his head out to observe what was passing below. This was the Shot Window, an ominous word those days, but it has nothing to do with shooting and means 'a sheet'. In braid Scots we read, 'the schot I closet' for the weather. In Scott's *Bride of Lammermore* [sic][15] we have references to this window when parchment or oiled linen sometimes served, letting in a meagre glim.

The windows were ill-sashed but they admitted an ample draught, otherwise they served for observation and it was not desirable in view of weather and other conditions to make them too large. The tower window was used by my lady and was made comfortable with cushions: they are familiar features in many old castles. Yet, to a building, windows are everything: they are as important as eyes are to us, for out of them a home takes its view, while in them the outlook of the inhabitants is framed. And so the guidwife became no longer content with a sheet of horn (hard, animal skin) but hankered after this more transparent material, 'so glass it maun to be'. We still speak of a lanthorn, a horn lantern.'

Proprietors of Pilmuir House

Wade's *Short history* tabulates the owners of Pilmuir House, those who possessed Kirklands, and those who acquired both properties (Table 15.1).[6]

The most interesting of the early owners of Pilmuir House was William Borthwick. The son of Alexander Borthwick of Johnstonburn and his wife Sibilla Cairns, William Borthwick became a Surgeon Apothecary in Edinburgh. He was apprenticed to James Borthwick of Stow for five years. He married his master's eldest daughter.

Figure 15.10 A built-up window. *In the course of restoring the house, Wade took particular delight in opening windows that had been closed when a windows tax was imposed in England in 1696. The date of the corresponding tax in Scotland is uncertain*

William Borthwick became a member of the Town Council, a Member of Parliament and Surgeon Major to the Forces in Scotland. He was married thrice. He had two daughters by his first marriage. In 1667, he married Marjorie Stewart, by whom he had a son, Harry. His third wife was Euphemia Young, by whom he had four sons and two daughters.

An unfortunate mistake occurred in the Register of the Privy Council of Scotland.[○] A libel on the character of William Borthwick, Surgeon Apothecary, was due to a coincidence, in that there are many references to another William Borthwick, MD, physician in Pittenweem, who married his ward, treated her shockingly and made many appearances before the Privy Council. The index reads:

> 'Borthwick, Mr William, HM Surgeon and MD in Pittenweem, exempt from attending the Host...Anent a petition presented by William Borthwick, Surgeon Apothecary, showing that there be one proclamation ordaining all inheritors to attend his Majesty's Host.'

Other references to Borthwick relate to his unhappy matrimonial affairs, which were, in fact, those of William Borthwick, Physician in Pittenweem, not of William Borthwick of Pilmuir, Surgeon Apothecary.

Table 15.1 Owners of Pilmuir House and/or Kirklands

Ownership	Period	Owners
Owned Pilmuir House only	1567	David Lamb
	1621–53	William Cairns and Agnes Brown
	1653–85	Richard Cairns
	1685–90	William Borthwick
	1690–1706	Henry Borthwick, 13th Lord Borthwick
	1706–11	Henry Borthwick, 14th Lord Borthwick
	1711	William Borthwick of Fallahill
	1778	Alexander Hunter
	1778–85	James Craig
	1785	Major Peter Grant
	1785	Catherine, Margaret and Jean Grant (1/3 sold to Lord Sinclair)
	1785–1842	Catherine Grant (until 1814), Margaret and Jean Grant
	1842	Robert Bruce Baird
Owned Kirklands only	1553–75	Laurance Cockburn
	1558 (added land)	Laurance Cockburn
	1884	William Robertson of Ladybank
	1804	George Bogie of Woodhall
	1838	William Bogie
	1839–70	Miss Agnes and Alexander Aitchison, George More
	1870–77	James More
Owned Pilmuir and Kirklands	1877	Robert Bruce Baird
	1909	Miss Helen Baird
	1925	Mrs Cecilia Baird or Mathieson and Mrs Elizabeth Baird or Blunt
	1925–29	Henry Wade and CMM Fraser-Tytler or Wade
	1929	Henry Wade

Indenture

Made at Edinburgh on the twenty second day of February 1653

Between

JAMES BORTHWICK, Surgeon, Burgess of Edinburgh

And

WILLIAM BORTHWICK, son of Alexander Borthwick of Johnstoun-bourne

WHEREBY

WILLIAM BORTHWICK becomes bound apprentice and servant

To

JAMES BORTHWICK, Chyrurgeon

'to his art and callinge of Churgerie for all the days,

space, years and terms of five years'

Renovation of Pilmuir House

Henry Wade described the condition of the House when he and his wife first gained access to it, and the work they undertook to improve and restore the building and its environs.[6]

> 'When we obtained possession of Pilmuir at the May Term in 1926 we had already considerable knowledge of the building and its story obtained from the Report of the Royal Commission on the Ancient and Historical Monuments of Scotland, County of East Lothian, published in 1924.'[P]

In Wade's words, some of which have been paraphrased:

The two windows to the left on the first floor, the drawing room, have been built up. The windows in the room above have been blocked in a similar manner. The dressed stone around each window has been left exposed. Of the four windows facing to the East one has been blocked. It is on the attic floor, a bedroom. In this case it has been harled over so that its presence can only be surmised. The circumstances that led to the original closure of the windows was the imposition of the Window Tax, a Tax levied in England in 1696, and repealed on the 24th July 1851, when a tax on inhabited houses was substituted.[16] The first task we undertook was to open up the four windows to the West. In the album[E] there is illustrated[17] the windows before they were opened, during the course of

continued

opening, and the final result. A turret stair window, which had originally opened to the outer surface, was discovered: the bathroom and pantry beneath being additions to the original structure of the building. The closed window to the east was opened up several years later and this has led to the discovery of the buried window.[18]

For four months a most expert cabinet maker and joiner (Tommy) worked in Pilmuir House, renovating it, and in the course of his work revealed certain most interesting features, the most astonishing being the discovery of the buried ambry and the ancient coin found in the dust of its floor. The incidents occurred when he was engaged in removing the original panels in the East room on the first floor, to clean them, the stiles being undisturbed. When a panel on the South East wall was removed, the ambry was discovered and in the dust an ancient coin was found - a twopenny piece Scots, of Charles 1st dated 1632.[19] On removing the panel in a similar situation in the drawing room to the West a similar ambry was revealed in the kitchen. In the storeroom two ambries are still in use.

The problem that faced us from the first was one which unfortunately led to the mutilation of so many old houses in Scotland, the provision of adequate facilities for domestic staff. Granted that Pilmuir was a gem of the period, how were these to be provided? There existed at present a kitchen; storehouse, pantry and a washhouse build across the lower closed windows to the West; and an outside lavatory. I sought the advice of a distinguished architect and he came out and produced plans for adding a baronial[Q] wing to the West – in my opinion a misguided judgement! Another distinguished architect, a personal friend, also proposed a baronial wing. I then became my own architect and laid down the following criteria: It shall be erected 9 feet to the West of the house, be no higher than the wall, be dry by being enclosed in a rock asphalt tank made by Walker and Co. It shall be harled in a separate grey; and contain a larder; a boot-room; a lavatory; a coal house; a wash-house with a bath; a laundry with a refrigerator; and a bedroom and bathroom. The result, illustrated in photographs 19–22 of the album, was eminently successful.[20]

The water supply came from a well within the grounds, the Lady's Well. From this source the Manse House and Lodge were supplied, as also Kirklands Farm House and Steading. It has never been known to fail. It had one handicap: the water was hard. A serious handicap from the domestic point of view, and required that the boiler and hot water pipes had to be cleaned out every four months. To overcome this difficulty, we introduced water softeners. Permutit, where one thousand gallons of soft water was obtained after regeneration by fifteen pounds of common salt. Fortunately later on we were able to introduce the County Supply, the Lady's' Well being retained for outside use.

Recently we have had it[R] introduced by the Lothian Power Company (now nationalized). The work was carried out for Messrs Barton by one of their electricians, Crosby, a genius, who made an excellent job. In the course of his work he had to take down a partition in the garret and in so doing he came upon a cavalry man's boot trees probably those of Captain Borthwick mortally wounded at Ramilles (1706). The boot trees are marked Levy Ply, (Plymouth). I corresponded with the Town Chamberlain of Plymouth and the correspondence is to be found in the Chronicle.[21]

Built into the North West wall of the garden at Pilmuir are four recesses facing south, the nature of which was the subject of many speculations on our part. The mystery was cleared up finally by finding an illustration in the *Weekly Scotsman*

continued

which explained their purpose: they are bee boles. On my suggestion Miss Sheila Forman[5] wrote an article on the subject. In the October and November numbers of the *Scottish Beekeeper* for 1950 are illustrations of bee boles.[22,23] The Chronicles give further information. SB4 on p 11 refers to fines paid in wax; the information being obtained from Extracts from the Records of the Burgh of Edinburgh 1403–1528. [24]

On p 13 of the Inventory of Ancient and Historical Monuments of Scotland it mentions that some hundreds of yards South East of the house is a contemporary dovecot which contains stone boxes for over 1,000 birds. On pp 111–113 of the Chronicles of Pilmuir, a short historical sketch is given of dovecots in Scotland, and the laws concerning them.[25] It answers the question put to the candidate for entrance to the Faculty of Advocates by an eminent judge: 'Wha may hae doon?' [Who may own doves?].

Figure 15.11 The Cadger's Well. *A cadger was often a delivery man or street seller but sometimes a beggar. To cater for these itinerants, this old well was maintained*

Figure 15.12 The bee boles. *Within the boles are skeps (baskets) for bees*

Death of Marjorie Wade

The marriage between Henry Wade and Marjorie Fraser-Tytler was tragically brief. In 1929, Mrs Wade was obliged to undergo an apparently simple operation for the common condition of uterine leiomyofibroma, a condition commonly designated 'fibroid'. The procedure was performed by David Wilkie, Wade's close colleague and friend, at their nursing home at 35 Drumsheugh Gardens, Edinburgh. Visiting the patient on the evening of 12th December 1929, seven days after the operation, Wade and Wilkie were called back to be told that Mrs Wade had died suddenly. She had suffered a pulmonary embolism.

Many years later, Wade referred obliquely to his wife's death when he said: 'There is no operation, however simple, but is attended with the possibility of a fatal consequence. The unavoidable consequence of the pulmonary embolism must ever be borne in mind'.[11] Yet Noel Gray (p 226) recalled that, in the course of their 30 years' collaboration, Wade never spoke of his loss, although, privately, he commemorated her death by acts such as a donation to St Leonard's School.

The Pilmuir Trust

Henry Wade had intended to leave Pilmuir House to the Royal College of Surgeons of Edinburgh as a country residence for the President and as venue for surgical and scientific meetings and hospitality. At the biennial College dinner in 1953, however, the Chair was taken by Mr FE Jardine (p 110), who had been President of the College from 1947 to 1949. Shortly before the Loyal Toast, it is said that Jardine lit a cigarette. Wade was so incensed that he returned home and amended his provisions. He decided that the Pilmuir estate would be held in trust. The estate was valued at £74,754/14/0d. Pilmuir House was assessed at £3,900, Kirkland Farmhouse at £6,750 and the other buildings, including the Old Manse, at £2,000. Wade's first purpose was that 'the house, with its furniture, should be occupied, lived in, maintained and preserved for all time'. His second intention was that the income from the residue of this estate should be used to maintain Pilmuir House but that the balance of any income should be used 'for schemes related to medical education, for research for medical education, for programmes of buildings for purposes related to medicine or its advancement or for the welfare of those who practice medicine'.

Figure 15.13 Henry Wade in his garden. *It is clear that one of Wade's quiet pleasures was the abundant wildlife of the ancient estate. Here he is feeding the birds during his retirement*

Henry Wade's Trust Disposition and Settlement was dated 29th September 1954. It was registered in the Books of Council and Session on 28th February 1955. He had appointed as testamentary trustees, William Annan Wightman, Chartered accountant, Edinburgh; Mrs Christian Helen Fraser-Tytler CBE, Old Clune House, Aldourie, Inverness-shire; Edith Christian Lady Broun Lindsay, Colstoun, Haddington, East Lothian; and William Edgar Gray Muir, Writer to the Signet, Edinburgh; and the survivors of them, 'to dispose of the residue of his Estate in accordance with a Deed of Directions dated and registered of even dates with the said Trust Disposition and Settlement'. It was a slow process and by November the Honorary Secretary of the RCSEd learned that the agent acting for the Wade trustees had still not yet 'ingathered' the estate.[26] The trustees sold Wade's house at 6 Manor Place, Edinburgh, on 23rd April 1956 to Bowhill Gibson and Laing, Chartered Architects. The documents do not record the price.

The Deed of Directions for the administration of Wade's estate, defined in the trust disposition, 'set forth that the residue of the Testator's means and estate would include the estate of Pilmuir House', then described as fully furnished, and 'the gardens, together with the Glebefield lying to the South, and the Paddockfield lying to the North thereof [all referred to as 'Pilmuir'], and the farm and lands of Kirklands, and Pilmuir Old Manse, all lying in the Parish of Bolton and County of East Lothian'. In summary, the deed confirmed that 'Pilmuir House with its furniture should be occupied and lived in, kept and preserved for all time as an unspoiled example of early seventeenth century Scottish Domestic Architecture'. As outlined in the Trust Disposition, the residue of the estate was to form a fund applied in the first instance to keeping Pilmuir in good repair and in the second place to fulfil the schemes of the RCSEd.

The Deed called for an administrative body. This body was required to include a representative of the RCSEd. The College decided that this should be the President, Professor John Bruce CBE. The other members of the administrative body were Mr Leslie Grahame MacDougall RSA, who represented the Society of Antiquaries of Scotland; the Honourable William Douglas Watson, who represented the Society of Writers to Her Majesty's Signet; and three of the trustees: Mrs Fraser-Tytler, Lady Broun Lindsay and Mr WEG Muir. The first meeting of the administrative body of the Sir Henry Wade Pilmuir Trust took place on 24th January 1958.

At once, Pilmuir proved to be a liability. From the capital funds of the Trust, the trustees were compelled to pay annual architects' and builders' fees and faced solicitors' bills and other costs. Mr Stuart had occupied Pilmuir House, the stables, the garage and the paddock for a rental of £150 per annum, but several other parties were now interested in renting the property. They included Sir Walter Mercer (p 346), Mr Stuart himself and Sir Kerr Fraser-Tytler, who was successful in his approach. He asked for immediate improvements in the property,

Figure 15.14 Henry Wade in retirement. *The photograph is of an elderly Wade with one of his favourite dogs, a* Dandie Dinmont. *The name of the Border breed evokes memories of Walter Scott's* Guy Mannering

which had been neglected. They cost £1,500. The garden was over-grown, and new gardening implements were necessary. The cost of maintaining the estate grew. Inspections revealed occasional dry rot. In 1969, alterations to the rooms and kitchen called for £17,900. A renovation of the cottage cost £1,440 in 1971 and repairs to the house in 1972 cost a further £7,089.

Within a few months, Dr Lamont gave up the lease of the Manse and Mr Stuart requested it on the same terms as Sir Kerr Fraser-Tytler had been granted for the 'Big House'. There were recurrent difficulties in finding tenants. In 1963, General Sir John Kennedy found the 'Big House' too small and Sir John Erskine became an interested party. The Trust derived only a modest income to set against their obligatory commitments. By 1973, the rent derived from the lease of the 'Big House' had risen to no more than £250 per annum, while the insurance value of Kirklands farm steading was only £35,000. It was a year that saw 34% of the value of the trust's investments, £94,725, wiped from the stock market. No tax relief was allowed until 1990. Even in 1964, the trustees had been compelled to sell the Wade Blue China at Christie's for £756. Subsequent calculation showed that, had these circumstances been allowed to continue, the Trust would have been exhausted by the year 2002. Fortunately, a ruling by the Inland Revenue in 1997 allowed some costs to be exempt from tax on condition that rooms in Pilmuir House were established as a Wade Museum – open, from time-to-time, to the public. This condition is still fulfilled.

CHAPTER 16

Later years: a retrospect

1945–1955

Fear no more the heat o' th' sun
Nor the furious winter's rages;
Thou thy worldly task hast done,
Home art gone, and ta'en thy wages.

(Shakespeare, *Cymbeline*)

Henry Wade was a solitary if not a lonely man. His success in surgery, science and soldiering concealed a quiet and undemonstrative personality. Yet he was determined, with a dry, surprisingly mischievous sense of humour and a taste for adventure. Experience widened Wade's horizons, while ambition ignited unsuspected aspects of his character. His personality rested on a strong inheritance. It was modulated by a firm spiritual upbringing in a household where his father was a man of the church. He achieved great success in the material things of life but much of his inner personality remained a private matter. He was reserved but not shy and by nature was hard working, with unobtrusive and unexpected outside interests that included antiquity, bees, petunias and Dandie Dinmont dogs. Few saw 'beneath the skin'. These qualities ensured that he had small numbers of close friends and trusted colleagues. Those who were intimates – his wife, David Wilkie and John Shaw – predeceased him, and he referred to them rarely, either in conversation or on paper.

Many factors beyond his control came into play as Wade's life advanced. One was national conflict: both he and his family were staunch royalists. Another was personal loss and suffering. With increasing fame and added responsibilities, there came a wider audience, a broader acquaintanceship. With advancing experience and skill, Wade was often called upon for his opinion in difficult surgical cases, to consult and to advise. He was a prized confident so that the element of trust played a large part in an increasingly successful surgical practice. Where despairing patients and anxious relatives sought comfort and when the best and most modern forms of surgery were stretched to their technical limits, he was a 'court of last appeal'.

Much of Wade's life and times may be learnt from James Ross,[1] President of the RCSEd from 1973 to 1976. Genial and forgiving, Ross

Chapter Summary

- **Philosopher**
- **Surgeon**
- **Benefactor**
- **Financier**
- **Victor**
- **Vanquished**
- **Academic**
- **Antiquarian**
- **Disciple**
- **Last years**
- **Conclusion**
- **The Sir Henry Wade Professorship**

observed and recorded through rose-tinted spectacles in *The Edinburgh School of Surgery after Lister*. Praising the positive qualities of surgeons, he seldom referred to the imperious demands of harassed consultants, their curt and irritable responses during prolonged outpatient appointments or their occasionally abrupt and dismissive words to patients fraught with pain and fear. Ross knew but did not describe the anger and frustration felt by the surgical operator when all was not well, when a mistake had been made or a diagnosis was incomplete or erroneous. He was aware that, under these circumstances, instruments might be hurled to the floor of the operating theatre and words directed at long-suffering Resident House Surgeons and nurses. Generous and tolerant, Ross measured the quantity of a surgeon's work not the quality, and he seldom revealed the merits, the scale or the value of the practices developed by those about whom he wrote.

Philosopher

Ross wrote of Wade's personal qualities perceptively, honestly and with affection,[1] quoting the words of RL Stewart – for many years an associate of Wade's in the Royal Infirmary of Edinburgh, the RIE:

> 'He [Henry Wade] was a fervent Lowland Scot and always an individualist in thought and deed, conforming to no pattern provided by his seniors. He drove himself hard throughout his working life, and though he had a reputation for some measure of irascibility, yet at heart he was the kindliest of men, always willing and ready to help and advise his juniors. He set the highest standards for himself in his work and truly earned the right to be considered the father and leader of modern urological surgery in Scotland.'

Wade had the dour determination and detachment that early twentieth century surgery demanded. These were also characteristics that made for success in the ancient Scottish game of golf.[A] In a letter from an Oxford photographer, we learn more of Wade's resilient approach to life; it could sometimes create tension. Gillman and Company Limited of 107 St Aldate's wrote on 5th March 1930:

Dear Sir,

We were very sorry to learn the print did not meet with your approval, though naturally we cannot carry in our eye, the print you recently sent us. There is no reason why we should not match it, but the mounting is a much more difficult proposition. We are therefore, sending you the negative, and trust you will be successful,

Yours faithfully

In the early 1950s, Mr JNJ Hartley (p 347), Conservator of the Museum of the RCSEd, often felt called upon to apologize for the abuse that Wade was inclined to hurl upon well-intentioned but careless Museum employees. However, the passage of time, the experience of war, adjustment to bitter personal loss and a growing breadth of vision mellowed this character and gave Wade a homespun philosophy of the greatest value to his students and assistants and of intense interest to the reader.[2] The most satisfactory way in which to convey his mature views is to quote from them directly.

'I can give you many instruments that will tell you when a man is ill, but none that will tell you when he is well.'

'There is no future for body or soul without the infallibility of belief.'

'The keystone of a comprehensive medical service is the general practitioner.'

'Mankind is lazy and the postponement of judgement is a not uncommon way out of a difficulty.'

'True estimations of the value of an observation can only be made by the man with a broad outlook.'

'The art of the surgeon in diagnosis is a knowledge of when not to operate...The art of the surgeon in treatment is a knowledge of when to conclude an operation.'

'The duty of the surgeon is not to prolong life but to promote happiness [with reference to patients suffering from tuberculosis who lay for months and years in Pension Hospitals]: There are some men in our hospitals with two legs who would be much healthier and happier on a Saturday afternoon at Tynecastle [football ground] with one.

> Robert Burns's advice
> *What's a' your jargon o' your Schools,*
> *Your Latin names for horns and stools?*
> *If honest Nature made you fools,*
> *What sairs your grammars?*
> is all right for the guidance of the natural genius. For lesser men, college classes are helpful.

As we cherish the fame of our country's surgery we should be careful to preserve this priceless treasure...in our desire for democratic opportunity...not to foster...one who, neither by natural inclination nor aptitude, can never make a surgeon.'

Wade's favoured hobby and pastime was his garden at Pilmuir House. He loved his trees, his shrubs and his flowers. A letter written by his friend David Wilkie in 1938, shortly before his death, reveals that Wade took a special interest in primulae. Photographs from a family album show that the wildlife was a further focus of interest. He was very fond of dogs.[2,B]

Surgeon

As Chapter 9 explains, much of Wade's character can be learned from his attitude to his patients, many of whom suffered intensely painful and disabling diseases. In dealing with ureteric calculus, no local anaesthetic was to be used. In men, pain was to be relieved by using a narrower catheter, and, in women, only appropriate encouragement and support were advised. This did not mean that Wade was either inhumane or insensitive: he simply practised Osler's *Aequanimitas* – the necessary detachment of the responsible consultant from the immediate suffering and the emotional demands of the patient. An innate kindness is revealed in a letter to a young boy who had sent him a present of a few handkerchiefs as thanks – presumably for surgical care after an accident. Wade said:

> 'it is very pleasant to have an occupation in life where your work is to make people well again who have been hurt, and I am sure, if when you grow up you become a Doctor, you will find great pleasure in your duties…[although] the responsibilities of an engine driver with the lives of 500 people dependent on him are often much greater than those of a Doctor.'

A popular student magazine, the *Gambolier* of 1912, portrayed Henry Wade at work:[C]

> 'When a hard-boiled Scotsman is gifted with scientific enthusiasm we expect something and we have got it in Mr Wade. His energy is proverbial, and anyone who has spent a day in the out-patient department of the Infirmary knows that 'when Wade is about things hum'. It is as an operating surgeon that he is making for himself a reputation. A rapid operator, with a fine aseptic technique, he spares no pains to husband all the resources of the patient both during and after operation. Whilst nothing comes amiss to Mr Wade, it is noticeable that he has a special preference for diseases of the urinary tract, and no surprise will be felt if this tendency should increase, for we feel sure that during the next decade there will be a greater degree of 'intensive culture' in the Edinburgh School of Surgery than has hitherto been the case. Apart from his profession, Mr Wade is known by many as a firm friend, whose original mind and strong individuality makes him always interesting whilst his keen sense of humour, with its soupçon of Bernard Shaw, make him no mean conversationalist.'

Ross described Wade operating to remove the prostate gland (p 239):[1]

> 'When performing the operation, he would look up at the gallery and remark in a loud voice to his assistant, 'Very difficult

case, this, Tammas'.[D] Then would follow a movement or two of his hand, deep in the abdomen, and out would come the adenoma, complete. He would hum a little, say nothing, and proceed to close [the wound].'

Ross records that General Frank Richardson, a historian who wrote later about Larrey (see below), told him that he had been Wade's house surgeon. 'I was useless', he said. Thus:

Wade: 'Frank, CAN'T you tie any knot but a granny?'

Wade (during a mammectomy operation): 'Come on, come on, get your great fat fingers out of here – she's bleeding like the Fountains of Versailles'. Frank went on, 'Wade was a confirmed addict of humming and singing during operations, often the latest pantomime song. How well I remember him at this, in 1927 I think, singing "My girl's got long hair" – slight pause while he coped with some intricate manoeuvre – "Got long ginger hair!"

In a discussion with the author, the late Noel Gray, a former House Surgeon of Wade's, recalled that the great man was a demanding but generous surgical teacher. Arriving in the anaesthetic room one afternoon in 1935, Mr Gray, at that time a fourth-year medical student, found that the consultant anaesthetist was still absent. Alone with a recumbent patient who had been prepared for thyroidectomy, he was startled when a head appeared around the door of the operating theatre and a stern voice demanded 'Get the patient under!' There were two bottles of anaesthetic on a nearby shelf – one of chloroform, the other of ether. The student seized the first, poured some of the liquid onto a pad of cotton wool, placed it over the face of the patient and was relieved when she lapsed into unconsciousness. Wheeled into the theatre, the operation was well under way when the student felt a sharp blow across his knuckles. In an attempt to maintain anaesthesia, his hand had moved into the operating field. Wade had a simple but effective way of dealing with such misdemeanours. After this brusque encounter, the student was astonished, some months later, by a kindly letter from Wade inviting him to be his House Surgeon.

Figure 16.1 Henry Wade in retirement. *Often a sombre and serious figure, many did not realize the mischievous humour that lay behind the elderly surgeon's guise*

Benefactor

By virtue of his position and of the authority that increased with age, Wade was often called on to write testimonials on behalf of young surgeons and nurses. His replies were invariably courteous and generous, although, in one instance, the style of the letter suggests that he was avoiding the issue by claiming to have been 'out of town'. The demands were considerable. In the period 1919–23, 25 people wrote asking for support.[3] Among these requests were three from his nursing staff at Leith Hospital. Of a Sister Fraser, Wade wrote characteristically:

> 'If it [the testimonial] is in part responsible for our losing your services from Leith Hospital, in common with many of my colleagues I will feel it has caused us a serious loss.'

Many applicants were ex-servicemen who had been with him in Gallipoli, Egypt or Palestine. Very often, they were candidates for the surgical Fellowship examination. Their letters came from all parts of the country, but some, like that from NJ Judah, were written from Egypt before a return to Britain (Figure 16.2). Judah's letter is of particular interest because Wade's reply, unusually, is written in his own hand, not dictated.[4]

In the case of William Brown, a friend who had served with Wade in the Scottish Horse Mounted Brigade Field Ambulance (Chapter 7), a request for support for an application for the position of Assistant Physician to the Aberdeen Royal Infirmary comes soon after a note telling Wade that:[5]

> 'I will send the films you need to prepare your lantern slides.'[6]

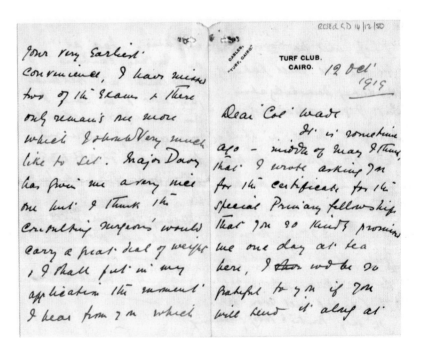

Figure 16.2 Letter from NJ Judah. *The letter, asking for a testimonial, was written to Henry Wade from Egypt in 1919*

This is one of the few indications that not all the photographs in Wade's collection were taken with his own camera.

Occasionally, a letter sheds light on the climate of the times. Thus, on 23rd June 1919, William Campbell, writing from the precincts of the University of Edinburgh, comments:

> 'Judging by the noise of hooters, it seems as if Peace has been signed.'

He adds:

> 'I am fed up with exams.'

Wade speaks warmly of Dr WT Gardiner, who had served as a regimental medical officer with the 52nd Scottish Lowland Division, in spite of being an Otolaryngologist and President of the Scottish Otological Society. He had been awarded the Military Cross. On another occasion, the Director of the Mayo Foundation asks Wade for his opinion of Dr Robert Mailer, who is applying for a visiting fellowship.

Financier

Thrifty but not mean, Wade hid a warm-hearted and kindly character behind a posture that could appear aloof or distant. His eminent predecessor, James Syme, is said 'never to have wasted a word, a drop of blood or a drop of ink'. Wade possessed some of Syme's qualities. He certainly dealt with artisans and businessmen in a firm, frugal and careful manner. Listing some required new fittings for his house at 6 Manor Place, Edinburgh (Chapter 9), he stipulated to Faraday and Sons of 146–150 Wardour Street, London, that:

> 'There should be an oak floor, Persian rugs laid out across a bright, old-fashioned room with a hearth fire. A large central light fitting is necessary and it should be of alabaster or preferably Mexican onyx, with the pendant close to the roof to give a shaded yellow tint. There should be a pair of electric candlesticks.'

The end of the First World War marked a turning point in Wade's finances. Now he began to earn sufficient money from his private practice to initiate a systematic policy of investment. Although he had started to exploit the stock market before 1914, the first concrete evidence of his financial thoughts came on 18th November 1919, when he wrote to Barclays Bank enclosing a cheque in payment for shares in Badcock and Wilcox. Later, in March 1920, they asked whether he wanted a share certificate sent to him. Towards the end of 1922, with the decision to buy a building to be used as a nursing home (p 166), it was time to call on the professional advice of Thomas

Stephenson, Stock and Share Brokers, of Glasgow.[7] Wade also took advice from J Miller Thomson and Co, WS, of 5 St Colme Street, Edinburgh. Wade explained to Thomas Stephenson that although he had balanced the books so far as the nursing home was concerned,[8] he still had £1,000 to invest. It is likely that he had been recommended to Thomas Stephenson by his elder brother, T Callander Wade (p 6), solicitor of Falkirk.

To take matters forward, Wade visited Glasgow. A series of 29 letters written between November 1922 and March 1923 reveals the sequence of events.[9] Wade says: 'I would like advice on ordinary shares in a sound concern'. Stephenson mentions a 5% War Loan, saying:

'Many industrials appear to be at a higher price than is justified.'

Stephenson adds:

'Coats are 'a fair lock up'. BAT [British American Tobacco] has a strong position in China.'

Wade settles for the purchase of BAT.[10] He sends a cheque for £901/17/0d. On 8th January 1923, Stephenson encloses the contract for the purchase of the 200 BAT ordinary shares at 88/6d each. A dividend for £26/2/6d follows. On 22nd February, Wade says that he still has some '£500 odd' to invest. Stephenson mentions Nobel preference and ordinary shares, Fife Coal and Forestal Land and Timber. The correspondence is followed by a request by Wade for a publication about 'principal public companies with shares'. Thomas Stephenson recommends the Stock Exchange Official Intelligence but comments that:

'It is pretty expensive [at £3/11/6d] and is not up to date.'

On 1st March, Wade sends £665/19/6d for the purchase of 200 Courtaulds ordinary shares, followed on 17th March by £75/1/–d for 100 Tharsis Sulphur Bearer shares.

The First World War led to an extreme loss from the country of physically and mentally alert staff from all walks of life. The civil service was not spared. There had been a cumulative deterioration in the quality of its work. Faced with an enhanced demand for the settlement of pension and benefit claims that had accrued over the five years prior to 1919, inaccuracies, errors and unfair decisions were commonplace. The offices of the Inland Revenue were understaffed and overworked. Correspondence with them sheds some light on the challenges faced by Wade and innumerable other ex-servicemen and women on their return home.

In 18 letters between Wade and the Income Tax authorities extending over the period from December 1919 to December 1929,[9] it proved necessary for Wade to defend his position vigorously against meticulous but insensitive civil service predators. It was in this way that on 26th December 1919, only a few weeks after his final release from military duties, Wade was compelled to explain to the Surveyor of Taxes, Edinburgh 5th District, that he, Henry Wade, had been absent on military duties for about five years and had not received the honorarium of £50 yearly that he would normally have expected as Lecturer in Clinical Surgery of the University of Edinburgh.[11] Nevertheless:

'the profit has worked out at the sum stated.'[12]

Stiff letters are exchanged with a Mr JW Sinton, who asks Wade on 27th February 1920 how much pay he received from 1st April 1919 until 21st May when he was demobilized.[13] After some petty remarks about whether returns have or have not been received, JW Sinton joins battle again:

'Does your statement include examination fees? Also fees earned but unpaid at 31.12.19? You appear to have debited a whole year's expenses but you had only 7–8 months of income. You have deducted ⅓ of the gross annual value of your house instead of the net value. What are the details of your house expenditure part of which may have been spent on 'other than professional items'? Capital costs may be contained in the £136 you claim as the cost of instruments.'

He goes on peremptorily:

'You better call and see me. Do not call between 12 and 2.'

A few days later Wade says:

'I shall be sending a complete statement of income for the year to April 1920.'

He added:

'The sum of 1/5d^E might appear to require an explanation which is that Lecturers receive the fees of their students and personally bear the expenses of rent and the cost of maintenance [of the lecture rooms – p 249]. In my case, the profit has worked out at the sum stated.'

JW Sinton attacks again. He asks Wade how much pay he received from 1st April 1919 until he was demobilized on 21st May. A stiff reply from the former Colonel explains his rank and says:

'I shall correspond with Messrs Holt, my Agent [solicitor] when I was an officer.'

Wade continues on 1st March:

'I have to thank you for pointing out the mistake made in adding only one quarter instead of 3/8 [of house repair costs] a foolish oversight on my part which I trust you will correct. Thank you for an invitation to call which I did in the middle of January but was not then afforded the opportunity of seeing you.'

Checkmate is secured for the Inland Revenue, when a Mr FI Keats writes on 10th March:

'I return Notice to you. An amended cheque for £167/13/10d will oblige.'[14]

Wade's financial problems were not confined to those stemming from the Inspector of Taxes. On 19th June 1919, he was obliged to explain to the Edinburgh Corporation Electric Lighting Department that the reason he had not paid his account was that he had been away on active service.[15] Two days later, the Department apologized for submitting incorrect charges of 6/10d and 20/– and sent him back a corrected notice.[16]

Victor

It was in the nature of things that Wade should receive many awards, both military and civil. Those that gave him the greatest pleasure were the former. The circumstances that led to his gallantry are described in Chapters 7 and 8. Wade was first mentioned in a dispatch from General Allenby GCMG KCB, dated 3rd April 1918, 'for gallant and distinguished services in the field'. The dedication read 'I have it in command from the King to record His Majesty's high appreciation of the services rendered'. The designation was signed by Winston S Churchill, Secretary of State for War, on 1st March 1919. Henry Wade by then was Temporary Lieutenant Colonel MD FRCS, Royal Army Medical Corps, although he remained a substantive Captain RAMC (TF). He was once more mentioned in a dispatch from General Sir EHH Allenby GCB GCMG, dated 5th March 1919. The dispatch was again signed by Winston S Churchill, Secretary of State for War, this time on 1st July 1919. Wade had now become a Temporary Colonel. He had been awarded the Distinguished Service Order (DSO; Chapter 8) in 1918 and became a Companion of the Order of St Michael and St George (CMG) in 1919.

His civilian honours were many and varied. Honorary Fellowship of the American College of Surgeons came in 1930. He was elected to the Fellowship of the Royal Society of Edinburgh on 7th March 1932 and to Honorary Membership of the American Urological Association on 1st June 1932. In the presentation scroll, he is shown erroneously as being President, not Vice President, of the Royal College of Surgeons of Edinburgh.

On 3rd March 1935, Wade became an Honorary Fellow of the Royal Australasian College of Surgeons and on 20th April an Honorary Member of the Los Angeles Surgical Society. At the same time, he was elected an Honorary Fellow of the Royal College of Surgeons in Ireland.

In 1937, Wade received an invitation from the Earl Marshal to attend the Coronation of King George VI. Like the many others honoured in this way, he was sent cards, a map and tickets that allowed him to be admitted to the North Aisle of the Nave of Westminster Abbey.

The doors of the Abbey open at 6 a.m.

The communication was followed by a foolscap booklet, *The ceremonies to be observed at the coronation of their most excellent Majesties,* and a small book, *Form and order of the service that is to be performed and the ceremonies that are to be observed in the coronation of their Majesties King George VI and Queen Elizabeth in the Abbey Church of St Peter, Westminster on Wednesday, the 12th day of May, 1937.*

Wade was elected an Honorary Fellow of the Royal College of Surgeons of England on 8th April 1943, at a time when the President was Sir Alfred Webb Johnson and the Vice President Sir Gordon Gordon Taylor. Wade was elected to the Athenaeum on 15th January 1945 and asked for a subscription of 15 guineas per annum, payable in three parts, together with an entrance fee of 30 guineas. He was advanced to the Honorary Fellowship of the Royal Society of Medicine on 22nd May 1951. The President was again Webb Johnson.

Wade was knighted in 1946.

Figure 16.3 Wade is elected Honorary Fellow of the Royal College of Surgeons of England. *Letter written to Wade on 13th April 1943 by Kennedy Cassels, Secretary of the Royal College of Surgeons of England, informs Wade of his election as Honorary Fellow*

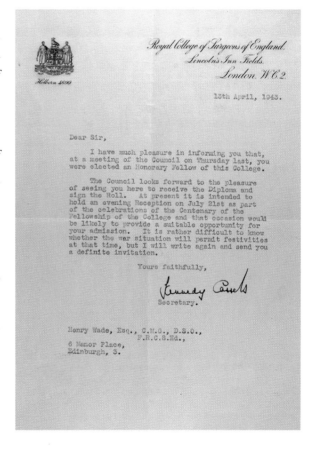

Figure 16.4 Diploma of Fellowship of the Royal College of Surgeons of England. *The ceremony took place on 13th April 1943. The presentation was made by Sir Alfred Webb Johnson, President of the Royal College of Surgeons of England. He was one of Wade's old friends and a wartime colleague*

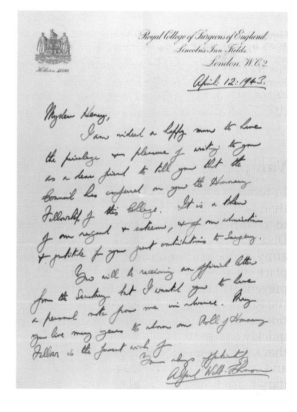

Figure 16.5 Personal letter written to Wade on 12th April 1943 by Sir Alfred Webb Johnson. *Webb Johnson writes: 'I am indeed a happy man to have the privilege and pleasure of writing to you as a dear friend to tell you that the Council have conferred on you the Honorary Fellowship of the College. It is a token of our regard and esteem and our admiration and gratitude for your great contributions to Surgery'*

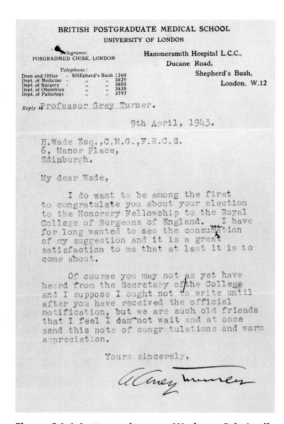

Figure 16.6 Letter written to Wade on 9th April 1943 by Professor A Grey Turner. *Grey Turner, another wartime friend and colleague (Chapter 7) writes from the British Postgraduate Medical School, Hammersmith, to add his congratulations on Wade's election to the Honorary Fellowship of the Royal College of Surgeons of England*

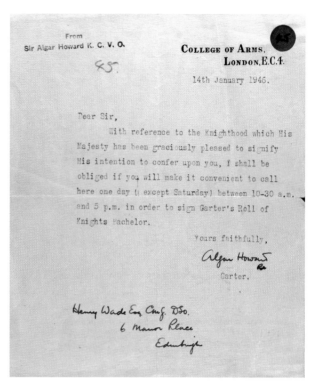

Figure 16.7 Letter to Wade on 14th January 1946 by Sir Algar Howard. *Howard asks Wade if he will please call at the College of Arms to sign the Garter's Roll of Knights Bachelor. It was the moment when Wade received his Knighthood*

Vanquished

In terms of character, men and women judge success less objectively than failure. Should we not be valued by our response to disaster, not to triumph? As Kipling said, 'If you can meet with Triumph and Disaster and treat these two impostors just the same...' By joining the army and spending nearly two years in South Africa, Wade lost his place on the fierce ladder of surgical promotion but the loss did not prevent success both in the 1903 examinations for the Fellowship of the Royal College of Surgeons of Edinburgh (RCSEd) and in the election to the Conservatorship of the College Museum. By responding so quickly to a second call to military service in 1914, it could be claimed that he lost even greater opportunities, but, unlike many of his friends and colleagues, he survived and reaped the rewards accorded to a military hero. When he failed to gain either of the two Edinburgh Chairs of Surgery in 1924–25, he could be forgiven for sensing bitterness and frustration. Yet neither failure prevented him from promotion to be Surgeon-in-Ordinary to the RCSEd and election to the Council of the College. Even to the most critical, it must be clear that he was a stoic, that he combined resilience with determination and that he was, on the surface at least, impervious to the world's judgement. That he bore the loss of his wife in 1929 without more than a transient interruption to his surgical labours was entirely in accord with these assessments. His heart may have been broken, but he was not prepared to share his sorrow with the world.

Academic

In his early cancer research, Wade displayed many of the qualities demanded of a successful research worker, and there is little doubt that had he so chosen, he could have risen to renown in this field. However, Wade was an outgoing individual who enjoyed very active participation in collaborative work that involved physical activity. He was not by nature a writer, although he published many papers of great interest. He was widely read but was content to express himself verbally rather than on paper. He displayed particular skills in explaining practical surgical questions in ways easily comprehended by young surgeons, and he accomplished this by publishing the lectures that he had given to local, national or international meetings. In the course of his work, he quoted Pasteur, Cohnheim, Virchow, Adami and Starling: he was thoroughly familiar with the greatest authorities of the Victorian age. He published neither books nor chapters in books, although, at an early age, his MD thesis and his long paper on experimental carcinogenesis demonstrated an innate ability for the lucid exposition of complex scientific argument. Only one of Wade's publications deals scientifically with physiological principles,[17] yet he acknowledged freely the momentous advances in surgery that had been brought about by this science.[2]

Although the editing of Wade's manuscripts might not have proved acceptable to modern medical journalists, the quaint layout of many of his

Figure 16.8 Henry Wade's book plate. *The plate bears his coat of arms (Auspicium feci melioris – 'Foresight makes for a happy life')*

papers was in the style of the time. To the frustration of readers, the texts were rarely supported by references, either from the historical or from the contemporary literature. He adopted occasional recondite and obscure usage, of which the word 'functionate' is one example. With the passage of time, Wade was occasionally called upon to compose obituary notices for friends and colleagues. He contributed moving obsequies to the *Edinburgh Medical Journal* to commemorate the deaths of Sir David Dalbreck Wilkie and Mr (Colonel) JJM Shaw.[18,19] Wilkie (p 42), a close friend, had died in 1938 in London at the age of 54 years. Shaw, an intimate and distinguished younger Edinburgh colleague, travelled to Egypt in 1940 as a Consultant Surgeon to the army and died from dysentery shortly after his arrival.

A list of Wade's published papers and communications is given in Appendix 16.1.

Antiquarian

Wade had a deep interest not only in the history of surgery but in the antiquity of his native land. He demonstrated his wide perspectives in his Ramon Guiteras lecture, in which he quoted John Hunter, James Mackenzie of Burnley, Claude Bernard and JBS Haldane.[20,F] It was in this lecture that he confirmed his insight into the state of mind of Napoleon before the Battle of Borodino (p 325).

Wade gave the Harveian Oration on 10th June 1938.[21] The oration was entitled *Harvey in Scotland*.

After brief accounts of the lives of William Harvey, of King Charles I and of Bishop Laud, Wade describes how Harvey was one of a small army of lay and clerical courtiers and personal attendants who accompanied Charles I as he left Whitehall on 11th May 1633 to ride to the Palace of Holyrood for the Scottish coronation.[G] Wade portrays vividly the story of the arrival in Edinburgh on 15th June 1633 and of the events of the coronation, after which the king 'touched aboute 100 persons that were troubled with the King's eiuell' (scrofula, or tuberculous cervical lymphadenitis). As part of the celebrations, Harvey was granted the freedom of the city of Edinburgh, while three of his surgical colleagues – Michell Andro (chyrurgeone to his majestie), Thomas Caldwell (barbour) and James Suricht or Sevricht (chyrurgeone) – received the Honorary Fellowship of the Incorporation of Barber Surgeons, the first time this honour had been bestowed.

During the 15-day stay in the capital city, Harvey journeyed to the Bass Rock, where he was able to study the behaviour of the prolific life of birds that he took to be 'soleand geese', but which were probably common guillemots. The owner of the Bass Rock, Sir Philip Lauder, made a great deal of money from the sale of the birds and their products. The animals were a delicacy, eaten like oysters. That Wade was so interested in Harvey's visit to Scotland and his ornithological exploits may be attributed to the circumstance that Wade's home, Pilmuir House, lay only a few miles from the rock.

continued

The occasion of the Royal visit of 1633 had been chosen by the King to per-suade the Scottish Parliament to re-enact the Revocation of 1625. This wise statute was based on a Scottish law, which determined that the Crown of Scotland, by custom, tradition and law, had full right to reassume public properties looted during Royal minorities. As Wade says, Charles was 'unmindful' of the fact that much of the loot had passed into the hands of the impoverished nobility. By altering the law, Charles alienated the nobles, setting in train the disasters that led, through the pedantic misjudgements of Laud, to common cause being struck between peers and people.

The King returned to Scotland in 1641, and Harvey, still his physician but now aged 63, again accompanied him. The reason for Harvey's visit to Aberdeen at that time remains 'a matter of conjecture'. It seemed likely to Wade that it was in connection with the union of two of Aberdeen's Colleges to form the new Caroline University.

On 24th November 1949, Wade presented the Vicary lecture to the Royal College of Surgeons of England. Wade chose as his subject, *The Barber Surgeons of Edinburgh.*[22]

Vicary had been the faithful servant of King Henry VIII of England. Wade recalled how Henry's sister, Margaret Tudor, had married King James IV of Scotland and described James's family history and interests. On 1st July 1505, the Barbers and Surgeons of Edinburgh appeared before the Lord Provost, Baillies and council-lors, seeking to be awarded a *Seal of cause and charter of privileges.* The Barbers and Surgeons argued that they 'had upheld an Altar within the College Kirk of St. Giles in the honour of God and St Mungo, their patron, and had paid their humble weekly penny which sustained and upheld the said altar in all necessary things'.

The *Seal of Cause* was duly agreed and affixed. The Barbers and Surgeons were the 10th Guild to be granted such recognition (p 358). Wade's manuscript includes a photograph of the famous Keir portrait of King James IV; a recon-structed view of Edinburgh drawn about 1450 and taken from a commemora-tive volume entitled *Edinburgh 1329–1929*; and a reproduction of the Incorporation prayer from the book of minutes of 1581. Wade also traces the story of Gilbert Primrose, an ancestor of Lord Rosebery (p 97), the distinctive requirements and conditions for the Barbers as opposed to the Surgeons, the temporary affiliation with the Apothecaries and the High Court action of 1722, in which the Barbers and Surgeons finally separated.

Disciple

Wade was interested intensely in the life and works of Dominique Jean Larrey (later Baron Larrey) (Appendix 2.1), with whom he clearly felt a particular affinity. Larrey was Napoleon's Surgeon General and is credited with the invention of the first mobile, 'flying', Field Ambulance (Appendix 2.1).[23] Quoting from General Count Philip de Ségur, Wade gave a graphic account of the fatal day on which the Battle of Borodino was fought:[24]

But the marches which he had just made with the army, the fatigues of the preceding days and nights, so many cares, and his intense and anxious expectation, had worn him [Napoleon] out; the chilliness of the atmosphere had struck to him; an irritating fever, a dry cough, and excessive thirst consumed him. During the remainder of the night, he made vain attempts to quench his burning thirst. This fresh disorder was complicated with an old complaint; he had been struggling since the day before with a painful attack of that cruel disorder [retention of urine] which had been long threatening him.

Napoleon's illness and inability to take decisions, Wade deduced, were the result of 'unbalanced' urinary disease following prostatic hypertrophy. The conclusion was beyond dispute: 'health is indispensable in war, and nothing can replace it'.

It was a measure of Wade's interest in his eminent predecessor that he arranged for the relevant parts of Larrey's work to be translated into English. The incomplete manuscript lies in the Library of the RCSEd. In front of the manuscript is a short extract from a Red Cross memorandum.[25] The story begins with a note on 2nd August 1919 from a Miss Agnes Muriel Johnston of 25 Drummond Place, Edinburgh. She had been reading the introduction to Larrey's memoirs, his *Relation Historique et Chirurgicale (1803)*, and the translation.[26,27] She says:

'The 1812 edition of the *Mémoires* is certainly a vast improvement on the 1803. Waller's translation misses out so much and is so inaccurate that it seems hardly worth regarding. I have been wondering whether you have asked anybody in America about the other translation. I know of two people whom I could ask to look at catalogues if you think it would be of interest to hear what the book is like. My memory is rather bad but was it not done by a man Hall of Philadelphia? Might I ask you to let me have the 'speech' which you made about the different editions when you have time? I enjoyed seeing your Egyptian curios so much.'

On 30th October 1919, Wade writes back:

'My sister Peggy [Margaret] has told me that you are now in Edinburgh. If so I wonder if you would be so kind as to look along some afternoon or evening so that we might have a further talk about the translation of Larrey's Egyptian campaign. I would like to show you a typed copy of the section of his work you did...I think it would be worth our while proceeding with it.'

Wade can now give her much more 'material help', by which it may be assumed he means money.[28] On 10th November 1919, he arranges a time to meet Miss Johnston.[29] In turn, on 9th December 1919, Miss Johnston wonders how Larrey is getting on.

'Even if you are not free I could have a talk with Miss Grey [Wade's secretary]. That is, if you don't mind me working at Manor Place as the books are there. I can bring an ordinary French Dictionary.'[30]

On the following day, Wade agrees;[31] however, Miss Johnston's time, as she explains on 8th November 1919, is now much more limited, as she is at work in Edinburgh. But she suggests Tuesday for a talk.[32,33] She writes again on 31st March 1920 to say:

'I believe 6 Manor Place is to be shut up while you are away.[H] Should I keep the last part of the translation to be typed later on? Miss Grey and I were saying it would be nice to go on with it while you are away.'[34,35]

Wade responds on 1st April 1920 and explains that he will leave next week and return in June. He recommends that she, Miss Johnston, negotiate with Miss Grey.[36]

Last years

On 16th December 1953, the RCSEd gave a dinner to mark Henry Wade's 50 years of service to the College. In turn, Wade presented to the College Museum his histological sections (Chapter 6). They came from the pioneer work that he had begun in 1904 and continued during the 1920s. As a mark of his affection for the College of which he had for so long been a Fellow, Wade had commissioned a replica in oils of the 'Keir' portrait of King James IV of Scotland, which hangs in the National Portrait Gallery of Scotland. Ross describes the occasion when Wade presented the portrait to the College:[1]

'Almost his last action, a few days before the brief illness from which he died, was to arrange for the President and one or two others to meet him at the artist's, Mr Harry Woolford's studio, to see the original portrait of King James IV, lent by Colonel Stirling of Keir, together with the copy which he [Sir Henry] was presenting to the College. The original had been executed by Daniel Mytens, court painter to King Charles the First, from a water colour afterwards destroyed in the fire at Whitehall and is believed to be the only authentic portrait of King James IV in existence. The thought of giving this likeness of the King from whom the College received its Royal Charter in 1506 gave him the greatest pleasure. The viewing took place although Sir Henry was by then too weak to be there.'

The portrait hung for many years in the Logan Turner room of the College, the President's room. It is now displayed in the Great Hall.

Henry Wade died at 3.20 on the afternoon of 21st February 1955 at

Figure 16.9 King James IV of Scotland. *This copy of the Keir portrait of King James IV of Scotland was presented to the Royal College of Surgeons of Edinburgh by Wade shortly before his death in 1955*

Figure 16.10 *The Wade burial stone. The stone in the Dean Cemetery, Edinburgh, which marks the burial place of Marjorie and Henry Wade*

his Edinburgh home – 6 Manor Place. He had been suffering from acute bronchitis and had been in declining health for some time. His funeral was held in Palmerston Place Church. Many who recalled his distinguished services in the First World War were in attendance, and former army colleagues acted as pallbearers. The stone that marks his grave, shared with Marjorie, his wife, stands in the burial ground of the Dean Church at the West End of Edinburgh. On 27th April, the President of the Royal College of Surgeons informed his Council that Miss Margaret Callendar Wade had presented to the College a drawing of her late brother. The drawing forms the frontispiece of this book. Wade had considered an alternative bequest but finally decided to settle £5,000 upon her, his sole surviving close relative.

Wade had intended to leave his estate to the RCSEd. Instead, Pilmuir House (Chapter 15) was held in trust. Among the items bequeathed to the College was his grandfather's grandfather clock and 100 of his own collection of books and papers. The books included Gallie's *Essays in surgery* (given to him by the author), a first edition of Reitz's *Commando* and 11 volumes of *Extracts from the records of the burgh of Edinburgh*.[37-39] The numerous items that he donated to the Museum of the RCSEd are described in Chapter 6.

Figure 16.11 Wade's grandfather clock. *The clock belonged to Wade's grandfather. The clock stands in the President's room – the Logan Turner room – of the Royal College of Surgeons of Edinburgh*

Conclusion

Wade lived from 1876 until 1955 – a period in surgery that linked Listerian antisepsis with the methods of *in vivo* diagnosis by scanning techniques, the understanding of organ transplantation, arthroplasty, the decline in peptic ulcer, cancer genetics and many other twentieth century discoveries. Wade saw and participated in the evolution of surgical specialism, the introduction of blood transfusion, the use of antibiotic and chemotherapy and the growth of laboratory medicine and microbiology. In his early life, Wade was both scientist and surgeon. He was a formidable military surgeon and, subsequently, a founder figure of surgical urology. In his later life, Wade lived for the RCSEd and his devotion to its cause was demonstrated by his intention to bequeath his estate to the College.

Henry Wade was a child of his time, brought up in the manse, educated in the strict Presbyterian environment of the Edinburgh Medical School. Loyalty to his profession, the RCSEd and his country were hallmarks of a long and distinguished career. But the disparate aspects of a long life that differentiate Wade from other surgical pioneers were the breadth of his scientific achievements, his contributions to military surgery and his political astuteness. During his lifetime, he became an outstanding figure of Scottish surgery. Now, 50 years after his death, it is possible to recognize that Henry Wade was a paradigm of British surgical science.

The Sir Henry Wade Professorship

In 1966, the Royal College of Surgeons of Edinburgh decided to establish a Wade Professorship in basic sciences. The *Lancet* of 26th March of that year carried a notice to the effect that:

> 'To honour the memory of the late Sir Henry Wade, the Royal College of Surgeons of Edinburgh has created an occasional professorship of surgical pathology. The incumbent will give talks and be available for consultation in the College museum. Professor William Boyd [Toronto] has accepted the first professorship.'

The professorship was made possible by funds gifted to the College by Sir Henry Wade. They were therefore independent of the moneys from his estate, which was incorporated in the Pilmuir Trust (p 304). In 1982, the Wade Professor received an honorarium of £1,000; in 1985, the amount is shown as £250.

Professor Boyd's lectures were entitled *'The place of the museum in a teaching school'* and *'The spontaneous regression of cancer'*. The Wade Professorship was tenable for three years. The first three incumbents were all pathologists. Professor Boyd was followed by Professor DF Cappell CBE, of the University of Glasgow at the Western Infirmary.

In 1970, he was succeeded by Dr Basil Morson, Director of Research at St Mark's Hospital, London, who spoke on problems of gastrointestinal surgery and, in particular, Crohn's disease. It is of great interest that, in their letters accepting the honour, both Professor Boyd and Professor Cappell acknowledged Henry Wade as a teacher, friend and colleague. William Boyd had been one of Wade's students, and Dan Cappell had sat with Wade on the General Medical Council.

At the same time as the establishment of the Wade Professorship, a series of Wade Demonstratorships were set up, with the aim of encouraging the training of overseas surgeons and assisting them in their careers. In the years between 1970 and 1981, the records suggest that the original purpose of the Wade Professorship gradually changed. The aims of the appointment became to counsel and supervise resident postgraduates, to regulate their sponsorship and to be available for their advice and assistance. The title of the position altered to Wade Professor of Surgical Studies. In 1982, Mr John Cook was appointed to the realigned post, and, in 1986, he was succeeded by the late Professor Adam Smith, who lent great distinction to the position during a period in office of 10 years. Mr Iain Mcintyre then held the position during his three years as Director of Education.

End Notes

Chapter 1

A. The Free Church, constituted at the Disruption of 1843, joined with the United Presbyterian Church in 1900 to form the United Free Church.

B. A 'call' is 'an invitation or summons to undertake the office of pastor, from God, one's conscience, or a congregation'.

C. The spelling of the family name needs to be distinguished from that of Callendar House, Falkirk – a mediaeval foundation near Henry Wade's home. Callendar House played an important part in six centuries of Scottish history. It is now a centre for historical research and is in the keeping of Falkirk District Council.

D. These letters were written by James Wade to his mother in 1922.

E. A letter to Henry Wade from his nephew Callander W Sinclair in 1922 described the illness of his father, Dr Eric Sinclair. His uncle, Henry Wade, replied in affectionate and sympathetic terms.

October 8th 1922

To Henry Wade from Callander W Sinclair, his nephew whose address is Kathor, Kenneth Street, Longueville, New South Wales.

Dear Uncle Harry,

Aunt Catherine will have been writing to Larbert during the past two or three week referring to the fact that Father has been ill. They have asked me to write to you & explain matters [in order that you may] (this last phrase is crossed out). On Saturday 16th Sept he was in normal health & worked in his garden doing much the same as he does every Saturday. It would [sic] a light day's work with no heavy lifting or digging. On Sunday morning he awoke to find a numbness & tingling of his right arm & hand. Further investigations during the day showed a more extensive nerve involvement. He could write but badly & he fumbled in touching things. He could walk but would be uncertain when the knee was fully extended. Sir Jarvie Hood's locum tenens, Dr Holmes a' Court is treating him but the symptoms & signs cleared up very rapidly. By the end of the week he had lost all his symptoms & 8 days up the road he was able to go to the town, & a week later to resume his full work.

 He proposes to make no alteration in his mode of living. Would you please explain this as far as you think advisable at Woodcroft?

With kind regards

Your nephew

Callander W Sinclair

December 1st 1922

My dear Callander,

I have always felt somewhat ashamed at not having corresponded with you more regularly than I have done. At the same time, you can understand that our channel of communication has been through Larbert where I have always received the most recent news of you and from which you have been informed of my various movements.

I appreciate very much that you have sent me so full and exact account of your father's health. As you are aware, my medical work being that of a surgeon I am not so familiar as I once was with the class of case the physician entirely deals with. At the same time, I remember enough and have seen enough to appreciate the exact state of affairs. I am sure that we are both in agreement that for a short interval of time a certain minute area of the brain had been rendered anaemic and consequently its functional activity temporarily upset. As you understand there are several causes that might account for this, the most serious being haemorrhage of [*sic*] embolism. Fortunately, it is clear that neither of these were in operation here and the almost certain explanation is a temporary contracture of the small blood vessels. To one of your years, such an occurrence would be a matter of no moment and its incidence you would be unconscious of. As years go on however, with all of us our blood vessels are liable to lose the tonicity they possessed when we were younger.

Seeing that we have commenced a correspondence, perhaps we might decide to keep it up at regular intervals, and when you are next writing to me you might let me know how you are enjoying your practice and what are the special difficulties you have met with and some of the triumphant cures you have obtained, of which I am sure you also have several.

Wishing you the compliments of the Season and with kindest regards,

I remain, Your affectionate Uncle, [signed] Harry

F.   This is the only surviving letter between Henry Wade and his youngest sister, Margaret.

G.   The Royal High School Archives are held by the City of Edinburgh.

H.   The Medical School building was designed by Robert Rowand Anderson. After competition, his final design was approved in 1876. The Medical School was erected between 1878 and 1884. The Graduation Hall, built between 1886 and 1894, lay to the east of the Medical School and was in continuity with it. The design was modified in its final form and completed through the generosity of Sir William McEwen, after whom it was named. A bell tower or campanile was considered in the design, but in the final analysis, the idea was not accepted. A drawing of the north façade is held among the Edinburgh University Rowand Anderson drawings. It is RRA 330.

I.   In 1869, the number was 560.

J.   The original sixteenth century Edinburgh Royal High School building came into use as a surgical hospital in 1832. A further large surgical hospital was erected in 1853 beside the original medical hospital. By 1864, however, this structure had deteriorated, and the architects reported to the managers that 'Nothing short of a new, medical building will answer the purpose'. By 1866, the condition of the 1853 surgical hospital also was described as entirely unhealthy. It became clear that the two structures required rebuilding and that they should be on the same site. Although strong voices stressed the desirability of keeping the new hospital near the University, a letter from the influential pen of James Syme emphasized that to rebuild on the same site would leave Edinburgh without a hospital for at least three years. He and many others preferred the idea of moving to an entirely new location. The site of George Watson's Hospital (School) would be available. A notorious 'battle of the sites' began. On 19th March 1869, Syme resolved that the medical and surgical hospitals should be both rebuilt on a new large site – the grounds of Watson's School. Although Syme died in June 1870, his influential and logical views had already been accepted, and the foundation stone of the new Royal Infirmary of Edinburgh was laid on 13th October of that year.

Equally complex and drawn-out arguments related to the provision of a hospital for infectious diseases. A Public Health (Scotland) Act had come into force in 1867 compelling the city of Edinburgh to accept responsibility for the care of those with 'fevers'. For many years, the Managers of the Royal Infirmary of Edinburgh were obliged to provide space for these numerous patients. They employed old Surgeons' Hall at High School Yards[10] – a building that became the University Department of Engineering in 1905 and remained so until the Department moved to King's Building in 1932. In 1906, the 1853 Royal Infirmary of Edinburgh surgical hospital building became the University's Department of Natural Philosophy, while the 'old' surgical hospital became the headquarters of the University Officers' Training Corps. The High School building emerged as the University's Department of Geography. When this became unavailable in 1870, the town turned to the Canongate Poorhouse, to the Poorhouse in Forrest Road and to rooms in Kings Stables Road. Finally, those planning and building the new Royal Infirmary of Edinburgh were relieved of the problem of providing beds for cases of infectious disease when the town bought both the old surgical hospital buildings and the medical building. It was demolished in 1884, paving the way for the construction of a new City Hospital for infectious disease, which was opened in 1903.

K. History repeated itself when patients were first admitted to the third 'new' Royal Infirmary of Edinburgh on 15th September 2002.

L. In 1883, there were no more than 12 professors and two lecturers within the Faculty of Medicine. However, the number of teachers grew steadily, beginning with the creation of a Lectureship in Tropical Medicine in 1898 – a position held by Dr John Thomson. A continued increase in the teaching staff followed in the second and third decades of the new century. There were not yet any chairs of Clinical Medicine, Bacteriology, Tuberculosis, Therapeutics, Psychiatry or Child Life and Health, while specialties such as Chemistry in relation to Medicine (Biochemistry), Neuropathology and Biophysics were still not recognized in Edinburgh.

Teaching in subjects where there was no chair or department was conducted either by lecturers, as in Child Life and Health (John Thomson) and Pathological Bacteriology (Dr Robert Muir), or by members of the Extramural School of Medicine (p 246) – individuals who were not members of the University. Thus, Thomas S Clouston of the Royal Edinburgh Asylum gave lectures on Mental Disease, while instruction in Tuberculosis was pursued in the Victoria Dispensary, which was established by Robert Philip in 1887.

M. The Medical Act of 1858 established a General Medical Council that was to prepare a register of all those qualified to practise medicine and surgery. The Medical Schools of the Universities and Royal Colleges had representatives on the Council. It was stipulated that evidence of infamous conduct in any respect would result in the name of the miscreant being removed from the register.

N. Before the eighteenth century, the completion of the training of an apprentice Barber Surgeon was recognized by success in an examination that granted a 'mastership'. In 1770, a diploma was introduced. It was renamed a Licentiateship in 1815. An individual and separate examination for Fellowship of what was now the Royal College of Surgeons of Edinburgh (FRCSEd) was discontinued temporarily in 1850, as it was believed that to become a Fellow it was sufficient for an experienced and well-known surgeon to be nominated. However, a Fellowship examination was reintroduced in 1885 in the face of competition from the other Royal Surgical Colleges.

The Diploma of Licentiate of the Royal College of Physicians of Edinburgh (LRCPEd) and the Diploma of Licentiate of the Royal College of Surgeons of Edinburgh (LRCSEd) merged (Chapter 13) and came to constitute a 'double qualification': LRCSEd, LRCPEd. The corresponding qualification of the Royal College of Surgeons of England was MRCS, LRCP. In 1884, the Faculty of Physicians and Surgeons of Glasgow had come to be included in the arrangement, so that a 'triple qualification' was born: LRCPEd, LRCSEd, LFPSG. The Glasgow faculty, granted a Royal dispensation to use the title 'Royal' in 1909, became a Royal College in 1962, so the triple qualification was now LRCPEd, LRCSEd, LRCPSG.

Recent changes had occurred in the style of the university degrees in Scotland, and, in 1889, the Universities (Scotland) Act determined that the qualifying degree would alter to MB, ChB. The title Doctor of Medicine (MD) remained as the higher degree in Medicine, but a separate Mastership in Surgery, the ChM degree, was introduced.

A Diploma in Public Health (DPH) was added to the qualifications granted by the RCSEd in 1889. Like other diplomas other than the Fellowship, it was discontinued in 1948. By this time, the University of Edinburgh, like sister institutions, was granting its own Diplomas in Public Health, Tropical Medicine and other disciplines.

O. On qualification, all medical graduates are now 'Dr'. By tradition, the majority of surgeons throughout the United Kingdom and Ireland are accorded the title 'Mr'. In Scotland, however, ophthalmologists, otolaryngologists, obstetricians and gynaecologists are designated 'Dr'.

The question of whether a newly qualified doctor should be called 'Dr' or 'Mr' did not arise until postgraduate training embraced specialization. In Wade's day, the principal distinction was between medicine and surgery. Obstetricians, by tradition, were associated with the Royal College of Physicians of Edinburgh, so Professor James Young Simpson was FRCPEd in contrast with his opponent Joseph Lister, who was FRCSEd.

Chapter 2

A. The Secretary for the Colonies, Joseph Chamberlain, had little faith in the intentions of Paul Krueger, President of the Transvaal. In turn, Krueger feared that Chamberlain's aim was the third conquest of the Transvaal and Orange Free States and their return to subjugation within the British Empire.

B. The Duke of Wellington and the adjutants General Sir John MacDonald and Sir George Brown ignored progress made on the continent. The Iron Duke believed that musketry was superior to artillery. He had won earlier battles with the old smooth bore Brown Bess musket and believed 'What could be done before, could be done again'.

C. Many were passing through on their way to England, as convalescents.

D. Their proposals were debated on 16th May 1901.

E. Alexander Ogston (1846–1929) was among the most distinguished surgeons of his time. Professor of Surgery in Aberdeen, he was an early disciple of Listerian antisepsis and discovered and named the staphylococcus. He then devoted 20 years to the condition of the Army Medical Service, accompanied the army to Suakin in the Sudan in 1885 and cared for the wounded before returning to the Military Hospital, Netley. The service was seriously deficient and in need of reform. Ogston joined the subcommittee set up by the British Medical Association to review the problem. Many changes he recommended were accepted by the Secretary of State for War, Lord Lansdowne. A Royal Warrant for the Medical Service to become a Corps of the army came into effect on 1st July 1898. Officers were granted military rank. In 1900, Ogston joined Lord Roberts' advance to the Modder River. However, he contracted enteric fever, narrowly survived and was invalided home in July of that year.

F. George Chiene (1873–1951), elder son of John Chiene, graduated in 1897. Chiene was House Surgeon to Thomas Annandale. In the spring of 1900, Chiene travelled to South Africa with the Edinburgh and East of Scotland (voluntary) Hospital. He was in South Africa, therefore, at the same time as his father (p 23). Later that year, the hospital was taken over by the military, and the staff returned home. In 1903, Chiene became Assistant Surgeon to the Royal Infirmary of Edinburgh, becoming full Surgeon in 1922. In the First World War, he served initially at Craigleith Hospital (now the Western General Hospital), but in 1918 he was sent to France. He retired in 1937. Chiene was an admired teacher, a skilled general surgeon and an advocate of local anaesthesia: he pioneered the use of stovocaine in 1904. His *Handbook of surgery* was published in 1923.[3]

G. David Wallace (1862–1952) was surgeon to the Edinburgh Hospital in South Africa. Later, as a territorial, he was on the staff of the Scottish General Hospital when it was mobilized in 1914. Wallace graduated from the University of Edinburgh and became Lecturer and then Senior Lecturer in Clinical Surgery and, from 1908 to 1923, Surgeon to the Royal Infirmary of Edinburgh. John Chiene, for whom he served as House Surgeon, encouraged him to acquire an interest in the evolving speciality of urological surgery – a subject in which he was followed by Henry Wade. He became KBE in 1920 and was President of the FRCSEd from 1921 to 1923.

H. Thorneycroft distinguished himself at the disastrous affair of Spion Kop on 24th and 25th January 1900. To the disbelief of the British public, 234 men had been killed and more than 1,000 wounded from a force of no more than a few battalions. James Wade survived.

I. The General Census of 1901 showed that the head of the Wade family at Broomage House, Larbert, was Mrs Eliza Wade, with whom resided

Grahame Wade (son), Henry Fairlie Wade (son) and Mary Russell Wade (daughter), together with two maidservants. The record is doubly inaccurate: first because Henry Wade had only one first name, second because he was in South Africa at the time of the census. An individual named Henry Fairlie was present in the Wade's house at the time of the census, but he was not a member of the family.

J. The British had adopted the Lee–Enfield rifle, now fitted with magazines holding 10 rounds. However, the change from the older Lee–Metford had meant a change in sighting. The result was that 25,000 reserve troops were dispatched to South Africa with rifles that fired 18" to the right at a distance of 500 yards. The Gatling and Gardner machine guns had been succeeded first by the four-barrelled Nordenfeldt machine gun, which fired 200 1" rounds each minute, and then, in 1884, by the Maxim water-cooled semiautomatic weapon, in which the recoil of each explosion was used to load, fire and eject continuously. The British started the war with excellent 15-pounder Armstrong shrapnel-firing field artillery. Later, they came to use longer range, 12-pounder Naval guns, although the new lyddite high explosive was almost useless against dispersed troops.

   The Boers had learned their lesson. The Jamieson Raid had alerted President Krueger to the inadequate weapons and experience of his burgher forces. Every burgher was required by law to provide himself with a rifle and ammunition, but 9,996 of the 24,238 individuals commandeered in 1895 had no weapon. The available rifles were obsolete, and there was little ammunition. President Krueger acted swiftly. He instructed Joubert to equip each burgher with a second rifle and to order 37,000 of the latest Mauser weapons from Krupp, Germany. They were of superior quality. The ammunition for the rifles was smokeless, rendering their defensive lines invisible. Moreover, they had the advantage of using a large-calibre Maxim machine gun. From Maxim–Nordenfeldt, in Britain, Joubert requested 20 experimental 20-mm 'pom-poms'. At a cost of more than £1 million, the Boers also ordered four Creusot 155-mm heavy guns (the 'Long Tom'), six 75-mm field guns, four 120-mm howitzers, eight 75-mm field guns and 20 1-lb (454g) 'pom-poms' of an experimental type not yet available to the British. Late in the day Krueger demanded another eight 75-mm Creusots.

K. That there were only 137 candles is perhaps surprising. The stores included 143 surgical sponges; the 214 field dressings were accompanied by 227 boxes of safety pins. There were 10 lb of ether and 110 lb of chloroform. Cocaine had come into use as a local anaesthetic, and the supplies included 49½ drachms of this agent (Appendix 2.2).

L. The X-ray equipment comprised a large 14-inch spark coil; a 12-inch portable coil (of Hall-Edwards' own design); a Mackenzie Davidson localizing couch; a Mackenzie Davidson cross-thread localizer; a Hall-Edwards, localizing tube holder; two EPS accumulators (12-volt, 48-ampere hours); bichromate batteries of eight cells; 15 Cox 'record' X-ray tubes; two fluorescent screens; a cycle dynamo driver; a small dynamo for charging accumulators; an ammeter; a voltmeter; a large dynamo for lighting; tube holders, intensifying screens, etc; a portable developing sink; developing dishes, printing frames, drying stands, etc; and photographic plates, developers, chemicals, etc sufficient to last at least 12 months.

M. Cordite is a smokeless explosive made of gun cotton, nitroglycerine and petroleum jelly.

N. By the time of the 'Great' War of 1914–8, the painful lesson had been learned and antityphoid vaccination had become compulsory.

O. Passive immunization against typhoid, by the injection of a preformed antitoxin, was not realistic. The injurious agents of the typhoid bacilli, *Salmonella typhi* and *paratyphi A*, *B* and *C*, are endotoxins not exotoxins.

P. Aware of the deep and growing public concern over the early military failures in South Africa and the widespread anxiety regarding the casualty figures, the government moved quickly to set up the Royal Commission of 1901 (see Appendix 2.3).

Q. After the war, a further Royal Commission reported to Parliament in 1903. Evidence was taken from senior civilian surgeons who had served in South Africa. Among them were: Alfred Downing Fripp CB, CVO, MS, MB, FRCS and Sir Frederick Treves, Bart, CB, KCVO, FRCS (Appendix 2.4). See also: *Appendix to minutes of evidence taken before the Royal Commission appointed to consider and report upon the care and treatment of the sick and wounded during the South African campaign.* London: Stationery Office: 368 (3/–). A further 71 pages were added in the same year at an additional cost of 8d.

Chapter 3

A. First published in 1862, this essay, one of John Brown's most famous, refers to an operation performed by James Syme in Minto Hospital, Chambers Street, in 1828. John Brown was the family doctor to Syme and his family; Syme's daughter was the wife of Joseph Lister.

B. WS Greenfield occupied the Chair of Pathology from 1881 to 1912. He succeeded John Thomson (1831–42), William Henderson (1842–6) and William Rutherford Sanders (1869–81). Greenfield held the position of Professor of Clinical Medicine and had wards in the Royal Infirmary of Edinburgh. The tradition of linking clinical teaching with the duties of pathologist persisted until his retirement in 1912. After Greenfield, and during Wade's lifetime, came James Lorrain Smith (1912–31), A Murray Drennan (1931–54) and George Lightbody Montgomery (1954–71).

C. Robert Muir (1864–1959) became Senior Assistant in Pathology of the University of Edinburgh in 1892 and Pathologist to the Royal Infirmary of Edinburgh. Later, Muir was Lecturer in Pathological Bacteriology from 1894 to 1898, before becoming Professor of Pathology of St Andrews University and finally Professor of Pathology of the University of Glasgow from 1899 to 1933. Under his direction, the Glasgow School of Pathology confirmed its worldwide reputation.

D. In 2005, the initial postgraduate diploma is that of Member of the Royal Colleges of Surgeons (UK) (MRCS, UK). The further qualification of Fellowship is now designated a 'Specialty Fellowship' according to the field of surgery in which a candidate exercises his or her skills.

E. Francis Mitchell Caird (1853–1926), a distinguished Fellow of the RCSEd, was appointed Surgeon-in-Ordinary (senior consultant) to the RIE in 1903. He was elected Regius Professor of Clinical Surgery in 1908, remaining a senior surgeon to the RIE until 1919. In 1912, he served as President of the RCSEd. Caird was an authority on abdominal surgery, building on the pioneering work of Billroth and Mickulicz at a time when the resection of injured, strangulated or gangrenous intestine and the removal of cancers of the gut began to be possible and when the treatment of perforated peptic ulcer now offered hope of recovery. Caird's extensive experience, wise guidance and understanding played a large part in furthering Wade's training and advancement, and he was one of the young surgeon's most influential teachers. Wade acted as Caird's clinical assistant, accompanying him to operations on private patients and administering the chloroform used in anaesthesia. Caird was a skilled artist, and a beautifully illustrated book of his notes is a treasured possession of the RCSEd.

F. David (later Sir) Percival Dalbreck Wilkie (1883–1938), Wade's friend and younger colleague, became Surgeon to Leith Hospital in 1910 and to the RIE in 1912. The First World War intervened. Wilkie served on hospital ships and in France before joining Sir Harold Stiles (below). A craftsman, conservative and painstaking, Wilkie combined sound judgement with an aptitude for improvization. When the death of Alexis Thomson in 1924 coincided with the retirement of Sir Harold Stiles, Wilkie was appointed to the University Chair of Systematic Surgery. There were delays in providing a new building; however, an extension to the Department of Anatomy was converted to a surgical laboratory by October 1925. After Wilkie's premature death from gastric cancer, the building was renamed The Wilkie Surgical Research Laboratory. Early in the 1920's, he and Wade became partners in the establishment of a Private Clinic at 35 Drumsheugh Gardens. In 1929, Wilkie operated upon Mrs. Wade and had the appalling misfortune to observe her death one week later.

G. The story of the 1879 RIE, often termed the Florence Nightingale hospital after the advice she gave on the occasion of her visit to Edinburgh in 1856, is long and complex. It is summarized on pp 10 and 43.

H. Joseph Bell described how, in 1854, there was no Lady Superintendent of Nurses in the old Edinburgh Royal Infirmary. The matron was a housekeeper and had kept a baker's shop, and she knew no more of nursing than the poorest of the scrubbers. A house surgeon, assisted by nine women, cared for 72 patients, distributed in six wards and six little rooms. Two of the women were staff nurses:

> 'Wonderful women, of great natural ability and strong Scottish sense and capacity, of immense experience and great kindliness.'

The other seven were:

> 'Poor, useless drudges, half-charwoman, half-field worker, rarely keeping their places for any length of time, absolutely ignorant, almost invariably drunken, sometimes deaf, occasionally fatuous.

Poor, creatures, their work began at 11 p.m. when in a mournful procession, each with a blanket round her shoulders, they walked to the wards from a dormitory, so-called, in the east end of the grounds. There they were supposed to keep up the fire and nurse the patients till five when they had to set about cleaning the wards, scouring the tins and preparing for the patients' breakfast.

What wonder that at night they snored by the fire, often on a vacant bed, if they could get one; and when an accident came in their blear eyes and stupid heads were of little use except to rouse up one or two house surgeons to help the one on duty. Serious operations were doubled in risk by want of ordinary care.'

I.   Dawson Fyers Duckworth Turner (1857–1928) was Assistant Medical Electrician to the RIE in 1896, Medical Electrician in 1901 and Extra Medical Electrician in 1911. He also lectured in physics at Surgeons' Hall. Early in his career, he set up equipment in his own house at 37 George Street, Edinburgh, and, on 5th February 1896, only a few weeks after Röntgen's epoch-making discovery, he demonstrated X-ray photographs to the Edinburgh Medico-Chirurgical Society. The number of radiological examinations increased rapidly. In 1901, no more than 1,000 were recorded in the RIE. In 1914, 6,000 X-ray photographs were taken.

     Like so many of the pioneers, Dawson Turner suffered from the effects of unguarded use of primitive equipment and he sustained radiation burns and the loss of three fingers and an eye.

J.   The history of anaesthesia is surprisingly long.[34] The first mention of an anaesthetic agent in English was in 1562.

K.   Illustrations of this case are shown in Figures 3.8 and 3.9. The case was reported in the *Edinburgh Medical Journal* of 1920. Eleven years after the successful graft, swelling of the shoulder and the presence of a mass of heterogeneous bone indicated the growth of an osteosarcoma. Intracapsular amputation was performed but the patient did not long survive the operation. (pp 51–2, 217–18).

L.   The boy was Norman McOmish Dott (1897–1973), later to become one of the world's leading neurosurgeons. Dott's conversion from his first love, engineering, to medicine, came as a result of the road accident he sustained at the age of 16 years. Riding his motorcycle up Lothian Road, he fell, fracturing his left leg. Threatened with amputation, he was saved by the intervention of Henry Wade. Persuaded by the care he received, Dott became a medical student. Through the influence of the physiologist, Professor Sharpey Schafer, he began the study of the pituitary gland. Success in research led to a Rockefeller Surgical Fellowship spent in 1923–4 with Harvey Cushing in Boston. In turn, came surgical appointments at the Royal Hospital for Sick Children, Edinburgh, where his work extended from the repair of hair lip and cleft palate to the surgery of hypospadias and intussusception. This experience allowed Dott to devote increasing time to the surgery of neurological disease. His fame was recognized when he became a Freeman of the City of Edinburgh in 1962.

M.   The most notorious case of the late nineteenth century was that of the Crown Prince Frederick, later Emperor Frederick III of Germany. It was suspected that he had laryngeal cancer. Morell Mackenzie, the leading European expert, correctly insisted that operation be delayed until a biopsy had been examined. A report that confirmed the diagnosis was made by Rudolph Virchow. However, surgery was too late and the Emperor died in 1892.

N.   The occasion was the operation on 24th June 1902 on the new King, Edward VII. His illness delayed the coronation, but it precipitated an immediate increase in the frequency of the surgical procedure. By 1890, Lawson Tait had publicized the operation of appendicectomy in Great Britain. Treves published a full account of 'perityphlitis' (appendicitis) in 1897. Henry Wade chose appendicitis as the subject of a special display in the Museum of the Royal College of Surgeons of Edinburgh.

O. Syme was succeeded by James Spence (1871) and then by Patrick Heron Watson (1883), William Stewart (1906), Alexander Miles (1913), AA Scot-Skirving (1917), JW Struthers (1925) and David Wilkie (1925). From 1897, surgeons (in addition to consultant surgeons) were designated. In Henry Wade's time, they were William Stewart (1897), Alexander Miles (1897), AA Scot-Skirving (1906), JW Struthers (1911), A Pirie Watson (1925), JM Carlow (1926), JJM Shaw (1927), AP Mitchell (1938) and RL Stewart (1939).

P. Harold (later Sir Harold) Jalland Stiles (1863–1946) and Wade shared many interests. Stiles had been surgical pathologist to Professor Chiene. Stiles introduced to Edinburgh the method of paraffin wax embedding, the 'Naples' technique' (p 80), and applied it to the study of breast disease. He had a fervent interest in tuberculosis and encouraged his protégées, including John Fraser (p 188), to investigate this disease in children. Stiles translated Kocher's *Textbook of operative surgery* into English and spent the First World War, 'his ultimate and greatest teacher', in adult surgery, largely at Bangour Hospital (p 284). In 1919, he succeeded Francis Caird in the Regius Chair of Clinical Surgery. He resigned in 1925 at the end of his time as President of the RCSEd.

Q. Patrick Heron Watson (1827–1907) achieved fame and notoriety. He served in the Crimea, where he was twice taken ill with typhoid or typhus but survived. Ambitious for the Chair of Military Surgery, he took up general practice in Edinburgh and was one of the last to combine such work with surgery. He was a Lecturer at Surgeons' Hall (Chapter 13). In 1858, he contested the position of Assistant Surgeon unsuccessfully when Lister's position was confirmed. In 1870, the death of Professor Spence created a vacancy for the Regius Chair of Clinical Surgery. Heron Watson and Lister were both applicants. Lister was elected. Heron Watson was greatly admired and liked. He became Honorary Surgeon in Scotland to Queen Victoria and then to King Edward VII, and he twice served the RCSEd as President, on the second occasion during the celebration of the 400th anniversary of the College in 1905.

R. In 1818, it was agreed that the Infirmary should have six surgeons. There were to be two Consulting Surgeons, two Acting Surgeons and two Assistant Surgeons. The Acting Surgeons were placed in charge of the surgical beds in the hospital. The consulting appointments were of an advisory nature.

In 1854, Bell recorded that there were two Ordinary Acting Surgeons with three wards each and a specialist ophthalmic surgeon with two small eye wards.[8] Professor Miller, who occupied the Chair of Systematic Surgery, was a Consulting Surgeon. He had a small number of beds. By contrast, James Syme, the Professor of Clinical Surgery, had 72 beds.

By 1891, in addition to the holders of the Chairs of Surgery, Professor Chiene and Professor Annandale, there were three Acting Surgeons, each with a large number of beds, six Assistant Surgeons and six Specialists.

Chapter 4

A. The substance of this chapter is taken from Gardner DL. *Henry Wade (1876–1955) and cancer research: early years in the life of a pioneer of urological surgery*, published in the *Journal of Medical Biography* 2003;11:81–6. It is reproduced by permission of the Editor.

B. William Ford Robertson (1867–1923) was an individual of original mind and purpose. He graduated in medicine at Edinburgh in 1891 and held appointments as House Physician to the Royal Infirmary of Edinburgh and to the Royal Edinburgh Hospital for Sick Children. In 1893, he accepted the appointment of Pathologist to the Royal Edinburgh Asylum. He was barely 26 years of age and can have had little experience of neuropathology or, indeed, of any form of pathology. However, he had had an excellent education, was conversant with several European languages and profited by possessing considerable self-confidence, a characteristic that brought him a reputation as an influential teacher. Ford Robertson published an original work, *A Textbook of pathology in relation to mental diseases*, of great interest.[40] His fascination with neuropathology can be attributed to the teaching of William Russell, a clinician who had been a pathologist to the RIE from 1888 until 1891. Russell was a lecturer in the Extramural School of Medicine of the Edinburgh Royal Colleges (p 246), teaching on the pathology of nervous diseases. He was interested in carcinogenesis, and his concept that protozoa or blastomycetes might be the cause of cancer influenced Ford Robertson's views.

C. The evidence of a bacterial cause of general paralysis of the insane (GPI) came later, when in 1913 Noguchi and Moore demonstrated *Treponema pallidum* in brain tissue from cases of this disease. Wasserman had paved the way by showing that the cerebrospinal fluid in 90% of cases was positive in his serological test. Ford Robertson's hypothesis of the bacterial origin of cerebral syphilis was close to the truth.

D. Since 1899, Harvey Russell Gaylord (1872–1928) had been Director of the New York State Institute for the Study of Malignant Diseases. He had studied in Europe, and, in 1900, was the co-author with Ludwig Aschoff of a splendid text and atlas in German, *Kursus der Pathologischen Histologie mit einem mikroskopischen Atlas*, subsequently issued in an American edition. It is of historical interest that Gaylord was called on to perform the autopsy on the late President McKinley, who had been assassinated by shooting in 1901. Gaylord's views on carcinogenesis found their origins in publications by the Italian investigator, Sanfelice of Cagliari, Sardinia, and by the Edinburgh worker Russell (see B above), whose name was given to the inclusions termed Russell bodies. Both interpreted the structures they found in cancer cells as parasites, such as protozoa, or fungi, such as blastomycetes.

E. Koch formulated his three famous 'postulates' in 1880. To ascribe an organism as a cause of a disease, he required that 1. the micro-organism had to be present in all cases; 2. the organism had to reproduce the disease when inoculated into animals; and 3. the micro-organism had to be recovered from these animals and grown in pure culture.

Chapter 5

A. Wade's contemporaries as Assistant Pathologist to the RIE were Stuart McDonald and George Lyon, who ended their appointments in 1906, and William Elliott Carnegie Dickson and John Dixon Comrie, whose positions dated from 1906 to 1909 and from 1908 to 1910, respectively. In 1910, James Miller and Alexander Murray Drennan joined the laboratory staff.

B. The career of Professor WS Greenfield is outlined in Chapter 3.

C. Heating was a luxury not enjoyed in the mortuaries of many hospitals as recently as 1950. A bucket of hot water stood beside the dissecting table, allowing a pathologist to warm his/her hands periodically.

D. In other hospitals, the arrangements were simpler. In the Bruntsfield Hospital, Edinburgh, the chapel served as a mortuary, and a prosector was compelled to hang his clothes on the crucifix.

E. The surgeons were Mr Charles Walker Cathcart (Ward 18), Professor Francis Mitchell Caird (Ward 7), Mr David (later Sir David) Wallace (Ward 6 and, three years later, Ward 12), Mr James (later Sir James) William Beaman Hodsdon (Ward 18 in 1909 and Ward 16 in 1910), Mr Henry (later Sir Henry) Wade (Ward 13 in 1913), Mr John Wheeler Dowden (Ward 9), Professor John Wyllie (Ward 34) and Mr George Chiene (Ward 13 in 1911).The pathologists who examined and reported these cases were Mr Theodor Shennan, Dr Alexander Murray Drennan, Dr John Dixon Comrie, Mr Henry Wade, Dr William Elliot Carnegie Dickson, Dr George Lyon, Dr James Hunter Harvey Pirie and Dr James Miller.

   The name of a D Miller is appended to one report, but no record of his appointment can be traced, and his first initial may have been written in error.

F. The first report (a) was written by Mr Henry Wade and the second (b) by Dr Theodor Shennan (Appendix 5.1).

G. This custom was still accepted in Edinburgh in 1954.

H. By 1863, the US Army Medical Museum, Washington, had collected 1,349 anatomical specimens, the core of what was to become the world famous Armed Forces Institute of Pathology. The preservative used was 70% ethyl alcohol. It was 'secured by re-distilling the illicit liquors seized by the Provost Marshall.'[37]

I. The history of the microscope is said to begin with the instruments of Leeuwenhoek and Hooke. Reflected and transmitted light was employed. A discovery of the utmost significance was the value of 'clearing' specimens by immersing them in a fluid such as olive oil,[12] an approach that allowed internal structure to be revealed. Only with the development of microscope lenses corrected for spherical and for chromatic aberration, however, were the images obtained from compound microscopes sufficiently exact and sufficiently reliable to permit the formulation of a Cell Theory.

J. In 1926, Cheatle's method was employed in the Physicians' Laboratory. By 1927, more than 1,200 such sections had been prepared. They included the sections of lung studied in 1929 by Dr Agnes MacGregor, those of renal and prostatic disease made during 1923–8 by Wade (p 107) and those of breast cancer made by Dr Edith Dawson (p 84).

K. In the course of his studies of dye specificity, Ehrlich advanced the concept of dye binding and specific receptors, work that led to his studies of immunity and the concepts of antigens and antibodies. One of the earliest 'stains' was madder root. In ancient times, many natural vegetable and mineral dyes had been used, for example, in watercolour painting, printing and dyeing fabrics. In 1856, Perkin manufactured the first synthetic dye, mauve. The dye was tested in microscopy in 1862. Thereafter, the explosive growth of the European chemical industry led to the manufacture of rapidly growing numbers of other synthetic dyes. For the staining of microscope sections, Paris blue, basic fuchsin, aniline blue and picric acid were tested. The pioneering work of Paul Ehrlich included the use of at least 12 dyes. Among them were safranin, acid fuchsin and neutral red.

L. A microphotograph is an image of a small structure. A photomicrograph is an image recorded through a microscope.

M. Under WS Greenfield's direction, German (later Sir German) Sims Woodhead (1855–1921) was responsible for establishing a course in practical pathological histology – the innovative method for learning the nature of disease by examining sections of tissues with a microscope. The course formed the basis for his well-known *Practical Pathology*, which provided a valuable guide to students for over 30 years. Sims Woodhead was appointed as the first Superintendent of the Laboratory of the RCPEd when it opened in 1887. He moved in 1890 to be Director of the Laboratories of the Conjoint Board of the Royal College of Surgeons of England and the Royal College of Physicians of London. In 1892, his already formidable reputation was enhanced when he founded the *Journal of Pathology and Bacteriology*. In 1899, Sims Woodhead succeeded Charles Smart Roy, another Edinburgh graduate, in the Chair of Pathology of the University of Cambridge. The Pathological Society of Great Britain and Ireland was constituted in 1906 and the Journal became associated with it. Woodhead remained Editor-in-Chief until his retirement in 1921, when the *Journal* was adopted as the official organ of the Society.

N. James Ritchie (1864–1923) became Superintendent of the Laboratory of the RCPEd in 1907 and held the position until 1920. He had been Lecturer, Reader and Professor of Pathology at Oxford from 1890 to 1907. In 1913, he accepted the Chair of Bacteriology and Clinical Medicine of the University of Edinburgh – an appointment he held until his death in 1923.

O. James Dawson (1870–1927) was among the most distinguished of all Edinburgh pathologists. Graduating in 1904 at the relatively late age of 34 years, he began work in the laboratory in 1908, becoming neurological histologist in 1913. In 1915, he joined Lorrain Smith and Ritchie in studies of trench foot and the effects of poison gas. Throughout his life, Dawson battled courageously with ill health but, in 1919, he was obliged to accept six months' sick leave. He returned to work but died in 1927. He is remembered for his studies of disseminated (multiple) sclerosis and melanomata.[38,39] His monograph with JW Struthers on *Generalized osteitis fibrosa* is recognized as a classic.[40]

P. In his later years, James Dawson was supported loyally by his wife, Edith Kate Dawson MBE (1886–1983). Born in India but educated in this country, she taught in a missionary school in Rangoon before entering Medicine in Edinburgh and becoming a pathologist. After leaving Lorrain Smith's University department, she served the Laboratory of the RCPEd with distinction until 1948, when she returned to the University. She moved to the RCSEd in 1960. During her years there, she confirmed her international expertise in breast cancer. She was awarded a Doctorate of Science in her 84th year. The RCSEd retains her archives.

Q. Alexis Thomson (1863–1924) was House Surgeon to John Duncan and Thomas Annandale. In 1888–89, he exploited the new Laboratory of the Royal College of Physicians for investigations of bone and joint tuberculosis. He conducted classes in Anatomy and Pathology with Harold Stiles and became Assistant Surgeon to the RIE in 1892. The dress of the consultant in the 1890s was a frock coat with tails, and Alexis Thomson was among the first to abandon this style.[6] Supported by Sir James Paget and Lord Lister, he was elected Professor of Systematic Surgery in succession to John Chiene in 1909. With Alexander Miles, he published *A manual of surgery*.[41] In 1914, he joined the 2nd Scottish General Hospital, later becoming Consultant to the Third Army of the British Expeditionary Force but he was invalided home with trench fever from which he never wholly recovered.

R. John (later Sir John) Struthers (1823–1899) was Professor of Anatomy in Aberdeen from 1863 to 1889. He returned to Edinburgh and was President of the RCSEd from 1895 until 1897. He was keenly interested in medical education, stressed the need for a premedical course in basic science and emphasized the value of practical as opposed to predominantly didactic teaching. He was knighted in 1898. His elder son, JW Struthers, was also a distinguished Edinburgh surgeon (p 351). His younger son, Alexander, a fellow Resident House Surgeon with Joseph Lister in the first RIE, died during the Crimean war.

Chapter 6

A. David Waterston (1870–1942) was elected FRCSEd in 1898. He was chosen as Interim Conservator of the RCSEd in 1900 but quickly returned to a Lectureship in Anatomy under Sir William Turner (p 14). He was awarded the Crichton Research Scholarship in Anatomy on 13th October 1900. An astute and able teacher and anthropologist, he became Professor of Anatomy at King's College, London, in 1909. He was at the same time Dean of the Faculty of Science (Medical). In 1914, he was translated to the Bute Chair of Anatomy at St Andrews University. His interest in clinical medicine showed itself in his collaboration with Sir James Mackenzie of polygraph fame. Waterston gave the prestigious Struthers Lecture to the Royal College of Surgeons of Edinburgh in 1927 and, according to instructions left by his friend, examined Mackenzie's heart *post-mortem*.

B. Charles Walker Cathcart CMG (1853–1932) became Assistant Surgeon to the Royal Infirmary of Edinburgh in 1884 and Surgeon-in-Ordinary in 1901. He retired, as Consultant Surgeon, in 1918. He served as Lieutenant Colonel in the Territorial Forces from 1914 until 1919. His influence within the College and on the Museum was very great. He was Conservator from 1887 until 1900. Over a period of 45 years, he exerted a significant impact on College decisions. During his time as Conservator, he devoted a great deal of time to the preparation of the New (printed) Catalogue (p 109). He also played a prominent part in the establishment and management of the College Laboratory. A man of some determination, he announced his resignation on 19th October 1900 but withdrew it when the Museum Committee agreed that an additional £50 be granted to him as an honorarium to allow him to pay a Museum Assistant directly. He insisted that the arrangement was 'with the Conservator still taking the entire supervision of the Museum'. He remained a prominent member of the Museum Committee and became Convener in 1908 at the time that the 'New' or 'Upper' Museum (p 95) was being constructed. It was named after him. His contribution to the work of the Emergency Surgical Service at Bangour Hospital is outlined in Chapter 14.

C. The candidates were Edward William Scott Carmichael, proposed by Mr JM Cotterill and seconded by Mr AA Scot Skirving; Hubert Dunbar Shepherd, proposed by Mr JWB Hodsdon and seconded by Mr A Thomson; Mr Henry Wade, proposed by Mr CW Cathcart and seconded by Dr T Shennan; and John William Struthers, proposed by Dr WT Ritchie and seconded by Mr A Miles. Like Wade, Shepherd was a young anatomy teacher. He had graduated MB, ChB in 1900 and was two years junior to Wade but had been admitted to the Fellowship of the RCSEd on the same day as Wade. Shepherd held the position of Senior Demonstrator in Anatomy whereas Wade's appointment was that of Junior Extramural Clinical Surgery Tutor. Shepherd was therefore senior to Wade but lacked experience of military service.

D. At that time, the Council comprised Joseph Bell (President), Alexander G Miller, John Chiene (p 23), James Dunsmore, William Craig and CW MacGillivray, together with the *ex officio* office bearers, the Secretary/Treasurer, Francis Cadell, the Vice President and the College's representative on the General Medical Council.

E. It was at this time in 1903 that the College decided to devote two whole days to the occasion of the Quartcentenary. For this purpose they set on one side £500. On 27th July 1905, they determined to hold a divine service followed by luncheon, a welcome to guests, a Presidential address and an evening reception. On 28th July, there were to be a visit to the Museum and to Edinburgh hospitals, another lunch, a garden party at Heriot's School and a dinner.[52]

F. David Middleton Greig (1864–1936) came from a respected Dundee medical family. It was said that his grandfather, working as a doctor in pre-Listerian times, wore ruffles, knee breeches, hose and buckled shoes. Greig graduated MB, CM in 1885. He then served for three years with the army at home and in India. Entering practice in Dundee, he moved into operative surgery and, in this capacity, devoted 30 years to the Dundee Royal Infirmary while acting as Demonstrator in Anatomy at University College, a period interrupted by the South African War (Chapter 2). Subsequently, he held the rank of Major in the RAMC (T). As a lecturer on the surgical diseases of children, his skills were in constant demand in Angus, Perthshire and Fife. Greig was elected Conservator of the Museum of the RCSEd in 1921. From an early age, he displayed an academic approach to his subject. Greig's early published works included a report on war wounds sustained in South Africa. The key to his favoured subjects were his sustained attempts to unravel the causes of the skull defects so frequent among the children who were under his care as Medical Superintendent of the *Baldovan Institute for the Care and Education of the Feeble-Minded*. The College recognized the importance of publishing the Museum catalogue that he compiled painstakingly.[53] He was the first to describe hypertelorism, and his later work drew attention to an example of neanderthaloid skull development.[54] In 1934, he was awarded the degree of LLD by the University of Edinburgh.

G. Walter Mercer (1890–1971) was one of the most distinguished College Presidents of modern times. He joined a group at Bangour Hospital (p 284) in 1919 that included orthopaedic surgeons directed by Robert Jones. Mercer worked with John Fraser as Assistant Surgeon to the RIE in 1924. He (Mercer) maintained great skill in gastrointestinal surgery but moved to chest and heart surgery before accepting the new Edinburgh University Chair of Orthopaedic Surgery. In the RCSEd, his influence was equally great. He served on the Museum Committee and on the Council. Elected President, he held office twice. Following the closure of the School of Medicine of the Edinburgh Royal Colleges (p 246), he revived postgraduate surgical teaching, drawing young Fellows into committees and organizational activities. In 1955, Mercer presided over the celebrations marking the 450th anniversary of the founding of the Incorporation of Edinburgh Barber Surgeons and initiated the College Journal which came to be directed by John Bruce.

H. In 1903, the Convener (Chairman) of the Museum Committee was JM Cotterill. Other members included Alexander Miles, JWB Hodsdon and David Wallace. Andrew Logan Turner joined the Committee in 1907. By 1908, CW Cathcart assumed the Chair when JM Cotterill became President. The Committee's members were then Francis Caird, Theodor Shennan, David Wallace, Alexander Miles and Andrew Logan Turner. During the succeeding 12 years, there were occasional further changes in the composition of the Committee but these changes were minimized during the years of the First World War.

I. Walter Quarry Wood (1888–1962), elected President of the RCSEd in 1949, achieved renown as an academic anatomist. Armed with a prodigious memory and manual skill, he was awarded gold medals for both his MD and ChM theses. Quiet, unassuming, slightly built and courteous, he was the antithesis of the layman's image of the successful surgeon. 'He was, in fact, imperturbable'.[11] Quarry Wood enjoyed strong spiritual convictions. Many benefited from his surgical prowess but first, they had to survive the ordeal of his monosyllabic, self-effacing manner. Speaking to a patient with a gangrenous leg, Quarry Wood was liable to confine his remarks to 'It's got to come off'. The sufferer benefited from Quarry Wood's particular understanding of and skills in the treatment of cancer of the intestinal tract. Quarry Wood became Assistant Surgeon to the RIE in 1923 and Surgeon-in-Ordinary in 1939.

J. There remained the challenge of disposing of the old (1697) Surgeons' Hall. Estimates showed that it was worth only the ground on which it stood (£250), together with any remaining materials (£60). When the value of the house was included, the surgeons found that the assets accruing from the old structure amounted to £1,510. The oak panelling from the old hall was moved to Playfair's new building. On 19th July 1928, A Logan Turner announced that he would bear the cost of transferring to the College the old doorway from Surgeons' Square with the added inscription: '*The Tympanum and Lintel Of The Doorway Of The Original Surgeons' Hall Completed In 1697*'. Ultimately, the old building was bought by the University of Edinburgh for use as a Department of Geography.

K. On the ground floor, an oblique pedestrian link was provided. It is shown in drawings made in 1913. Later, a more direct, rectilinear and wider passage was constructed. It is delineated in plans drawn in 1960. A first-floor bridge connecting the Museum with rooms that had become the College Laboratory was completed in 1902. It was followed by a new bridge added in 1908.

L. When the new Barclay Hall at 9 Hill Square was reconstructed again in 1994, it was discovered that no metal tubes had been used and that simple electrical wires were attached directly to wooden slats.

M. The 'New' or Cathcart Museum became an essential part of the space used for displays. Many years later, during the Conservatorship of Eric Mekie, it was developed as a centre for postgraduate teaching. In 1988, a generous grant of £100,000 from the Sir Jules Thorn Foundation allowed the New Museum to be developed as a Museum of the History of Edinburgh Surgery, with the addition, in 1998, of a gallery displaying the story of *50 years of the National Health Service*.

N. James Norman Jackson Hartley (1889–1966) graduated MB, ChB with first-class honours in 1913, served in the army and undertook valuable studies of war wounds. Twice mentioned in dispatches, he was appointed OBE (Mil). Returning to Edinburgh, he became surgical assistant to Sir Harold Stiles (p 340) before being made Assistant Surgeon to the RIE and then, in 1927, Honorary Surgeon to the Cumberland Infirmary. He was an examiner to the Royal College of Surgeons of Edinburgh. It was said that 'his lean frame was strong enough to respond to the huge demands made on it by his intellectual urges, by long, arduous hours of operating day and night, by hospital outpatient sessions and by long country journeys at all times and seasons'. On his retirement in 1947, he was elected Conservator of the Museum, a position that he held with great distinction until 1955.

O. Until 1948, the costs were partly justified by the demands of undergraduate education. After the Extramural School of Medicine of the Royal Colleges closed in 1948, the expense was justified by the demands of postgraduate teaching (Chapter 13) and examination.

P. James Bell Pettigrew (1834–1908) was one of the most unusual academic figures of his time. An Edinburgh graduate, he was awarded a gold medal for his MD thesis and was Lecturer on Physiology at the School of Medicine, Surgeons' Hall. He was fascinated by the interaction of organic matter and the forces observed in nature in muscular contraction. This interest led him to the study of aerial navigation and flight. He experimented with flying machines and contributed on this subject in the *Encyclopaedia Britannica*. His dissections of muscle fibres, including those of the heart, were displayed in the Hunterian Museum of the Royal College of Surgeons of England, where he served as Assistant Curator before returning to Edinburgh to become Curator of the Museum of the

Edinburgh College. His work gained him the Godard prize of the French Academy of Sciences, and later he was elected FRS. Pettigrew succeeded to the Chandos Chair of Medicine and Anatomy of the University of St Andrews in 1875 after his publication of *Animal Locomotion*.

Q. A General Catalogue dated from 1807. In 1824, Hamilton, Watson and Knox strove to bring it up to date. Knox prepared an (Edinburgh) Bell Catalogue. The Mackintosh obstetrical specimens were added in 1837. In 1828, a Wilson Catalogue was presented to the College, while William MacGillivray made a First Printed Catalogue. The initial part was published in 1835. In 1888, Cathcart's plan for a New Catalogue was accepted. Advantage was taken of the new science of Histology centred on microscopy (p 78). Volumes 1 (1893) and 2 (1898) of the New Catalogue were prepared by Cathcart and Volume 3 (1903) by Theodor Shennan. Of the 1,284 items in Volume 2, largely nervous, alimentary and urinary, 314 were examined microscopically. In 1908, Wade introduced an additional system of recording, the Scroll Book, on the basis of his experience of laboratory work in the Royal Infirmary of Edinburgh. Fifteen years later, Greig adopted a typewriter, card indexing and loose-leaf sheets for his own system, the Greig Catalogue.

R. A dangerous precedent, as it depended on the interest and time of the Conservator to ensure that the work was almost wholly for the Museum. It led eventually to a situation in which an assistant might work entirely on general College duties.

S. Frank Evelyn Jardine (1886–1956) started his surgical career as House Surgeon to Francis Caird, to whom he became Assistant. He served as Lecturer in Anatomy to the Bristo Street Extramural School and was renowned as an accurate diagnostician and skilled operator. In the Royal Infirmary of Edinburgh, he was Assistant Surgeon under WJ Stewart and then Surgeon-in-Ordinary. He was Interim Conservator of the Museum of the Royal College of Surgeons of Edinburgh during the First World War and was Elected President in 1947.

Chapter 7

A. The Secretary of State for War was the elderly and Olympian Field Marshall – the Right Honourable HH Lord Kitchener of Khartoum, KG, KP, GCB, OM. The Chief of the Imperial General Staff was the imperturbable Lieutenant General Sir WB Robertson. The First Lord of the Admiralty was the impetuous and ambitious Winston Churchill. The First Sea Lord was the aged and petulant Admiral Sir John Fisher. A Directorate of Military Aeronautics was administered by the General Officer commanding the Royal Flying Corps, an organization with naval and military 'wings'.

B. At the outbreak of war with Germany, the Turks had on order two of the most modern Dreadnought British battleships, of which one was armed with 14 12"guns. The ships were promptly bought by Britain. However, the Turks acquired two German warships, the Dresden and the Goeben, and stationed them in the Black Sea.

C. The story of the Highland Mounted Brigade Field Ambulance (Territorial Forces) was recorded very fully.[10] They shared experiences similar to those of the SHMB Field Ambulance. The Highland Mounted Brigade Field Ambulance (Territorial Forces) left Hexham on 6th September 1915 by train for Devonport, where it joined the brigade. The Field Ambulance then embarked on His Majesty's Transport *Ardania* for Gallipoli, sailing via Malta and Alexandria.

D. The museum's displays are now in the Castle Museum, Edinburgh.

E. William Thomas Ritchie (1873–1945) graduated from the University of Edinburgh two years before Wade. Both were closely involved in the work of the Laboratory of the Royal College of Physicians of Edinburgh, where Ritchie conducted bacteriological research before becoming Assistant Physician to the RIE in 1911 and Physician-in-Ordinary in 1922. An authority on cardiac disease, Ritchie was the first to describe atrial (auricular) flutter. He published a monograph on this subject. He was posted from the 2nd Scottish General Hospital, Craigleith, to serve with the 1/3 Scottish Horse at Gallipoli and then in Egypt. Henry Wade was 'best man' at Ritchie's wedding in 1922. Ritchie was President of the RCPEd in the same years (1935–7) in which Wade held the Presidency of the RCSEd (Chapter 14).

F. The make of camera that Wade took with him remains uncertain. It is likely to have been a 4¼ × 2¼ (108 mm × 57 mm) large-format, folding Kodak camera. However, in the later parts of his collection of photographs, different negative formats appear, confirming that two or even three cameras may have been used at different times. There is also a small group of prints entitled 'Turkish photographs'. The content suggests strongly that they could only have been taken by a Turkish photographer and that therefore they were 'captured' by Wade when the enemy forces surrendered.

G. This car achieved fame, travelling with the brigade to Egypt as a brigade staff car. It was then transferred to the Arab Army. It landed near Jeddah with other armoured cars. Twenty miles of new road were provided for them. The car was known as 'Blue Mist' and survived the fighting up to and beyond Aleppo.

H. The new arrivals would recall that on 13th June the remnant of the 7th Royal Scots, a territorial regiment that had survived the railway disaster at Gretna Green, reached Gallipoli with the 156th Brigade of the Lowland Division. Three officers and 211 men had been killed and 246 seriously injured in one of the worst railway accidents ever to have occurred in Britain. Only six officers and 57 men under Colonel Peebles were able to board the *Empress of Britain* as she sailed.

Chapter 8

A. Dominique Larrey was Surgeon-in-Chief to Napoleon's Grande Armée. Wade had learnt of Larrey's 'flying ambulances' while working on the designs of his own mobile operating car. When the war ended, Wade arranged for the translation into English of a substantial part of Larrey's memoirs (p 324); Appendix 2.1.

B. Cercariae are the minute free-swimming larvae of the worm *Schistosoma haematobium*.

C. Major A Pirie Watson (1889–1943) was a territorial who had become Regimental Medical Officer to the 4th battalion of the Royal Scots in 1914. He had accompanied the 52nd Lowland Division to the Dardanelles when attacks were renewed in August 1915. He joined the Egyptian Expeditionary Force, was involved in the battle of Romani and served at a CCS during the battles for Gaza. He was present when Jerusalem was captured. After the war ended, in 1925, Pirie Watson became the Officer Commanding the Second Scottish General Hospital. He was initially Assistant Surgeon and then Surgeon-in-Ordinary to the RIE. He was elected to the Council of the Royal College of Surgeons of Edinburgh, but was able to combine these responsibilities with the challenge, in 1933, of being Assistant Director Medical Services, ADMS, to the 52nd Division.

D. Shells filled with bullets or metal particles, timed to explode near or above combatants, before impact.

E. When passive, anti-tetanus immunization was introduced, soldiers received approximately 1 fluid ounce (30 ml) of the unrefined horse serum. It was injected subcutaneously, into the foot. Serum sickness, a hypersensitivity reaction to the foreign proteins of the horse serum, was a common complication.

F. An obsolete term, based on the theory that there was pus in the blood. The assumption came from the appearance of blood seen in a glass tube: the leucocytes separated as a distinct, pale layer, simulating pus.

G. Other devices of value included the Balkan frame, or Balkan bed, and Pearson's callipers used with the Thomas splint; the callipers proved to be better than Steinmann's pins. Sinclair's glue could be used in fractures of the ankle region. For fractures of the upper extremity, the Hey Groves wire cradle arm splint was recommended, while, for fractured hips, pelvis or spine, a Jones abduction frame proved priceless.

H. Wade's notes record that the 'Turkish' photographs are of:
   • Izzih Pascha in the Mosque
   • General Kress von Kressenstein
   • Red Crescent workers
   • Kusainich
   • Abou Hunairia trenches
   • Turkish Field Ambulance
   • Turkish Field Ambulance at El Arish
   • Dressing station field ambulance at El Arish.

I. Wade kept incomplete records of the sequence of his many photographic negatives, prints and enlargements.

Chapter 9

A. A letter he received from Dr Bahr in June 1919 reminded him that Dr Bahr and his colleague 'Benzie' had both failed to detect the malarial parasites in Wade's blood.[47] Bahr asked whether Wade was surviving in 'that bleak town', Edinburgh.

B. The nature of the neoplasm remained uncertain, but it might have been a giant cell tumour or osteoclastoma rather than the myeloma described in Wade's notes.

Chapter 10

A. In 1927, he was made Consulting Surgeon to this institution – a position he retained until his death in 1955.

B. Arthur Henry Havens Sinclair (1868–1962) was President of the RCSEd from 1933 to 1935, immediately preceding Wade with whom he had a longstanding friendship. They travelled together to the United States in 1920. AHH Sinclair graduated from Edinburgh in 1893, becoming FRCSEd in 1900. He trained as an ophthalmic surgeon with Sir George Berry, became Assistant Ophthalmic Surgeon to the RIE in 1905, served in the Royal Army Medical Corps during the First World War and returned to become Surgeon-in-Ordinary to the RIE in 1922. He was responsible for the development of quantitative perimetry and introduced to Edinburgh the operation of intracapsular extraction of the lens of the eye. President of the Ophthalmological Society of the UK in 1931, he was Surgeon Oculist to His Majesty the King in Scotland for 24 years and devoted many years to the work of the WH Ross Foundation for the Study of the Prevention of Blindness.

C. John William Struthers (1874–1953) was a contemporary of Wade. His father, Sir John Struthers, had been President of the RCSEd from 1895 to 1897. JW Struthers was appointed Assistant Surgeon to the RIE in 1908. He became Surgeon-in-Ordinary in 1924. For 10 years he was College Secretary and Treasurer (p 268) – a period including Wade's Presidency. In February 1939, Struthers was appointed to the new position of salaried Conservator of the Museum and Director of Postgraduate Education. However, the Second World War intervened, and he intimated to the Royal College of Surgeons of Edinburgh that as he had accepted a salaried position at the East Fortune Sanatorium, he would be able to devote only two days each week to the College.

D. James Methuen Graham (1882–1962) graduated from Edinburgh in 1904, becoming FRCSEd in 1907. He was appointed Assistant Surgeon to the Royal Infirmary of Edinburgh in 1919 and Surgeon-in-Ordinary in 1928. He was elected President of the Royal College of Surgeons of Edinburgh in 1945. His ChM thesis, for which he was awarded the Chiene Medal, was on the techniques of blood transfusion. Later, he contributed strongly to the development of the Scottish Blood Transfusion Service. He was a pioneer of thyroid surgery and was skilled in the treatment of diseases of the oesophagus and pharynx.

E. The position of Full Surgeon (Surgeon-in-Ordinary) dated from 1st August 1716. Wade's position as Full Surgeon was renewed on 18th November 1929, with effect from 1st January 1930 (Table 10.1).

F. When a Peace Treaty was finally signed in 1919, Wards 5 and 6 were in the charge of Mr AA Scot Skirving. Professor Sir Harold Stiles had charge of Wards 7 and 8, Mr A Miles of Wards 9 and 10, Mr D Wallace of Wards 11 and 12 and Profession Alexis Thomson of Wards 13 and 14. Mr JWB Hodsdon bore the responsibility for Wards 15 and 16, Mr JW Dowden for Wards 17 and 18 and Mr WJ Stuart for the Leck Ward.[30]

A period of remarkable stability followed. By 1930, the Surgeons-in-Ordinary had become Mr G Chiene, Mr RL Stuart, Mr RW Struthers, Professor DPD Wilkie, Mr Henry Wade, Professor John Fraser and Mr JM Graham. There was no change until 1937, when Mr G Chiene retired. He was succeeded by Mr A Pirie Watson. The following year, Mr RW Struthers retired and Sir David Wilkie died.[31] They were succeeded by FE Jardine and by JR Learmonth, recently elected to the Chair of Surgery in succession to Wilkie. Shortly afterwards, Henry Wade himself was obliged to retire under the 15-year rule. His place was taken by JJM Shaw, while Mr RL Stuart's place was taken by W Quarry Wood.

G.   Much of the special work that Wade undertook in relation to urological surgery was in the Electric Diagnostic Theatre; radiological work of a more routine nature was performed in the separate Radiological Department. A distinct Department of Urology was not established until 1967.

H.   Robert Leslie Stewart (1896-1981) was an Edinburgh graduate. He qualified in 1917 and served in the Royal Navy before becoming an Assistant to Wade. On the basis of this experience, Stewart continued to specialise in urological surgery. He was appointed Consultant to the Leith Hospital and then Surgeon-in-Ordinary to the RIE. Among other positions he held was that of Surgeon to the Peebleshire Nursing Association.

I.   John James McIntosh Shaw (1889–1943) was a pioneer of plastic surgery, following in the footsteps of Harold Gillies. Like many, Shaw volunteered for military duties in August 1914, joining the expeditionary force sent to France. He served as Surgeon Specialist at the Battle of the Aisne and, much later, at the First Battle of Ypres. In 1918, he was awarded the Military Cross and the Croix de Guerre with Star. His name was associated particularly with the help he gave to the stricken population of Bailleul. Shaw served for several years in the field of reconstructive surgery at the Queen's Hospital, Sidcup, Kent, before returning to Edinburgh, where he became Surgeon to the Leith Hospital and then to the Royal Infirmary of Edinburgh, where he was Assistant Surgeon in Wards 13 and 14 to David Wilkie. He became influential in the world of University medicine and was an assessor on the Edinburgh University Court. In a wider sphere, he became a member of the Radium Commission. In 1939, as a colonel in the Army Medical Service, Shaw embarked for the Middle East. He had not been in Egypt long before news arrived of his sudden death from bacillary dysentery.

J.   David Band (1901–88) graduated in Edinburgh in 1923, served as Wade's House Surgeon in 1925 and became FRCSEd in 1926. Clinical Tutor with Wade in 1929, he was Surgeon to the Leith Hospital and to the Hospital for Diseases of Women in Archibald Place, becoming Lecturer in Clinical Surgery and later Reader in Urology to the University of Edinburgh. Assistant Surgeon to the Western General Hospital, he was appointed later as Consultant Urological Surgeon. His extensive clinical research, begun with Wade, was concerned closely with renal physiology, radiography and tuberculosis. Like Wade, he served as President of the Section of Urology of the Royal Society of Medicine. He was also President of the University of Edinburgh Graduates Association from 1966 to 1968. A Foundation Member of the British Association of Urological Surgeons, he was part of the team that assisted Michael Woodruff when he performed the first successful renal transplant in the United Kingdom on 30th October 1960. Band was a member of the Royal College of Surgeons of Edinburgh Museum Committee and of the Council of the College.

K. The possibility of advancement to the Chair of Systematic Surgery in the University of Edinburgh arose shortly before Wade became Surgeon-in-Ordinary 17th November 1924.

L. John Fraser (1885–1947) graduated from the University of Edinburgh with honours in 1907. In 1910, he was awarded the Lister Prize for Surgery. His studies of tuberculosis in children led to international fame. Much of his work was in association with the Laboratory of the Royal College of Physicians of Edinburgh (p 83). Fraser showed that 60% of the cases of bone and joint tuberculosis in Edinburgh children were attributable to the bovine bacillus. He served in Flanders. Wounded and awarded the MC, he nevertheless published many scientific papers, collaborated with Cannon and Hooper in a study of gum arabic/saline in the correction of 'shock', and joined the Medical Research Committee (later the Medical Research Council). Fraser was an extraordinarily skilled operator. As Regius Professor, he tested cervical sympathectomy for cardiac pain and the correction of congenital ductus arteriosus. He showed that direct injuries to the heart could be repaired and initiated surgical techniques for breast cancer, lymphoma and lipidosis.

M. Scialytic lamp. The name seems to have been derived from the word *scie* (French: saw), indicating the saw-like to-and-fro movements that the lamp could make during an operation.

N. In 1995–6, 61,621 patients were admitted to the RIE; 28,806 were treated in surgical wards. They remained in hospital for an average of four days. There were a further 15,369 'day' surgical cases who did not remain in hospital after their treatment. Consequently, approximately 120 operations were performed daily. In 2000, there were 52,447 episodes of hospital care and 41,957 patients are recorded as having had continuous inpatient care. The mean duration of a period in hospital was five days. Because of changes in the style in which hospital statistics are expressed, it is difficult to compare these figures with those recorded for earlier years. Contemporary surgery is practised in a substantial series of specialities, the sum of which is not readily comparable with the overall practice of surgery in 1900. Under the headings of Accident and Emergency surgery, Otolaryngology, General Surgery (including Vascular Surgery), Gynaecology, Ophthalmology, Orthopaedics, Surgical Paediatrics and Urology, there were 16,920 continuous 'stays' in 1995–96, and 70.3 % of these patients were subjected to surgical operations. After 14,916 surgical inpatient 'stays', 88.2% of surgical patients returned to their usual place of residence. No more than 264 patients (1.6%) died in hospital – a figure to be compared with the 7.2% deaths in 1878 among 107 operations and 6.9% deaths in 1899 from 400 operations.

O. Each year, a printed report (*Reports regarding the affairs of the Royal Infirmary of Edinburgh*, the RIER) was prepared on the state of the hospital during the preceding 12 months. The report followed a standard pattern and comprised sections devoted to lists of the Managers and Officers, the Medical, Surgical and other staff; a summary of the reports by the Managers; an abstract of the Accounts; a report by the Committee of Contributors; an extensive section detailing all financial contributions made from people and organizations in Edinburgh, outside Edinburgh and outside this country; and a list of church parishes that made contributions.

There followed a list tabulating patients' occupations and their places of residence and the regulations about admission to the hospital. Thus, no patient with an infectious disease was allowed entry, and individuals were not permitted access to the Lock (venereal disease) wards. The affairs of trusts such as the Murray Keith Trust were reported. Within the back cover of the Annual Report were printed a form of bequest; the system of endowing beds; the procedure for completing cheques and remittances; and the ways of addressing hospital officials. Within the front cover were printed a list of waiting days and hours and the days and times when emergencies were received by the different clinical units; rules for patients; arrangements for ambulance wagons; and information about the Samaritan Society.

P. An entirely separate Committee of Medical Managers reported (RIEM) to the governing body of the Royal Infirmary of Edinburgh. The committee minute books of the Medical Managers, Finance, Law, House, Murray House and Nursing Committees were always reviewed, their minutes frequently reduplicated in full. Then came discussion on building works such as the alterations proposed in 1925 to Wards 13 and 14 and the debatable matter of the building of a new maternity hospital; letters of thanks; intimations of legacies; donations, for example of portraits; appointments, for example of House Surgeons, Clinical Assistants, Pathologists, Assistant Surgeons and Surgeons; retirements (the pioneer radiologist, Dr Dawson Turner retired in 1925); the chaplaincy; the provision of a shelter for friends visiting patients; and lastly, the 40-day rule – a regulation that required an explanation for every patient who had been in the RIE for 40 or more days, constituting what, in modern terms, would be called 'bed-blocking'. Misdemeanours and unexplained deaths under anaesthesia were reported and action reviewed. The Law committee dealt, among other matters, with trusts and executors, the deceased, feu duties and property.

Chapter 11

A. These records were stored in the basement of the Red Home of the Royal Infirmary of Edinburgh. They were copied as microfilm. Many years later, they were scanned electronically and stored in the archives of the Lothian Health Services Trust in the Special Collections Division of the University of Edinburgh Library.

B. This responsibility was reaffirmed on 17th November 1924, 7th December 1925 and (erroneously) 21st February 1927. It was followed by a further reappointment made on 5th December 1927, with effect from 24th December 1927. A subsequent reappointment was made on 3rd December 1928. It was effective from 24th December of that year. Wade was designated as having charge of the Diagnostic Theatre for one year from 24th December 1929. This position was renewed annually until the year of Wade's retirement, 1939.

C. Ward and operation books are catalogued under the Lothian Health Board acronym of LHB1, Royal Infirmary of Edinburgh.

D. This, the Fairmilehead Cripples Hospital, would become the Princess Margaret Rose Hospital in 1932.

Chapter 12

A. The pain of a bladder stone has always been one of the worst forms of human suffering. To remove a stone posed a hideous challenge both for a patient driven to surgery in the days before anaesthesia and antisepsis and for the operator. Thomas Hollier successfully removed a stone the size of a tennis ball from Samuel Pepys's urinary bladder in 1657. The diarist was aged 24 years. The patient's neck, arms and legs were bound, and strong men restrained him as the perineum was incised. The wound was not stitched. Recovery took 35 days.

B. Early in 1920, a letter of application from Wade to the Superintendent of the Royal Infirmary of Edinburgh, Lt Colonel Sir John Fayrer, Bart, CBE, requested permission from the Infirmary Managers to be absent for a period of three months from about 3rd April. Wade wished to spend much of his time in Baltimore but then to visit other centres. The Superintendent replied that permission would be granted on condition that suitable arrangements for carrying out his (Wade's) work could be made with Professor Alexis Thomson.

C. Envelope 14.3 of the Wade papers includes a list of illustrations for an article on prostatism by Henry Wade. 14/3/1/1 comprises 60 captions, six of infant pelvis, some of normal young and older adults and many others showing prostatic disease, including chronic lobular prostatitis, and operations of various kinds for this condition. 14/3/2/1 includes 93 similar captions for what is obviously a second version of the same draft article. Envelope 14/3/3/1 is an outline of a lecture on the surgical treatment of prostatism, of which the subheadings are: Introduction, Definition, Varieties of prostatic disease producing prostatism, The effect of these upon the patient when untreated, Treatment: non-operative and operative, Indications for radical treatment, and Choice of treatment. 14/3/4/1-23 is a draft of an article on the treatment of prostatism. 14/3/5/1-6 is an incomplete draft of the same article/chapter. 14/3/6/1-7 is an old, rough draft of another article on prostatism, perhaps the one for the *Annals of Surgery* (Figure 12.7), while 14/3/7/1-7 is a similar but not identical draft of paper on prostatism.

D. The collected Wade papers include the pathological records of 15 fatal cases of prostatic disease from the Royal Infirmary of Edinburgh compiled during the years 1909–12. The reports are typed on foolscap paper, some with purple carbon copies. The style is often very brief. Four short summaries at the end of one file are written longhand. They may be the first drafts of cases reported by Henry Wade during his time as Assistant Pathologist to the Royal Infirmary of Edinburgh. Case 94 of 1908, for example, was a necropsy undertaken by Henry Wade on 12th March 1908. The patient was aged 67 and died on 1st March 1908.

E. The archival envelope containing the Wade papers 14/5/1-9 includes a number of draft papers, occasional chapters, lecture notes and other manuscripts.

Chapter 13

A. Francis Mitchell Caird (p 41) was elected to the Regius Chair of Clinical Surgery in 1908. A brief comment on the Edinburgh Chair of Systematic Surgery is given in Chapter 10.

B. The Archives of the SMRC are in the Library of the RCSEd.

C. Minto House was the site of James Syme's private hospital.

D. Argyle Square occupied the land to the south of North College Street (now Chambers Street) on which the National Museum of Scotland was built.

E. An incidental but recurrent and vexed question that arose at this time was the question of the precedence of the Edinburgh Royal Colleges. All was not sweetness and light. On 16th December 1910, there was a debate at the Council of the RCSEd as to whether, if agreement could not be reached, the matter would have to be taken to the Lyon Court. Some years later, the matter was resolved by the Crown in favour of the Physicians.

F. The cost of new buildings and the burden of their maintenance were indeed high, the College's income modest. The RCSEd owned the School of Medicine. They were obliged to lease the lecture rooms to those who wished to use them. The fees were composite and had been raised to £365 in July 1900. The resulting income covered part of the expenses of heating, lighting, maintenance, salaries and wages. The Lecturers themselves were paid a fee by each student for each teaching term attended.

By 12th October 1920, serious difficulties were beginning to appear in the running of the lecture rooms: the Lecturers, of whom there had originally been 12, were one year behind with the payment to the College of their agreed rent. Moreover, the College Clerk was being called on to collect the individual rents. When an architect's report showed in June 1923 that the provision of a much needed central lavatory, alterations to the macerator in the tank room, the cleaning of the lecture theatres and the upkeep of the heating system would impose a large cost, the President's Council decreed that no more than £1,500 should be spent.[40] By February 1924, however, £995 had already been disbursed and £735 more was owed. To deal with these charges, the College was obliged to sell £2,000 3½% NSW stock, so that £1,249 could be transferred to meet the architect's claims.

These responsibilities were symbolic of longstanding and recurrent problems. An analysis of the cost of the 24 tons of coal used in heating the lecture rooms during 1922 led to an additional charge of £45 being requested from the Lecturers. Not unnaturally, they disputed the claim. The terms of the tenancy, dating back to 1909, then compelled the Council to 'go into the whole matter' by appointing a small committee comprising: the President, the Secretary/Treasurer, Mr Wallace and Mr Sym. Their report revealed that the long-serving Dr Ryland Whitaker (see below) had allowed matters to drift.[41]

The Council therefore decided to terminate the group lease, enabling arrangements for the future to be made with individual teachers, of whom only five remained of those who had signed the composite lease in 1909. At a meeting, the Lecturers agreed to new terms, under which the College undertook to maintain and clean the lecture rooms, while each individual Lecturer contributed to the cost of cleaning the laboratories and the retiring rooms. Although the Lecturers hoped that their costs would be unchanged, the College soon found it necessary to impose a 5% rise. The arrangement worked well, with the exception of Dr Whitaker, who at first refused to pay his rent.[42] However, he had seen the light of reason by 24th January 1928.

G. Report of the Lister Memorial Scheme Committee – a 13-page addendum to the Council's minutes of 7th February 1939.

H. Within the Extramural School of Medicine, Wade's fellow teachers in 1910–11 included A Scot Skirving, George Chiene, JW Struthers and JM Beasley (Surgery). In 1930–31, among the names were those of A Pirie-Watson and DS Middleton; George Chiene, WJ Stuart, JW Struthers, JM Graham and DS Middleton (Clinical Surgery) together with Agnes Macgregor (Pathology).

I. Dr Joseph Ryland Whitaker (1846–1932) was a highly successful Lecturer in Anatomy in the SMRC during the period 1894–1932. His recipe for success was 'anatomy with laughter', a style he illustrated with 'Whitaker's hymns'.

   Joseph Ryland Whitaker is not to be confused with his successor, Dr Charles Richard Whittaker (1879–1967). Senior Demonstrator in Anatomy, CR Whittaker resigned from the School of Medicine in 1933 but continued to devote his life to teaching anatomy and pathology, writing a popular *Manual of surgical anatomy*. Honorary Professor of Anatomy of the Royal Scottish Academy, he lectured under licence at the School of Medicine until 1948. His classes were chiefly at the Marshall Street Dispensary.

J. The rise to prominence of the Medical School of Leiden can be traced back to the emergence of Salerno, Montpellier and Padua as great centres of medical learning.

K. In the 1930s, a medical student could obtain a perpetual hospital ticket for the medical and surgical practice of the RIE. The ticket was issued 'subject to the Regulations of the Managers' and 'entitled the Holder to visit the wards and operating theatres and attend post-mortem examinations'. 'A medical student, while on the list of one clinic, could feel entitled to visit the other wards'. 'In Wade's case, many undergraduates from other units joined his classes'.[4]

L. Arthur Logan Turner (1865–1939) was the distinguished second son of Sir William Turner, Professor of Anatomy and Principal of the University of Edinburgh (p 14). House Surgeon to Professor Thomas Annandale, a hand injury took Logan Turner from his ambition to be a general surgeon to the practice of otolaryngology, a subject in which he became one of the country's foremost experts. From the Deaconess Hospital, Edinburgh, he moved to be Ear, Nose and Throat Surgeon to the RIE from 1906 until 1924, when he retired as a Consultant Surgeon. In the war of 1914–18, he served as Ear, Nose and Throat Surgeon to the Second Scottish General Hospital, Craigleith. Having written a biography of his famous father in 1919, in 1927 he edited a commemorative volume at the time of the Lister Centenary. Honoured with the LLD of the University of Edinburgh, he was President of the RCSEd from 1925 to 1927, held senior offices in many eminent societies and was active in the British Medical Association. Among the other books that he inspired and edited were a *History of the*

University of Edinburgh 1883–1933. He is remembered for his *Story of a great hospital: the Royal Infirmary of Edinburgh* (1937), where he served on the Committee of Management. His generosity to the Royal College of Surgeons of Edinburgh was renowned and the President's room is named after him.

Chapter 14

A. The work of the College, its aims and purposes, its contributions to the affairs of state and government and, not least, the life and work of its staff were recorded month by month in the minutes of the College committee. The minutes do not reveal every detail of Wade's collegiate life but they provide a vista, a backcloth, for an understanding of his life's work.

B. The Barber Surgeons, incorporated in 1505, were one of 14 Edinburgh crafts. The crafts were the Surgeons, Goldsmiths, Skinners, Furriers, Hammermen, Wrights, Masons, Tailors, Baxters, Fleshers, Cordiners, Websters, Waulkers and Bonnetmakers. The term 'Cordiner' (cordwainer) is of particular interest. It derives from the description for a worker in 'cordwain', that is, a shoemaker. Cordwain implied an association with the Spanish city of Cordova. It was used, *inter alia*, to describe shoes made from a pliable fine-grained leather. Originally goatskin, the leather came to be made from horsehide.

C. Despite political differences that culminated in the creation of an Irish Republic, the Royal College of Surgeons in Ireland is content to continue the use of the prefix 'Royal'.

D. The Royal College of Surgeons of Edinburgh ended its ancient allegiance to the Town of Edinburgh in 1851. Cresswell wrote:[1] 'The Widows' Fund was brought to a close as was the connection of the Surgeons with the Incorporated Trades. The Convenery and the Municipal Corporation, which had lasted 350 years, was completely severed. Mr Syme was the College President at the time'.

E. The consecutive printed pages of Council Minutes were numbered carefully. Although these printed Minutes bore the date of each meeting, there was no systematic pagination. Occasionally, pages were assembled in an incorrect order.

F. In 1903, the year of Wade's appointment as Conservator, the Council comprised D Argyle Robertson, Joseph Bell (President), John Chiene (p 23), Alexander G Miller, William Craig and Charles W MacGillivray, together with the Secretary/Treasurer, Francis Cadell, the Vice President and the representative of the College on the General Medical Council.

   In 1914, the President was Dr Harry Moss Traquair, an ophthalmic surgeon; the Secretary/Treasurer was Mr WJ Stuart. The Council members were CW MacGillivray, JM Cotterill, JWB Hodsdon, CW Cathcart, G Mackay and David Wallace. The amount of time that could be given to College affairs diminished and facilities deteriorated. Many of the wartime Council meetings were held at 6 Chester Street.[51]

G. The life of Arthur Logan Turner is outlined in Chapter 13.

H. Archibald Adam Scot-Skirving CMG (1868–1930) was House Surgeon to Professor John Chiene. Scot-Skirving served for one year in a field hospital in South Africa during the war of 1899–1902 (p 24). He was appointed

CMG. In the war of 1914–18, he was consultant at the Second Scottish General Hospital, Craigleith and at Bangour before spending a year with the British Expeditionary Force in Flanders. Scot-Skirving was Senior Surgeon to the Leith Hospital from 1906–16. He was appointed Assistant Surgeon to the RIE in 1910, Surgeon-in-Ordinary from 1916 to 1928 and was a Lecturer in Systematic Surgery to the Extramural School of Medicine of the Edinburgh Royal Colleges. He published *Surgical Applied Anatomy.*

I. William James Stuart (1873–1959) was loved for his calm and equable nature, for his devotion to his church and for dedication to fresh air and exercise. Scorning a car, he rode to the RIE by bicycle and continued hill walking late into life. One race through snow-covered Border hills to save an injured patient recalls the adventures of young Robert Knox,[56] the tales of Dr Clement Gunn[57] and Mr Gideon Gray in Walter Scott's *Surgeon's Daughter.*[58] Stuart became Honorary Assistant Surgeon to Leith Hospital in 1906 and to the RIE in 1907, where he was made Surgeon-in-Ordinary in 1923. During the First World War, Stuart served for two years in the Macedonian campaign at Salonika. He was elected President of the RCSEd in 1937. He returned to consultant duties when the Second World War began and became CBE in 1952.

J. An outline of Mr James Methuen Graham's life is given in Chapter 10. His promotion of blood transfusion was of lasting importance.

K. William A Cochrane (1893–1944) played an influential part in the recognition of orthopaedics as a speciality. At the end of the First World War, Bangour Hospital was the main orthopaedic surgical centre in Scotland. Here, Cochrane came under the powerful influence of Harold Stiles (p 340) and Robert Jones, who visited the unit periodically. After time in the United States, Cochrane became FRCSEd in 1921. He played a large part in the establishment of the Fairmilehead Hospital for Cripples, soon to be renamed the Princess Margaret Rose Orthopaedic Hospital. Another factor leading him to orthopaedics was the wound he sustained at the battle of the Somme. In collaboration with PD Wilson, he published *Orthopaedic surgery* in 1926 and *Fractures and dislocations* in 1928. Cochrane had strong interests in preventative health and postoperative care that were conspicuous during the Second World War when he was a consultant to Scottish Command.

L. John Wheeler Dowden (1866–1936) was House Surgeon to both Professor Thomas Annandale and to Joseph Bell, and he became a Fellow of the RCSEd in 1894. A thoughtful clinician and respected surgeon, it is likely that it was from Bell that he acquired the habit of placing hard evidence before speculation. He lectured in the SMRC from 1902 to 1914. He was appointed Assistant Surgeon to the RIE in 1901, becoming Surgeon-in-Ordinary in 1912. He held this position until 1924, when he moved to the Chalmers Hospital. In 1914, his devotion to orthopaedics showed when, as a Captain in the RAMC, he specialized in the early treatment of fractures at the Second Scottish General Hospital at Craigleith. Dowden was President of the RCSEd from 1931 to 1933 and therefore the predecessor to AHH Sinclair (p 351) in this office. Good humoured, Dowden was an enthusiastic sportsman and devoted to the arts.

M. At the opening of the new building of the Royal Australasian College of Surgeons, Melbourne, in April 1935, Wade's invited lecture was illustrated by 19 photographs of his studies of renal tumours (p 236).

N. The office of President was one of the most ancient in the land. Its origins lay in the Incorporation of Barber Surgeons of the Town of Edinburgh, of which the chief officer was the Deacon (p 358).

  In modern times, one Council member was invariably chosen to preside. The position was one of power and prestige. Much of the power was exercised indirectly, by influence. Provided his or her – there had not yet been a woman – actions were within the law of the land, however, the President had the authority to 'hire or fire', spend or save and mend or destroy, almost at will. He could therefore exercise an almost mediaeval authority. He was supported by a Vice President and a Secretary, who combined this office with that of Treasurer. The Presidency was held by 38 individuals during Wade's lifetime (Table 14.1). With few exceptions, nineteenth and early twentieth century Presidents served for two years. Sir William Turner held the office for one year only, in 1882. By contrast, Patrick Heron Watson (p 340), first elected in 1877, was chosen again in 1903, with the purpose of leading the College through the celebration of its quartcentenary in 1905.

O. Matters commonly discussed at meetings of the College's Council included:

  - bequests
  - General Medical Council matters, including disciplinary procedures
  - postgraduate teaching
  - building works
  - financial questions
  - prizes and awards
  - congresses
  - intercollegiate concerns, conferences and celebrations
  - representation on sister bodies and committees
  - colonial and dominion matters
  - prestigious lectureships
  - research and travel grants
  - Diplomas
  - Library matters
  - School of Medicine examinations
  - Museum matters
  - students
  - expenses, particularly those of examiners
  - nursing matters, including the Queen's Institute of District Nursing wages and salaries
  - Fellowship and Fellowship examinations
  - national events: war, the Royal family, the National Insurance Act and the Workman's Compensation Act
  - role of women in medicine and surgery
  - Honorary Fellowships
  - election of lecturers in the School of Medicine
  - election of ordinary examiners
  - property, its acquisition and upkeep
  - election of Fellowship examiners
  - prizes and awards

P. 'Club practice', a reference to days when patients joined together and contributed a small weekly sum to pay for medical care.

Q.	The subject is covered fully by McCrae.[22]

R.	Professor Halsted, of Johns Hopkins Hospital fame, and Sigmund Freud, the psychiatrist, were among those ensnared as a result of testing the drug upon themselves. There is no evidence that Joseph Bell, a prototype of Sherlock Holmes, was a cocaine addict but the fictitious detective certainly was.

S.	Gertrude Marian Amalie Herzfeld (1890–1981) became a Fellow in 1920. She was a true pioneer. Born in London, she graduated in medicine from the University of Edinburgh in 1914. She was attached to the RAMC Cambridge Hospital, Aldershot, before moving first to Bolton and then back to Edinburgh. She became Consultant Surgeon to the Bruntsfield Hospital for Women and Children (1920–55) and to the Royal Edinburgh Hospital for Sick Children (1920–45). A Lecturer in the Surgery of Childhood, she achieved national recognition not only for her skilled and compassionate surgery but for the part she played in furthering the cause of women in medicine through her presidency of the Medical Women's Federation.

T.	Harry Moss Traquair (1879–1954) qualified MB with honours in 1901 and took the Diploma in Public Health in 1902. After time in Halle and a period spent in South Africa for health reasons, he became a Fellow of the RCSEd in 1904 and was elected President in 1939. Becoming MD in 1913, he was appointed Senior Ophthalmic Surgeon to the RIE, a position from which he retired in 1943 to become Consultant Surgeon. Traquair achieved fame for promoting pioneer work on the visual fields undertaken by GA Berry and AHH Sinclair, and his close collaboration with the recently appointed Norman Dott was of immense value to the new science of neurosurgery. Dott admitted freely that much of his progress in this field would not have been possible without Traquair's help and encouragement. Traquair was President of the RCSEd in 1939–41 and of the Ophthalmic Society of Great Britain in 1943–44.

U.	From the year 1856, a Consulting Surgeon was no longer on the active staff of the hospital, although he retained the right to practise privately.

V.	The members were Mr TG Addley, Dr JR Anderson, Dr Gladys Boyd, Dr JF Lambie, Dr DG Leys, Dr D Dale Logan, Dr G McFeat, Sir William Marshall, Colonel Stewart Middleton, Dr AF Wilkie Millar, Dr GW Miller, Dr JB Miller, Dr F McE Sinclair, Dr John Smith and Colonel AD Stewart. The minutes record that FE Jardine and Professor James Learmonth were among those who attended.

W.	Noel Gray (1910–1999) took his seat as a Fellow of the RCSEd on 20th October 1943. As a fourth-year student, he was taught surgery by Henry Wade. Later, Gray served as Wade's House Surgeon. After the Second World War ended, Noel Gray and JC 'Jock' Milne, together with ADR Batchelor, Norman Dott and others, formed an admirable partnership and constituted the backbone of the surgical care provided by Bangour Hospital as part of the National Health Service.

Chapter 15

A.	The uncommon name Tytler is said to have occurred in the English Hundred Rolls (1273) and may have been derived from the mediaeval

English titeler (a tatler), although this is considered improbable. In mid-sixteenth century English, a tatler was a 'tell-tale'.

B. Henry Wade was a member of Gullane Golf Club from 1904 until 1914, when it is believed his membership was placed 'on hold'. The club has no record of the resumption of his membership in 1919.

C. Originally the parlour of a two-roomed house with only one outer door opening into the kitchen.

D. The *Chronicles of Pilmuir* is a foolscap 270-page bound volume, with spine and corners bound in leather. The name Henry Wade extends diagonally across the lower right corner of the cover. Like the title, the name is in gilt. The same title and name are inscribed on the spine. Only 146 pages of the volume are used – pages 49–52, 59, 61 and 152–270 are blank. There is no introduction or preface, but a list of contents occupies pages 267–270.

E. The album is in the possession of the Pilmuir Trust.

F. In the General Register of Sasines, First Series, volume VII, f.269, on the date of registration, 24th March 1621, it is recorded that it was then purchased by William Cairns and Agnes Brown from the Earl of Lauderdale. Pages 1–4 of the *Chronicles of Pilmuir* contain a copy in Latin and pages 6–10 a translation. Pages 12–15 are photostatic copies of the original.

G. Volume I, page 592, of 18th November 1567.

H. An individual was declared an outlaw by the blowing of three blasts on a horn.

I. On pages 88–94 of the *Chronicles of Pilmuir,* references to Pilmuir in the barony of Bolton in the Constabulary of Haddington in the County of Edinburgh are set forth, being taken from RMS Register of Sasines. The first is on 13th April 1366. Fifty-two references are listed.

J. Wade recorded the meeting: 'This afternoon my secretary Miss Gray and I attended by appointment at the old Register House and met Mr McInnes, Curator of Historical Records. The introduction came through Miss Gray. He was a friend of her father's and I found a bond between us when he informed me that he had compiled the records dealing with the ancient Sea Laws, for an article contributed, by my brother Callander, to the Stair Society'.

K. Oxgang: An ancient measure of land equivalent to one eighth of a carucate. A carucate was the area of land that could be ploughed in one year by one plough and eight oxen.

L. An ornamental design resembling the leaf (with five leaflets) of a cinquefoil (plants of the genus *Potentilla*, of the rose family) especially inscribed in an arch or a circle.

M. The structure of Pilmuir from the standpoint of the architect and antiquarian is given in the Royal Commission on East Lothian, Inventory number 20, pages 11–13 (B1), and the National Art Survey of Scotland, Volume IV (B9).

N. *Ballad Minstrelsy of Scotland*, Glasgow, 1871, Maurice Ogle and Co (B). Pages 619–25 give the poem and full details of the catastrophe.

O. Volume XI, 1683–1686, 3rd edition (B3).

P. On pages 11–13 of the inventory, full information is detailed under

Bolton – Castellated and Domestic Structure, 20, Pilmuir House. Facing page 11 is an illustration of Pilmuir House showing the present front of the house facing south. On page 12 are grouped seven outline drawings to scale showing the contour of the building and the individual rooms within.

Q. The turreted style, of French origin, characteristic of Scottish country houses.

R. This ambiguous statement probably refers to the water supply but may be a comment on electricity.

Chapter 16

A. Wade wrote to the Secretary, Gullane Golf Club, on 11th February 1920 apologizing for overlooking his payment of the annual subscription of one guinea.

B. Lecture to the Newcastle-upon-Tyne and Northern Counties Medical Society due to be given on 10th May 1945 but postponed on account of Victory in Europe celebrations until 4th October 1945.

C. *The Gambolier* was a student magazine published by Edinburgh University students during the years before the First World War.

D. Mr TI Wilson, FRCSEd was Wade's assistant in the 1930s and a distinguished Fellow of the College.

E. Approximately 9p in the decimal currency introduced in 1971.

F. The Ramon Guiteras lecture was given in 1932 in Minneapolis, US, in honour of Dr Guiteras, founder of the American Association of Urologists.

Wade's surgical philosophy drew an analogy between the stream of disease and the urinary system. His conclusion remained: 'Health is indispensable in war, and nothing can replace it'. His lecture finished with an emphasis on investigative medicine, particularly on searches for the explanation as to why urinary obstruction disorganizes chemical balance. Wade was thanked by Dr Herman L Kretschmer on behalf of the association and in memory of Dr Guiteras, and by Dr George R. Livermore.

G. Comrie JD. *History of Scottish medicine*. London: Baillière, Tindall and Cox, 1932. A shorter, first edition was published to coincide with the inauguration of the Section for Medical History at the 1927 meeting of the British Medical Association.

H. Within a few days, Henry Wade sailed for the United States (p 186).

References

Chapter 1

1. Fraser WH, Morris RJ. *People and society in Scotland.* Edinburgh: John Donald in association with the Economic and Social History Society of Scotland, 1990.

2. Scott I. *The life and times of Falkirk.* Edinburgh: John Donald, 1994.

3. Anonymous. Obituary: Sir Henry Wade. *BMJ* 1955a;**1**:607–8.

4. Anonymous. Obituary: Henry Wade. *Lancet* 1955b;**1**:516–7.

5. Graham JM. In memoriam: Henry Wade. *J R Coll Surg Edinb* 1955;1:75–8.

6. Robinson R, LeFanu W. *Henry Wade. Lives of the Fellows of the Royal College of Surgeons of England 1952–64.* Edinburgh, London: E and S Livingstone 1970: 419–20.

7. Stewart R. Henry Wade. *J Path Bacteriol* 1956;**71**:550–3.

8. Wade TC. *Story of the Falkirk West United Free Church.* Falkirk: F Johnston, 1926.

9. Comrie JD. *History of Scottish medicine, Volume I and II.* London: Baillière, Tindall and Cox, 1932.

10. Logan Turner A. *Story of a great hospital. The Royal Infirmary of Edinburgh 1729–1929.* Edinburgh: Oliver and Boyd, 1937. Re-issued: Edinburgh: Mercat Press, 1979.

11. Fraser AG. *The building of the old college. Adam, Playfair and the University of Edinburgh.* Edinburgh: Edinburgh University Press, 1989.

12. Risse GB. *Mending bodies, saving souls. A history of hospitals.* New York, Oxford: Oxford University Press, 1999.

13. Ross JA. *The Edinburgh School of Surgery after Lister.* Edinburgh, London, New York: Churchill Livingstone, 1978.

14. Logan Turner A, ed. *History of the University of Edinburgh* 1883–1933. Edinburgh, London: Oliver and Boyd, 1933.

15. Chiene J. *Looking back, 1907–1860.* Edinburgh: Darien Press, 1908.

16. Wade H. The art of the surgeon in diagnosis and treatment. *Newcastle Med J* 1946;**23**:22–7.

17. Creswell CH. *The Royal College of Surgeons of Edinburgh. Historical notes from 1505 to 1905.* Edinburgh, London: Oliver and Boyd, 1926.

18. Dingwall H. *A famous and flourishing society. The history of the Royal College of Surgeons of Edinburgh, 1505–2005.* Edinburgh: Edinburgh University Press, 2005.

Chapter 2

1. Montgomery, Field Marshall Viscount, of Alamein. *A history of warfare.* London, Glasgow: William Collins Sons, 1968.

2. Packenham T. *The Boer War.* London: Weidenfeld and Nicolson, 1979.

3. Pemberton W. *Battles of the Boer War.* London: Pan Books, 1964.

4. Featherstone D. *Weapons and equipment of the Victorian soldier.* London: Arms and Armour Press; 1996.

5. Holmes R. *Redcoat. The British soldier in the age of horse and musket.* London: Harper Collins, 2001.

6. Adams A. Alexander Ogston and the Army Medical Services. Formation of the Royal Army Medical Corps 1 July 1898. *Scottish Med J* 1998;**43**:156–7.

7. Blair JSG. *Arduis Fidelis. Centenary History of the Royal Army Medical Corps.* Edinburgh: Scottish Academic Press, 1998.

8. Cantlie N. *A history of the army medical department.* Edinburgh, London: Churchill Livingstone, 1974.

9. Drew R. *Commissioned officers in the medical services of the British Army, 1660–1960.* London: Wellcome Historical Medical Library, 1968.

10. Mitchell T, Smith G. Casualties in Egypt and Palestine, 1915–1918. In: *History of the Great War based on official documents. Medical services: casualties and medical statistics of the Great War.* London: Stationery Office, 1931: 268–73.

11. Horsley V. The destructive effects of projectiles. *Proc Roy Inst Great Britain* 1893;**14**:228–38.

12. MacCormac W. The war in South Africa – case notes. *Lancet* 1900;**i**:59.

13. Makins G. *Surgical experiences in South Africa, 1899–1900.* London: Smith, Elder and Co, 1901.

14. Simpson RJS. Medical history of the South African War. *J R Army Med Corps* 1910;**14**:23–38, 125–41, 259–71, 487–505.

15. Stevenson WF. *Report on the surgical cases noted in the South African War, 1899–1902.* London: Stationery Office, 1905.

16. Tatham CJW. *Report on the surgical cases noted in the South African War.* London: Stationery Office, 1905.

17. Treves F. The wounded in the present war. *BMJ* 1900;**i**:1156–62.

18. Chiene J. *Looking back 1907–1860.* Edinburgh: Darien Press, 1908.

19. Ogston A. Report upon micro-organisms in surgical diseases. *BMJ* 1881;**1**:369–75.

20. Chiene GL. *Handbook of surgery.* Edinburgh, London: E&S Livingstone, 1923.

21. Wade H. The art of the surgeon in diagnosis and treatment. *Newcastle Med J* 1946;**23**:22–7.

22. *Report of the Edinburgh and East of Scotland South African Hospital.* Edinburgh: Oliver and Boyd, 1901.

23. Greig DM. A case of gunshot wound from the South African War. *J Roy Army Med Corps* 1994;**2**:590.

24. His Majesty's Stationery Office. *Minutes of evidence taken before the Royal*

Commission appointed to consider and report upon the care and treatment of the sick and wounded during the South African Campaign. London: HM Stationery Office, 1901: 1–565.[R]

25. Hall-Edwards J. Report of the X-ray department. In: Countess Howe, ed. *The imperial yeomanry hospitals in South Africa 1900–1902. Volumes 1–3.* London: Arthur L Humfreys, 1902.

26. Singer C, Underwood E. *A short history of medicine.* Oxford: Clarendon Press, 1962.

27. Reitz D. *Commando. A Boer journal of the Boer War.* London: Faber and Faber, 1929.

28. Churchill W. *London to Ladysmith via Pretoria.* London: Longmans Green, 1900.

29. Churchill W. *Ian Hamilton's march.* London: Longmans Green, 1900.

30. His Majesty's Stationery Office. *Minutes of evidence taken before the Royal Commission on the War in South Africa. Volume I: 1–534.* London: Stationery Office, 1903.

Chapter 3

1. Daiches D, Jones P, Jones J, eds. *A hotbed of genius. The Scottish enlightenment.* Edinburgh: Edinburgh University Press, 1986.

2. Osler W. *Aequanimitas, with other addresses to medical students, nurses and practitioners of medicine.* London: HK Lewis, 1906.

3. Burdon Sanderson J. An address on the relation of science to experience in medicine. *BMJ* 1899;**2**:1333–5.

4. Howell J. *Technology in the hospital. Transforming patient care in the early twentieth century.* Baltimore, London: Johns Hopkins University Press, 1995.

5. Logan Turner A. *Story of a great hospital. The Royal Infirmary of Edinburgh 1979–1929.* Edinburgh: Oliver and Boyd, 1937.

6. Chiene J. Looking Back, 1907–1860. Edinburgh: Darien Press, 1908.

7. Watson WNB. An Edinburgh surgeon of the Crimean war – Patrick Heron Watson 1832–1907. *Med Hist* 1966;**10**:166–76.

8. Bell J. The surgical side of the Royal Infirmary of Edinburgh, 1852–92: the progress of a generation. *Edinb Hosp Rep* 1893;**1**:1–18.

9. Koch R. Die Aetiologie der Tuberkulose. *Berliner klinische Wochenschrift* 1882;**19**:221–30.

10. Ogston A. Report upon micro-organisms in surgical diseases. *BMJ* 1881;**1**:369–75.

11. Kitasato S. Ueber den tetanusbacillus. *Ztschr Hyg u Infektionskrank* 1889;**7**:225–34.

12. Welch WH, Nuttall GHF. A gas-producing bacillus (*Bacillus aërogenes capsulatus nov spec*) capable of rapid development in the blood-vessels after death. *Johns Hopkins Hospital Bulletin* 1892;**3**:81–91.

13. Gradle H. *Bacteria and the germ theory of diseases.* Chicago: WT Keener: 1883.

14. Ross R. The role of the mosquito in the evolution of the malaria parasite. *Lancet* 1898;**2**:488–9.

15. Ivanowski DA. Ueber die Mosaikkrankheit der Tabakspflanze. *Bull Acad Imp Sci St Petersb* 1892;**3**:67–70.

16. Loeffler, FAJ Frosch P. Bericht der Kommission zur Erforschung der Maul- und Klauenseuche bei dem Institut für Infektionskrankheiten. *Z Bakteriol* 1898;**23**:371–91.

17. Stanley WM. Isolation of a crystalline protein possessing the properties of tobacco mosaic virus. *Science* 1935;**81**:644–5.

18. Ehrlich P. *Das Sauerstoff-Bedürfniss des Organismus. Eine farbenanalytische Studie.* Berlin: A Hirschwald, 1885.

19. Behring EA, von Kitasato S. Ueber das Zustandekommen der Diphtherie-Immunität und der Tetanus-Immunität bei Thieren. *Deutsche medizinische Wochenschrift* 1890;**16**:1113–4.

20. Wright AE, Leishman WB. Remarks on the results which have been obtained by the antityphoid inoculation. *BMJ* 1900;1:122–9.

21. Ehrlich P, Lazarus A. *Anaemia.* London: Rebman Limited, 1910.

22. Röntgen WC. Ueber eine neue Art von Strahlen. *Sitzungs Bericht der phys-med Ges Wurzburg* 1895;132–41.

23. Becquerel AH. Sur les radiations émises par phosphorescence. *Comptes Rendue de l'Academie Scientifique de Paris* 1896;**122**:420–1.

24. Curie P, Curie M. Sur une substance nouvelle radio-active, contenue dans la pechblende. *Comptes rendue de l'Academie Scientifique de Paris* 1898;**127**:175–8, 1215–7.

25. Calder J. *The history of radiology in Scotland.* Edinburgh: Dunedin Academic Press, 2001.

26. Keys TE. *The history of surgical anaesthesia.* New York: Schuman's, 1945 (reprinted with corrections and additions, 1963).

27. Masson AHB. Anaesthesia in Edinburgh 1900–1950. In: *Essays on the history of anaesthesia: selected and revised contributions by members of the History of Anaesthesia Society, Series 1, 1986–89.* London: Royal Society of Medicine, 1996: 65–70.

28. Trendelenburg F. Beiträge zu den Operationen an den Luftwegen. *Archiv für klinische Chirurgie* 1871;**12**:112–33.

29. Bowman A. *The life and teaching of Sir William Macewen. A chapter in the history of surgery.* London, Edinburgh, Glasgow: William Hodge, 1942.

30. Berger P. De l'emploi du masque dans les operations. *Bulletin de la Societé des Chirurgiens de Paris* 1899;**25**:187–96.

31. Wangansteen OH, Wangansteen SD. *The rise of surgery from empiric craft to scientific discipline.* Minneapolis: University of Minnesota Press, 1978.

32. Halstead WS. *Johns Hopkins Hospital Reports* 1891;**2**:308–10.

33. Halstead WS. *Johns Hopkins Hospital Reports* 1894;**4**:plate XII

34. Guthrie D. *A history of medicine.* London, Edinburgh, Paris: Thomas Nelson and Sons, 1945.

35. Rutkow I. *Surgery: an illustrated history.* St. Louis: Mosby-Year Book, 1993.

36. Ellis H. *A history of surgery.* London: Greenwich Medical Media Limited, 2001.

37. Wade H. Excision of ulna for infective osteomyelitis; nephropexy for moveable kidney. 1910. *Proceedings of the Edinburgh Medico Chirurgical Society*, 14th December 1910.

38. Wade H. Nephrectomy for acute consecutive suppurative nephritis; cellulitis and osteomyelitis. *Proceedings of the Edinburgh Medico Chirurgical Society*, 21st December 1912.

39. Wade H. Treatment of simple fractures. *Lancet* 1912;**i**:798.

40. Wade H. Osteosarcoma treated by bone graft. *Edinb Med J* 1920;**24**:37.

41. Wade H. Intussusception of the stomach and duodenum due to a gastric polypus. *Lancet* 1913;**ii**:1204.

42. Wade H. Intussusception of the stomach and duodenum due to a gastric polypus. *Surg, Gynecol Obstet* 1913;**20**:184–90.

43. Fitz RH. Perforating inflammation of the vermiform appendix. *Trans Assoc Am Phys* 1886;**1**:107–44.

44. Treves F. Perityphlitis. In: Albutt TC, ed. *A system of medicine, volume III*. London, New York: Macmillan and Macmillan Company, 1897: 879–937.

45. Langenbuch, CJA. Ein Fall von Extirpation der Gallenblase wegen chronischer Cholelithiasis; Heilung. *Berlin Klinische Wochenschrift* 1882;**19**:725–7.

46. Carmichael EWS, Wade H. A case of primary sarcoma of the liver in a child aged four months. *Lancet* 1907;**i**:1217–9.

47. Wade H, Watson BP. The anatomy and histology of an early tubal gestation, with lantern demonstration. *Lancet* 1908;**i**:1844–5.

48. Macewen W. *Pyogenic infective diseases of the brain and spinal cord*. Glasgow: J Maclehose and Sons, 1893.

49. Macewen W. Tumour of the dura mater – convulsions – removal of tumour by trephining – recovery. *Glasgow Med J* 1879;**12**:210–3.

50. Ehrlich P. *Die experimentelle Chemotherapie der Spirillosen (Syphilis, Rückfallfieber, Hühnerspirillose, Frambösie)*. Berlin: J Springer, 1910.

51. Masson AHB. *A history of blood transfusion in Edinburgh*. Edinburgh: Edinburgh Blood Transfusion Service, 1993.

52. Boyd D. *Leith Hospital 1848–1988*. Edinburgh: Scottish Academic Press, 1990.

Chapter 4

1. Carmichael EWS, Wade H. A case of primary sarcoma of the liver in a child aged four months. *Lancet* 1907;**i**:1217–9.

2. Wade H. Renal tumours. *Aust N Z J Surg* 1935:1–15.

3. Huxley J. *Biological aspects of cancer*. London: Allen and Unwin, 1958.

4. Adami JG. *The principles of pathology. Volume 1: general pathology*. London: Hodder and Stoughton and Oxford University Press, 1909: 768–80.

5. Hadfield G, Garrod LP. *Recent advances in pathology*. London: J and A Churchill, 1934: 52–5, 75–81.

6. Willis RA. *Pathology of tumours*. London: Butterworths, 1967: 28–66.

7. Baillie M. *The morbid anatomy of some of the most important parts of the human body*. London: J Johnson and Nicol G, 1797.

8. Home E. *A short tract on the formation of tumours*. London: Longman, 1830.

9. Cameron GR. *Pathology of the cell*. Edinburgh, London: Oliver and Boyd, 1952: 173–4.

10. Müller J. *Über den feinern Bau und die Formen der krankhaften Geschwülste. Lief 1*. Berlin: G Reimer, 1838 (English translation: C West, 1840).

11. Hughes Bennett J. *On cancerous and cancroid growths*. Edinburgh: Sutherland and Knox, 1849.

12. Rokitansky C. *A manual of pathological anatomy*. London: Sydenham Society, 1854.

13. Virchow R. *Cellular pathology as based upon physiological and pathological histology*. London: John Churchill, 1860 (translated from the second edition of the original by Frank Chance).

14. Young JZ. *An introduction to the study of man*. Oxford: Oxford University Press, 1971: 303, 328.

15. Pott P. *Chirurgical observations relative to the cataract, the polypus of the nose, the cancer of the scrotum etc*. London: for L Hawes, W Clarke and R Collins, 1775.

16. Yamagiwa K, Ichikawa K. Ueber die künstliche Erzeugung von Karzinom. *Verhandlungen der Japanese pathologische Gesellschaft* 1916;**6**:169–78.

17. Becquerel AH. [Radioactivity.] *Comptes Rendue Academie Science Paris* 1896;**122**:420–1.

18. Frieben EAFA. Cancroid des rechten Handrückens. *Dtsch Med Wochenschr* 1902;**28**:335.

19. Cohnheim Julius F. *Vorlesungen über allgemeine Pathologie, Band 1*. Berlin: August Hirschwald, 1877.

20. Jensen CO. Experimentelle Untersuchungen über Krebs bei Mäusen. *Zentralblatt für Bakteriologie und Parasitologie* 1903;**34**:28–34, 122–43.

21. Ehrlich P. *Das Sauerstoff-Bedürfniss des Organismus. Eine farbenanalytische Studie*. Berlin: A Hirschwald, 1885.

22. Twort FW. An investigation on the nature of ultra-microscopic viruses. *Lancet* 1915;**2**:1241–3.

23. Gaylord HR. The protozoon of cancer. *Am J Med Sci* 1901;**121**:503–39.

24. Robertson WF, Wade H. Cancer and *Plasmodiaphorae*. *Lancet* 1904;**ii**:469.

25. Annotation. Exhibition of specimens illustrating *Plasmodiophora* and finger and toe disease, given to the Pathological Museum Section of the Oxford meeting of the British Medical. *Lancet* 1904;**ii**:469, 547.

26. Robertson WF, Wade H. Researches into the etiology of carcinoma: on the presence of *Plasmodiaphorae* in carcinomatous tumours and the successful cultivation of the parasites. *Lancet* 1905;**i**:215–21.

27. Editorial. The etiology of carcinoma. *Lancet* 1905;**i**:244–5.

28. Robertson WF, Wade H. Researches into the etiology of carcinoma. *Lancet* 1905;**i**:321.

29. Annotation. Researches into the etiology of carcinoma. *Lancet* 1905;**i**:321–2.

30. Annotation. Researches into the etiology of carcinoma. *Lancet* 1905;**i**:328.

31. Beatson GT. The etiology of carcinoma. *Lancet* 1905;**i**:644–5.

32. Robertson WF, Young MCW. Further researches into the etiology of carcinoma: note upon certain histological features of carcinomatous tumours revealed by an improved ammonio-silver process. *Lancet* 1907;**ii**:358–61.

33. Robertson WF. Note on the presence and significance of certain rod-shaped bodies in the cells of carcinomatous tumours. *Lancet* 1908;**i**:225–6.

34. Robertson WF. Experimental evidence of the infective origin of carcinoma and of the transmissibility of the disease from the human subject to the mouse. *Lancet* 1909;**i**:1591–3.

35. Robertson WF, Young MCW. The protozoal origin of tumours. *Lancet* 1909;**ii**:465.

36. Wehr V. Demonstration der durch Impfung von Hund auf Hund erzeugten Carcinomknötchen. *Verhandlungen der deutsche Gesellschaft für Chirurgie* 1878;**17**:52–3.

37. Wade H. *A contribution to the problem of cancer research based upon the results of an experimental investigation of infective sarcoma of the dog* [MD thesis]. Edinburgh: University of Edinburgh, 1907.

38. Wade H. An experimental investigation of infective sarcoma of the dog, with a consideration of its relationship to cancer. *J Path Bacteriol* 1908;**xii**:384–425.

39. Rous FP. A transmissible avian neoplasm (sarcoma of the common fowl). *J Exp Med* 1910;**12**:696–705, 1911;**13**:397–411.

40. Robertson, W Ford. A textbook of pathology in relation to mental diseases. Edinburgh:WF Clay,1900.

Chapter 5

1. Wade H. The art of the surgeon in diagnosis and treatment. *Newcastle Medical Journal* 1946;23(2): 22–27.

2. Royal Microscopical Society. A celebration of the tercentenary of the microscope in living biology. The first American meeting of the Society held at Bethesda, Maryland, 1963. *J Royal Microsc Soc* 1964;**83**:1–228.

3. Hartley W. *The light microscope. Its use and development.* Oxford: Senecio Publishing Company, 1993.

4. Bernard C. *Leçons de physiologie expérimentale appliquée à la médecine.* Paris: JB Baillière, 1855.

5. Ehrlich P, Lazarus A. *Anaemia.* London: Rebman Limited, 1910.

6. Ross J. *The Edinburgh School of Surgery after Lister.* Edinburgh, London, New York: Churchill Livingstone, 1978.

7. Foster W. *Pathology as a profession in Great Britain and the early history of the Royal College of Pathologists.* London: Royal College of Pathologists, 1981.

8. Rokitansky C. *A manual of pathological anatomy*. London: Sydenham Society, 1854.

9. Virchow R. *Cellular pathology as based upon physiological and pathological histology*. London: John Churchill, 1860 (translated from the second edition of the original by Frank Chance).

10. Adami GJG, McCrae J. *A textbook of pathology for students of medicine*. Philadelphia, New York: Lee and Febiger, 1912.

11. Jacyna LS. The laboratory and the clinic: the impact of pathology on surgical diagnosis in the Glasgow Western Infirmary 1875–1910. *Bull Hist Med* 1988;**62**:384–406.

12. Bracegirdle B. *A history of microtechnique. The evolution of the microtome and the development of tissue preparation*. London: Heinemann Educational Books, 1978.

13. Rochow TG, Tucker PA. *Introduction to microscopy by means of light, electrons, X-rays or acoustics*. New York, London: Plenum Press, 1994.

14. Ritchie J. *History of the Laboratory of the Royal College of Physicians of Edinburgh*. Edinburgh: Royal College of Physicians of Edinburgh, 1953.

15. Hamilton TD. Notes on preparation by Cheatle's method of thin microscopic sections of whole organs embedded in paraffin: technical study. *J Roy Microsc Soc* 1930;**50**:200–09.

16. Gough JWJ. Pneumoconiosis in coalworkers in Wales. *Occup Med* 1947;**4**:86–97.

17. Gough J, Wentworth JE. The use of thin sections of entire organs in morbid anatomical studies. *J Roy Microsc Soc* 1949;**69**:231–5.

18. Wade H. *A contribution to the problem of cancer research, based upon the results of an experimental investigation of infective sarcoma of the dog* [MD thesis]. Edinburgh: University of Edinburgh, 1907.

19. Wade H. An experimental investigation of infective sarcoma of the dog, with a consideration of its relationship to cancer. *J Path Bacteriol* 1908;**12**:384–425.

20. Monti A. *The fundamental data of modern pathology. History, criticisms, comparisons, applications*. London: New Sydenham Society, 1900.

21. Browning CH, Mackenzie I. *Recent methods in the diagnosis and treatment of syphilis. The Wasserman serum reaction and Ehrlich's salvarsan*. London: Constable and Company, 1911.

22. Mortimer PP. The bacteria craze of the 1880s. *Lancet* 1999;**353**:581–4.

23. Gradle H. *Bacteria and the germ-theory of diseases*. Eight lectures delivered at the Chicago Medical College. Chicago: WT Keener, 1883.

24. Klein E. *Micro-organisms and disease: an introduction to the study of specific micro-organisms*. London, New York: Macmillan, 1896.

25. Crookshank EM. *An introduction to practical bacteriology based on the methods of Koch*. London: HK Lewis, 1886.

26. Sternberg G. *A manual of bacteriology*. New York: William Wood, 1893.

27. CM 15th December 1998.

28. CM 20th October 1897.

29. MC 15th December 1897.

30. MC 15th December 1898.

31. CM 30th July 1899.

32. CM 18th October 1899.

33. CM 15th December 1899.

34. CM 26th July 1900.

35. CM 8th July 1902.

36. CM 12th May 1904.

37. Henry RS. *The Armed Forces Institute of Pathology. Its first century 1862–1962*. Washington, DC: Office of the Surgeon General, Department of the Army, 1964: 17–22.

38. Dawson JW. The histology of disseminated sclerosis. *Trans R Soc Edinb* 1916;**1**:517–740.

39. Dawson JW. The melanomata. *Edinb Med J* 1925;**32**:501–732.

40. Struthers JW, Dawson JW. Generalised osteitis fibrosa with parathyroid tumour and metastatic calcification including a critical discussion of the pathological processes underlying osseous dystrophies. *Edinb Med J* 1923;**30**:421–564.

41. Thomson A, Miles A. *Manual of surgery*. Edinburgh, London: Young J Pentland, 1904.

42. Aschoff L, Gaylord H. *Kursus der Pathologischen Histologie mit einem mikroskopischen Atlas*. Wiesbaden: Verlag von JF Bergman, 1900.

Chapter 6

1. Cresswell CH. *The Royal College of Surgeons of Edinburgh. Historical Notes from 1505 to 1905*. Edinburgh: Oliver and Boyd, 1926.

2. Dingwall H. *A famous and flourishing society. The history of the Royal College of Surgeons of Edinburgh, 1505–2005*. Edinburgh: Edinburgh University Press, 2005.

3. Hartley JNJ. The early history of the museum of the Royal College of Surgeons of Edinburgh. *Edinb Med J* 1948;**60**:513–32.

4. Tansey V, Mekie DEC. *The story of the Museum of the Royal College of Surgeons of Edinburgh*. Edinburgh: Royal College of Surgeons, 1978. (The original 110 page manuscript, with 68 photographs, one in colour, is held in the library of the Royal College of Surgeons of Edinburgh).

5. Virchow R. *Cellular pathology as based upon physiological and pathological histology*. London: John Churchill, 1860. (Translated from the second edition of the original by Chance F.)

6. Cameron G. *Pathology of the cell*. Edinburgh, London: Oliver and Boyd, 1952.

7. Harris H. *The birth of the cell*. New Haven, London: Yale University Press, 1999.

8. Mortimer PP. The bacteria craze of the 1880s. *Lancet* 1999;**353**:581–4.

9. Goodsir J. History of a case in which a fluid periodically ejected from the stomach contained vegetable organisms of an undescribed form. *Edinb Med Surg J* 1842;**57**:430–43.

10. Pettigrew JB. *Animal locomotion or walking, swimming and flying with a dissertation on aëronautics*. London: Henry S King and Co, 1873.

11. Ross J. *The Edinburgh School of Surgery after Lister*. Edinburgh, London, New York: Churchill Livingstone, 1978.

12. MC 15th December 1897.

13. MC 16th July 1907.

14. MC 16th December 1910.

15. MC 2nd May December 1856.

16. CM 20th October 1897.

17. PCM 15 December 1908.

18. Lonsdale H. *The life of Dr Robert Knox*. 1870.

19. McLaren I. Robert Knox MD, FRCSEd, FRSEd 1791–1862: the first conservator of the college museum. *J R Coll Surg Edinb* 2000;**45**:392–7.

20. Gardner DL. Robert Knox and Joseph Lister: pioneers of vascular physiology. *J R Coll Physicians Edinb* 2003;**33**(Suppl 12):42–5.

21. Chalmers J. *Audubon in Edinburgh*. Edinburgh: NMS Publishing, 2003: 83–103.

22. Royal College of Surgeons of Edinburgh. CMR 21st October 1914.

23. MC 19th October 1920.

24. MC 11th November 1920.

25. CM 1st May 1930.

26. CM 8th October 1907.

27. Treves F. Perityphlitis. In: Albutt TC, ed. *A system of medicine, volume III*. London, New York: Macmillan, 1897: 879–937.

28. MC 17th October 1888.

29. MC 7th October 1901.

30. HWP 14/11/08

31. HWP 14/11/01

32. HWP 14/11/02

33. Cox FEG, ed. *The Wellcome Trust illustrated history of tropical diseases*. London: Wellcome Trust, 1996.

34. MC 13th March 1904.

35. MC 19th October 1904.

36. Bowman, AK. *The Life and Teaching of Sir William Macewen. A Chapter in the History of Surgery*. London, Edinburgh, Glasgow: William Hodge and Company Limited, 1942.

37. MC 9th July 1907.

38. MC 17th May 1910.

39. PCM 8th October 1914.

40. PCM 15th May 1929.

41. PCM 9th October 1922.

42. PCM 15th November 1914.

43. PCM 19th November 1914.

44. PCM 28th January 1919.

45. CM 21st October 1914.

46. MC 15th October 1916.

47. MC 17th July 1917.

48. MC 19th May 1919.

49. PCM 30th September 1919.

50. PCM 28th January 1920.

51. PCM 11th May 1921.

52. CM 21st October 1903.

53. PCM 17th July 1922.

54. Greig DM. A neanderthaloid skull presenting features of cleidocranial dysostosis and other peculiarities. *Edinb Med J* 4th Series 1933; 40: 497–557.

Chapter 7

1. Cruttwell C. *A history of the Great War 1914–1918.* Oxford: Clarendon Press, 1936.

2. Keegan J. *The first world war.* London: Pimlico edition, 1999.

3. Taylor A. *The first world war. An illustrated history.* Harmondsworth: Penguin Books, 1966.

4. Churchill WS. *The world crisis 1915.* London: Thornton Butterworth Limited, 1923.

5. MacMunn G, Falls C. *History of the Great War based on official documents by direction of the Historical Section of the Committee of Imperial Defence. Military Operations, Egypt and Palestine. From the outbreak of war with Germany to June 1917.* London: Stationery Office, 1928.

6. MacPherson, Major General Sir WG. *History of the Great War based on official documents. Medical services, general history. Volume III. Medical services during the operations on the Western Front in 1916, 1917 and 1918; in Italy; and in Egypt and Palestine.* London: Stationery Office, 1924.

7. MacPherson WG, Mitchell TJ. *Official history of the war. History of the Great War based on official documents. Medical services, general history. Volume IV. Medical services during the operations on the Gallipoli Peninsula; in Macedonia; in Mesopotamia and North-West Persia; in East Africa; in the Aden Protectorate; and in North Russia. Ambulance transport during the war.* London: Stationery Office, 1924.

8. Blair JSG. *In arduis fidelis. Centenary history of the Royal Army Medical Corps.* Edinburgh: Scottish Academic Press, 1998.

9. Wade H. Student life in the Scottish Horse Field Ambulance. *The Student* 1920:43–6.

10. Anonymous. *With the 1st/1st South Midland Mounted Brigade Field Ambulance in Egypt, Gallipoli, Palestine, Salonika, 1914–1918.* Aston: Globe Printing and Binding Works, Darwin Book Company.

11. MacEchern D. *The sword of the north*. Inverness: Robert Carruthers and Sons, Courier Office, 1923: 285–300.

12. McPherson J. *Battle cry for freedom*. London: Penguin Group, 1990.

13. Larrey D. *Mémoire de chirurgie militaire et campagnes*. Paris: De l'imprimerie de J Smith, 1812.

14. Abadie J. *Wounds of the abdomen*. London, Paris: University of London Press, Masson et Cie, 1918.

15. Macdonald L. *1915. The death of innocence*. London: Hodder Headline, 1993.

16. Hamilton I. *Sir Ian Hamilton's dispatches from the Dardanelles*. London: George Newnes, 1915.

17. Carlyon, LA. *Gallipoli*. London, New York, Toronto, Sydney, Auckland: Bantam Books, 2001.

18. Ross J. *The Edinburgh School of Surgery after Lister*. Edinburgh, London, New York: Churchill Livingstone, 1978.

19. McCusatra L. *Gallipoli days and nights*. London, New York, Toronto: Hodder and Stoughton, 1916.

20. Drew R. *Commissioned officers in the medical services of the British Army, 1660–1960*. London: Wellcome Historical Medical Library, 1968.

21. Cantlie N. *A history of the army medical department*. Edinburgh: Churchill Livingstone, 1974.

Chapter 8

1. Ludwig E. *Napoleon*. London: George Allen and Unwin, 1927: 116–37.

2. Anonymous. Obituary: Sir Henry Wade. *BMJ* 1955;**1**:607–8.

3. Anonymous. Obituary: Henry Wade. *Lancet* 1955;**i**:516–7.

4. Graham JM. In memoriam: Henry Wade. *J R Coll Surg Edinb* 1955–6;**i**:75–8.

5. MacMunn G, Falls C. *History of the Great War. Based on official documents by direction of the Historical Section of the Committee of Imperial Defence. Military operations, Egypt and Palestine. From the outbreak of war with Germany to June 1917*. London: Stationery Office, 1928: 1–445.

6. Wells HG. *The outline of history being a plain history of life and mankind*. London: George Newnes Limited, 1930.

7. Cruttwell CRMF. *A history of the Great War 1914–1918*. Oxford: Clarendon Press, 1936: 204–27, 339–58.

8. Keegan J. *The First World War*. London: Pimlico, 1999: 234–69.

9. Overy R, ed. *The Times history of the world*. London: Times Books, Harper Collins, 1999: 250–1.

10. Wade H. The influence of the war on the modern treatment of fractures. *BMJ* 1921;**1**:1–12.

11. Wade H. Surgical work in Palestine, Mesopotamia and Macedonia. In: MacPherson WG, Bowlby AA, Wallace C, English C. *History of the Great War, based on official documents. Medical services: surgery of the War*. London: Stationery Office, 1922:310–27.

12. Larrey DJ. *Mémoire de chirurgie militaire et campagnes. Tome 1.* Paris: De l'imprimerie de J Smith, 1812.

13. Gardner DL. War wounds 1815 and 1915. *Seminar delivered to the Department of Pathology, University of Edinburgh, 12 March 1997.*

14. Gardner DL. War wounds: 1815 and 1915. The contrasting experiences of Charles Bell and Henry Wade. *Seminar delivered to the Postgraduate Medical Centre, Wythenshawe Hospital, Manchester, 1 April 1998.*

15. Gardner DL. Henry Wade: from Dunkeld to Damascus, 1914–1919. *Lecture to the Faculty of Pre-Hospital Care of the Royal College of Surgeons of Edinburgh and the Military Surgery Society, 16th May 1998.*

16. Mitchell TJ, Smith GM. Casualties in Egypt and Palestine, 1915–1918. In: *History of the Great War. Based on official documents. Medical services: casualties and medical statistics of the Great War.* London: Stationery Office, 1931: 208–17.

17. Ellis H. *A history of surgery.* London: Greenwich Medical Media Limited, 2001.

18. Gray HMW. *The early treatment of war wounds.* London: Joint Committee of Henry Frowde and Hodder and Stoughton at the Oxford University Press Workshop, 1919: 1–79.

19. Abadie J. *Wounds of the abdomen.* London, Paris: University of London Press, Masson et Cie, 1918: 171.

20. Wade H. The significance of haematuria: a British Medical Association lecture delivered to the Northampton Branch, November 10th 1931. *BMJ* 1932;**i:**177–80.

21. Cox FEG, ed. *The Wellcome Trust illustrated history of tropical diseases.* London: Wellcome Trust, 1996.

22. HWP 14/9 (17th March 1919).

Chapter 9

1. HWP 14/78 (15th June 1919).
2. HWP 14/80 (7th September 1919).
3. HWP 14/76,77 (20th April 1919).
4. HWP 1/1/35 (7th June 1919).
5. HWP 1/1/27 (2nd July 1919).
6. HWP 16/7 (5th June 1919).
7. HWP 14/116 (17th October 1919).
8. HWP 16/40 (22nd December 1919).
9. HWP 8/1 (15th April 1922).
10. HWP 8/19 (12th February 1914).
11. HWP 1/2/19 (15th December 1922).
12. HWP 8/42 (29th November 1922).
13. HWP 8/39 (22nd March 1923).
14. HWP 8/10–16 (11th June 1919).
15. HWP 6/10 (29th November 1922).

16. HWP 6/17 (13th February 1923).

17. HWP 6/18 (20th December 1922).

18. HWP 6/20 (19th October 1922).

19. HWP 6/9 (20th November 1919).

20. HWP 6/25 (24th October 1922).

21. HWP 16/67 (6th September 1922).

22. HWP 14/1 (15th August 1919).

23. HWP 1/1/43 (18th October 1920).

24. HWP 1/1/45 (undated).

25. HWP 1/1/64 (11th February 1920).

26. HWP 1/1/12 (24th January 1920).

27. HWP 2/58 (5th January 1920).

28. HWP 1/2/5 (28th April 1922).

29. HWP 1/1/15–18 (15th February 1920 et seq).

30. HWP 1/4/35 (27th November 1919).

31. HWP 1/4/67 (undated).

32. HWP 1/4/68 (31st October 1922).

33. HWP 1/4/43–53 (27th June 1922 et seq).

34. HWP 1/4/9 12th March 1920).

35. HWP 2/78 (undated).

36. HWP 1/2/46–67 (6th April 1922–24th March 1923).

37. HWP 1/2/71 (17th August 1922).

38. HWP 1/3/8 (23rd January 1923).

39. HWP 1/1/72 (4th March 1920).

40. HWP 14/16/28 (undated).

41. HWP 1/2/74 (20th April 1922).

42. HWP 1/2/1 (10th October 1922).

43. HWP 1/1/63 (24th April 1922).

44. HWP 14/7/2 (undated).

45. HWP 6/5 16th (March 1920).

46. HWP 14/7/1 (undated).

47. HWP 14/14/7,8 (undated).

Chapter 10

1. Young J. *An Introduction to the Study of Man*. Oxford, London, New York: Oxford University Press, 1971.

2. Billings JS. The history and literature of surgery. In: Dennis FS, editor. *System of Surgery*. Philadelphia, 1895. p. 17–144.

3. Craig W. *History of the Royal College of Physicians of Edinburgh*. Oxford, London, Edinburgh, Melbourne: Blackwell Scientific Publications, 1976.

4. Guthrie D. *A History of Medicine*. London, Edinburgh, Paris: Thomas Nelson and Sons Ltd, 1945.

5. Gallie W. *Essays in Surgery*. Toronto: University of Toronto Press, 1950.

6. Keynes G. *Blood transfusion*. Bristol: John Wright & Sons Ltd; London: Simkin Marshall (1941) Ltd, 1949.

7. Masson A. *A History of Blood Transfusion in Edinburgh*. Edinburgh: Edinburgh Blood Transfusion Service, 1993.

8. Keys T. *The History of Surgical Anesthesia*. New York: Schuman's, 1945.

9. Singer C, Underwood E. *A Short History of Medicine*. 2ed. Oxford: Clarendon Press, 1962.

10. Dingwall HM. *A History of Scottish Medicine. Themes and influences*. Edinburgh: Edinburgh University Press, 2003.

11. Logan Turner A. *Story of a Great Hospital. The Royal Infirmary of Edinburgh 1729–1929*. Edinburgh: Oliver & Boyd, Tweeddale Court; London: Oliver & Boyd: 33, Paternoster Row, 1937

12. Catford EF. *The Royal Infirmary of Edinburgh 1929–1979*. Edinburgh: Scottish Academic Press, 1984

13. Comrie J. *History of Scottish Medicine*, volume I. 2nd edn. London: Baillière, Tindall & Cox, 1932.

14. RIEM 21st July 1926.

15. RRIE 5th October 1925.

16. Johnston IDA, Hunter AR Eds. *The Design and Utilization of Operating Theatres*. London: Edward Arnold, 1984.

17. Howell J. *Technology in the Hospital. Transforming patient care in the early twentieth century*. Baltimore, London: The Johns Hopkins University Press, 1995.

18. RIEM 15th April 1925.

19. RIEM 13th March 1929.

20. RIEM 11th June 1929.

21. RIEM 28th July 1927.

22. RIER 1st October 1924.

23. Birkmeyer JD, Stukel TA, Siewers AE, Goodney PP, Wennberg DE, Lucas FL. Surgeon volume and operative mortality in the United States. *New England Journal of Medicine* 2003;349(22), 2117–27.

24. RIEM 7th January 1924.

25. Bell J. The surgical side of the Royal Infirmary of Edinburgh, 1852–92: the progress of a generation. *Edinburgh Hospital Reports* 1, 1–18. 1893. 27–3–0003.

26. Creswell C. *The Royal College of Surgeons of Edinburgh. Historical notes from 1505 to 1905*. Edinburgh, London: Oliver and Boyd; 1926.

27. RIEM 3rd July 1928.

28. Wade H. Lancet 1912;1:798. (A contribution to a discussion following a paper on The treatment of simple fractures, presented by CW Cathcart at a meeting of the Edinburgh Medico-Chirurgical Society. Wade used splints exceptionally but massage was invaluable).

29. Ross J. 1978. *The Edinburgh School of Surgery after Lister*. Edinburgh, London, New York: Churchill Livingstone, 1978.

30. RRIE 26th August 1919.

31. RRIE 30th September 1939.

Chapter 11

1. Young JZ. *An introduction to the study of man*. Oxford: Oxford University Press, 1971.

2. McCrae M. *The National Health Service in Scotland. Origins and ideals, 1900–1950*. East Linton: Tuckwell Press, 2003.

3. Ellis H. *A history of surgery*. London: Greenwich Medical Media Limited, 2001.

4. *Reports of the Royal Infirmary of Edinburgh:* 1919–1939.

5. Wade H. The art of the surgeon in diagnosis and treatment. *Newcastle Med J* 1946;**23**:22–7.

6. Thomson AL. *Half a century of medical research*. London: HM Stationery Office, 1973–75

7. Public Health Laboratory Service. *Annual Reports*: London: PHLS, 1914–1948.

8. RIEM 17th March 1925.

9. PCM 19th November 1914.

10. Stanley WM. Isolation of a crystalline protein possessing the properties of tobacco mosaic virus. *Science* 1935;**81**:644–5.

11. Calmette A, Guérin C, Négre L, Boquet A. Sur la vaccination préventive des enfants nouveau-nés contre la tuberculose par le B.C.G. *Annals de l'Institut Pasteur* 1927;**41**:201–32.

12. RIEM 6th November 1924.

13. RIEM 15th July 1924.

14. RIEM 11th March 1928.

15. RIEM 13th March 1929.

16. Masson AHB. Anaesthesia in Edinburgh 1900–1950. In: Essays on the history of anaesthesia: selected and revised contributions by members of the history of anaesthesia. London: Royal Society of Medicine, 1996: 65–70.

17. Morton WTG. *Remarks on the proper method of administering sulphuric ether by inhalation*. Boston: Dutton and Wentworth, 1847.

18. Simpson JY. Discovery of a new anaesthetic agent, more efficient than sulphuric ether. *Lond Med Gaz NS* 1847;**5**:934–7.

19. Simpson JY. On a new anaesthetic agent, more efficient than sulphuric ether. *Lancet* 1847;**ii**:549.

20. RIEM 15th January 1926.

21. RIEM 30th March 1928.

22. RIEM 14th February 1929.

23. PCM 12th December 1922.

24. PCM 21st July 1924.

25. Kirkup JR. The history and evolution of surgical instruments. I. Introduction. *Ann R Coll Surg Eng* 1981;**63**:281–5.

26. Bowman A. *The life and teaching of Sir William Macewen. A chapter in the history of surgery*. London, Edinburgh, Glasgow: William Hodge and Company, 1942.

27. Guthrie D. *A history of medicine*. London, Edinburgh, Paris: Thomas Nelson and Sons, 1945.

28. Singer C, Underwood EA. *A short history of medicine*. Oxford: Clarendon Press, 1962.

29. Wangensteen OWS. *The rise of surgery from empiric craft to scientific discipline*. Minneapolis: University of Minnesota Press, 1978.

30. Porter R. *The greatest benefit to mankind. A medical history of humanity from antiquity to the present*. London: Harper Collins, 1997.

31. Macewen W. Cerebral abscess. *BMJ* 1879; **II**:1022.

32. Macewen W. *Pyogenic infective diseases of the brain and spinal cord: meningitis, abscess of brain, infective thrombosis*. Glasgow: James Maclehose and Sons, 1893.

33. Macewen W. Tumour of the dura mater – convulsions – removal of tumour by trephining – recovery. *Glasgow Med J* 1879;**12**:210–13.

34. Cushing HW. *Intracranial tumours*. Springfield: CC Thomas, 1932.

35. Carrel A, Guthrie CC. The transplantation of veins and organs. *Am Med* 1905;**10**:1101–2.

36. Carrel A. Experimental surgery of the thoracic aorta by the method of Meltzer and Auer. *Ann Surg* 1910;**52**:83–95.

37. Jonnesco MT. Angine de poitrine guérie par la résection du sympathique cervico-thoracique. *Bull Acad Méd Paris* 1920;**84**:93–102.

38. Carrel A, Lindbergh C. A apparatus for the perfusion of whole organs. J Exp Med 1935;62:409–32.

39. PCM 2nd February 1918.

40. Wade H. The influence of the war on the modern treatment of fractures. *BMJ* 1921;**I**:327–30.

41. Brown J. *Horae subsecivae. Rab and his friends*. Edinburgh: David Douglas, 1889: 363–87.

42. Halsted WS. The results of operations for the cure of cancer of the breast performed at the Johns Hopkins Hospital from June 1889 to January 1894. *Johns Hopkins Hosp Rep* 1894;**4**:297–350.

43. Handley WS. *Cancer of the breast and its treatment*. London: J Murray, 1922.

44. Landsteiner K. Zur Kenntnis der antifermentativen, lytischen und agglutinierenden Wirkungen des Blutserums und der Lymphe. *Centralblatt für Bakteriologie, Parasitenkunde und Infektionskrankheiten* 1900;**27**:357–62.

45. Levine P, Stetson RE. An unusual case of intra-group agglutination. *JAMA* 1939;**113**:126–7.

46. Masson A. *A history of blood transfusion in Edinburgh*. Edinburgh: Edinburgh Blood Transfusion Service, 1993.

47. RIEM 30th December 1927.

48. Domagk G. Ein Beiträg zur Chemotherapie der bakteriellen Infectionen. *Dtsch Med Wochenschr*1935;**61**:250–3.

49. Fleming A. On the antibacterial action of cultures of a penicillium, with special reference to their use in the isolation of *B. influenzae*. *Br J Exp Path* 1929;**10**:226–36.

50. Schatz A, Bugie E, Waksman SA. Streptomycin, a substance exhibiting antibiotic activity against Gram-positive and Gram-negative bacteria. *Proc Soc Exp Biol* 1944;**55**:66–9.

51. Symposium. Aureomycin – a new antibiotic. *Ann NY Acad Sci* 1948;**51**:175–342.

52. Kendall EC, Mason HL, McKenzie BF, Koelsche GA. Isolation in crystalline form of the hormone essential to life from the suprarenal cortex; its chemical nature and physiologic properties. *J Biol Chem* 1934;**114**:57–8.

53. Waksman SA, Lechevalier HA. Neomycin, a new antibiotic active against streptomycin-resistant bacteria, including tuberculosis organisms. *Science* 1949;**109**:305–7.

Chapter 12

1. Anonymous. Obituary: Sir Henry Wade. *BMJ* 1955;I:607–8.

2. Anonymous. Obituary: Henry Wade. *Lancet* 1955;i:516–17.

3. Ross JA. *The Edinburgh School of Surgery after Lister*. Edinburgh, London, New York: Churchill Livingstone, 1978: 78–90.

4. Ellis H. *A history of surgery*. London: Greenwich Medical Media, 2001: 120–2.

5. Bell C. *Illustrations of the great operations of surgery*. London: Longman, 1821.

6. Cresswell C. *The Royal College of Surgeons of Edinburgh. Historical notes from 1505 to 1905*. Edinburgh, London: Oliver and Boyd, 1926.

7. Wade H. *A contribution to the problem of cancer research, based upon the results of an experimental investigation of infective sarcoma of the dog* [MD thesis]. Edinburgh: University of Edinburgh, 1907.

8. Gardner DL. Henry Wade (1876–1955) and cancer research: early years in the life of a pioneer of urological surgery. *J Med Biog* 2003:11:81–6.

9. Wade H. The choice of methods employed in the surgical diagnosis of renal disease. *Med Chir Trans* 1922;36:169–83.

10. Wade H. The art of the surgeon in diagnosis and treatment. *Newcastle Med J* 1946a;23:22–7.

11. Wade H. The diagnosis of renal and vesical disease in general practice. *Clin J* 1935a;64:66–71.

12. Wade H. The balanced urinary system: the Ramon Guiteras lecture. *J Urol* 1932;28:381–403.

13. Wade H, Dick IL. Suppression of urine and deficiency of renal secretion. *Trans Med Chir Soc Edinb* 1933–34;41:193–220.

14. Desormeaux AJ. *De l'endoscope et ses applications au diagnostic et au traitement des affections de l'urèthre et de la vessie*. Paris: JB Baillière, 1865.

15. Wade H. The diagnosis and treatment of calculus in the pelvic portion of the ureter. *Edinb Med J* 1920;24:392–401.

16. Wade H. The significance of haematuria. *BMJ* 1932;I:1–12.

17. MacIntyre J. Roentgen rays. Photography of renal calculus. *Lancet* 1896;ii:118.

18. Wade H. The clinical significance of the form and capacity of the renal pelvis. *Trans Med Chir Soc Edinburgh* 1924–25;38:13–9.

19. Wade H, Band D. Uroselectan: excretion urography. *Trans Med Chir Soc Edinb* 1929–30;44;203–20.

20. Swick M. Darstellung der Niere und Harnwege im Röntgenbild durch intravenöse Einbringung eines neuen Kontraststoffes, des Uroselectans. *Klin Wochens* 1929;8:2087–9.

21. von Lichtenberg A, Swick M. Klinische Prufung des Uroselectans. *Klin Wochens* 1929;8:2089–91.

22. Wade H. The role of excretion urography in the diagnosis of disease. *BMJ* 1933a;I:353–5.

23. Wade H. The treatment of tuberculous disease of the kidney from the standpoint of the surgeon. *Edinb Med J* 1933b;40:166–75.

24. Wade H. The surgical pathology of tuberculous disease of the urinary tract. *Ir J Med Sci* 1928;6:245–58.

25. Wildbolz H. *Chirurgie der Nierentuberculose. Stuttgart*: F Enke, 1913.

26. Thomson-Walker J. *Surgical diseases and injuries of the genito-urinary organs*. London, Toronto, Melbourne: Cassell and Company, 1936.

27. Wade H. Renal tumours. *Aust N Z J Surg* 1935b;5:3–17.

28. Wade H. The treatment of ureteric calculi. *Proc R Soc Med* 1935c;28:582–90.

29. Wade H. Urological reflections. *Proc R Soc Med* 1946b;39:751–4.

30. Wade H. The treatment of tumours of the urinary bladder. *Trans Med Chir Soc Edinb* 1926–27;41:1–19.

31. Wade H. The treatment of malignant tumours of the urinary bladder. *Surg Gynecol Obstet* 1931;52:312–23.

32. Young HH, Davis DM. *Young's practice of urology*. Philadelphia: WB Saunders, 1926.

33. Wade H. Vesical exclusion. *Proc R Soc Med* 1937–1938;31:277–92.

34. Wade H. The expectancy of life after ureteral transplantation. *Edinb Med J* 1939;46:61–82.

35. Wade H. Prostatism: the pathological basis of the operative treatment. *Lancet* 1913;ii:299–300.

36. Wade H. Prostatism. The surgical anatomy and pathology of the operative treatment. *Ann Surg* 1914a;37:321–59.

37. Wade H. Treatment of prostatism. *Int Clin II Series* 1914b;24:1–12.

38. Walker KM. *The enlarged prostate and prostatic obstruction*. London: Humfrey Milford/Oxford University Press, 1933: 208–17.

39. Millin TJ. Retropubic prostatectomy. A new extravesical technique. *Lancet* 1945;2:693–6.

40. McGill AF. On supra-pubic prostatectomy, with three cases in which the operation was successfully performed for chronic prostatic hypertrophy. *Trans Clin Soc Lond* 1888;21:52–7.

41. Fuller E. Six successful and successive cases of prostatectomy. *J Cut Genito Disease* 1895;13:229–39.

42. Freyer PJ. A clinical lecture on total extirpation of the prostate for radical cure of enlargement of the organ. *BMJ* 1901;II:125–9.

43. Freyer PJ. One thousand cases of total enucleation of the prostate for radical cure of enlargement of that organ. *BMJ* 1912;II:868–70.

44. Freyer PJ. *Clinical lectures on enlargement of the prostate.* London: Baillière, Tindall and Cox, 1920.

45. Nitze M. Eine neue Modifikation des Harnleiterkatheters. *Zentralblatt für Krankheit Harn und Sex Organe* 1897;8:8–13.

46. Young HH. A new procedure (punch operation) for small prostatic bars and contracture of the prostatic orifice. *JAMA* 1913;60:253–7.

47. Caulk JR. Infiltration anesthesia of the internal vesical orifice for the removal of minor obstructions: presentation of a cautery punch. *J Urol* 1920;4:399–408.

48. Walker K. Perurethral operations for prostatic obstruction. *BMJ* 1925;I:201–4.

49. Proust R. *Manuel de la prostatectomie périnéale pour hypertrophie.* Paris: C Naud, 1903.

50. Proust R. *La prostatectomie dans l'hypertrophie de la prostate. Prostatectomie périnéale et prostatectomie transvésicale.* Paris: Masson et Cie, Editeurs Libraires de l'Académie de Médecine, 1904.

51. Young HH. Conservative perineal prostatectomy. *JAMA* 1903;41:999–1009.

52. Young HH. Early diagnosis and radical cure of carcinoma of the prostate. Being a study of 40 cases and presentation of a radical operation which was carried out in four cases. *Johns Hopkins Hosp Bull* 1905;16:315–21.

53. Muir EG. Carcinoma of the prostate. *Lancet* 1934;i:667–72.

54. Murphy LJT. *The history of urology.* Part 1. The history of urology to the latter part of the nineteenth century by Ernest Desnos,1914 translated and edited by LJT Murphy, pp 1–190; Part 2. The development of modern urology by 1972, by LJT Murphy, pp. 191–531. Springfield: Thomas, 1972.

55. Pousson A, Dennos, E. *Encyclopédie française d'urologie.* Paris: Maloin and fils, 1914.

56. Ballenger EG. *History of urology.* Baltimore: Williams and Wilkins, 1933.

57. Guthrie D. *A history of medicine.* London, Edinburgh: Thomas Nelson and Sons, 1945.

58. Guyon JCF. *Leçons cliniques sur les maladies des voies urinaires.* Paris: JB Baillière, 1881.

59. Thompson H. *Clinical lectures on diseases of the urinary organs.* London: J Churchill, 1868.

60. Blandy JP, Williams JP. *The history of the British Association of Urological Surgeons.* London: Royal College of Surgeons of England, 1995:15.

Chapter 13

1. Comrie JD. *History of Scottish Medicine*. London: Baillière, Tindall & Cox, Volume II, 1932.

2. Creswell C. *College of Surgeons of Edinburgh. Historical Notes from 1505 to 1905*. Edinburgh: Oliver and Boyd, 1926.

3. Dingwall H. *A Famous and Flourishing Society. The History of the Royal College of Surgeons of Edinburgh, 1505 – 2005*. Edinburgh: Edinburgh University Press, 2005.

4. Guthrie D. *Extramural Medical Education in Edinburgh and the School of Medicine of the Royal Colleges*. Edinburgh and London: E & S Livingstone, 1965

5. Logan Turner A. *Story of a Great Hospital. The Royal Infirmary of Edinburgh 1729–1929*. Edinburgh: Oliver and Boyd, 1937.

6. Porter R. *The Greatest Benefit to Mankind. A Medical History of Humanity from Antiquity to the Present*. London: Fontana Press, 1997 (paperback edition 1999).

7. Kaufman MH. *Medical Teaching in Edinburgh during the 18th and 19th Centuries*. Edinburgh: The Royal College of Surgeons of Edinburgh, 2003.

8. PCM 24th January 1928.

9. PCM 5th December 1929.

10. PCM 11th October 1928.

11. Renshaw J. Report on the state of the buildings of the Royal College of Surgeons of Edinburgh, 2004.

12. CM 14th May 1912.

13. CM 25th July 1912.

14. PCM 31st July 1914.

15. PCM 8th October 1914.

16. HWP 10/37.

17. CM 1918.

18. HWP 10/1–5.

19. HWP 10/20–22.

20. HWP 10/6,7,8.

21. HWP 10/17.

22. HWP 10/40.

23. HWP 10/45.

24. Ross, J. *The Edinburgh School of Surgery after Lister*. Edinburgh, London: Churchill Livingstone, 1978.

25. HWP 14/14/63.

26. CM 2nd February 1927.

27. PCM 9th July 1930.

28. PCM 2nd February 1918.

29. CM 12th July 1937.

30. CM 4th February 1944.

31. CM 19th December 1944.

32. PCM 7th March 1929.

33. PCM 13th October 1916.

34. CM 15th December 1897.

35. HWP 10/58.

36. HWP 10/66.

37. HWP 10/67.

38. HWP 10/61.

39. HWP 10/69.

40. PCM 25th June 1923.

41. PCM 11th May 1925.

42. PCM 22nd November 1927.

Chapter 14

1. Creswell CH. _The Royal College of Surgeons of Edinburgh. Historical Notes from 1505 to 1905_. Edinburgh, London: Oliver & Boyd, 1926.

2. CM 1956 p. 26.

3. PCM 7th May 1934.

4. CM 19th December 1934.

5. PCM 16th October 1935.

6. CM 3rd November 1925.

7. CM 5th February 1936.

8. Anon. Henry Wade. _Lancet_ 1955;268:516–7.

9. PCM 9th July 1930.

10. PCM 2nd May 1932.

11. CM 19th May 1926.

12. CM 17th Ocotber 1928.

13. CM 19th May 1926.

14. Logan Turner A. _Story of a Great Hospital. The Royal Infirmary of Edinburgh 1729–1929_. Edinburgh: The Mercat Press, 1937, reprinted 1979.

15. PCM 1st November 1921.

16. CM 25th July 1938.

17. CM 14th October 1935.

18. PCM 25th February 1923.

19. PCM 25th March 1930.

20. CM 23rd July 1937.

21. PCM 8th October 1918.

22. McCrae M. _The National Health Service in Scotland_. East Linton: Tuckwell Press, 2003.

23. CM 5th March 1934.

24. CM 19th December 1934.

25. HWP 14/7/2.

26. SCMWC 1941–1942 to 1946–1947.

27. SCMWC III 1941–1942.

28. CM 18th December 1928.

29. CM 5th July 1932.

30. CM 12th July 1937.

31. CM 21st July 1939.

32. Pater JE. *The Making of the National Health Service.* King's Fund Historical Series I. London: King Edward's Hospital Fund for London,1981.

33. Craig. *History of the Royal College of Physicians of Edinburgh.* Edinburgh, London: Blackwell 1976.

34. *Report of the Committee on Scottish Health Services* (Cathcart Report) 1936 Cmd 5204.

35. *Report of the Hospital Services (Scotland) Committee* (Mackenzie Report). HMSO 1926.

36. *Report on the Hospital Services of Scotland* (Walker Report), HMSO, 1933.

37. *Report of the Committee on Social Insurance and Allied Services* (the Beveridge Report), 1942, Cmd. 6904.

38. PCM 12th December 1922.

39. PCM 21st July 1924.

40. CM 25th July 1924.

41. CM 25th January 1923.

42. PCM 20th July 1916.

43. PCM 6th October 1915.

44. PCM 7th December 1915.

45. PCM 5th December 1919.

46. PCM 4th February 1920.

47. PCM 30th November 1931.

48. CM 16th May 1899.

49. CM 23rd January 1909.

50. CM 15th December 1908.

51. PCM 11th May 1916.

52. PCM 12th October 1916.

53. SCMWC 26th January 1945.

54. SYP 22nd August 1943.

55. Hendrie WF, Macleod DAD. *The Bangour Story. A History of Bangour Village and General Hospitals.* Aberdeen: Aberdeen University Press, 1991.

56. Gardner DL. Robert Knox and Joseph Lister. Pioneers of vascular physiology. *J Roy Coll Physicians Edinb* 2003;33:43–5.

57. Gunn CB. *Leaves from the Life of a Country Doctor.* Edinburgh: The Moray Press, 1935.

58. Scott W. *The Surgeon's Daughter.* London and New York: George Routledge & Sons. New edition with the author's notes, 1831.

Chapter 15

1. Barrott HN. *An Atlas of Old Edinburgh*. West Port Books, 2000.

2. Fraser WH, Morris, RJ. *People and Society in Scotland*. Volumes 1–3. Edinburgh: John Donald, in association with the Economic and Social History Society of Scotland, 1990.

3. Chambers R. *Traditions of Edinburgh*. Edinburgh: Chambers, an imprint of Larousse plc, 1868.

4. HWP 14/1/2, 34–45.

5. Forman SG. Pilmuir. A seventeenth century laird's house. *Scottish Field* 1949;97:26.

6. Wade, H. *A Short History of Pilmuir*. Unpublished.

7. Wade, H. *Chronicles of Pilmuir*. Unpublished.

8. Album of Wade's photographs of Pilmuir House.

9. Wade, H. *Chronicles of Pilmuir* pp 84–5.

10. RMS 11.6.10.

11. Wade H. *Chronicles of Pilmuir* pp 53–60.

12. Album 23–24.

13. Small JW. *Scottish Woodwork of the Sixteenth and Seventeenth Century, measured and drawn from the stone*. Edinburgh: David Douglas, 1878.

14. Fleming A. *Scottish and Jacobite Glass*. Glasgow: Jackson, Son & Co, p.80.

15. Scott W. *The Bride of Lammermoor*. The Waverley Novels, Bouverie edition, volume viii. London: The Daily News Limited, 1901, p. 127.

16. Wade H. *Chronicles of Pilmuir* pp 106–107.

17. Album A17, 18 and 22.

18. Wade H. *Chronicles of Pilmuir* pp 96 and 98–100.

19. Album A9 and 10.

20. Album 19–22.

21. Wade H. *Chronicles of Pilmuir* pp 152–3.

22. Forman S. Tribute in Wax. *Scotland's S.M.T. magazine*, page 59 (SB No.2).

23. The Scottish Beekeeper 1950;26(11):213.

24. Wade H. *Chronicles of Pilmuir* pp 141–143.

25. Wade H. *Chronicles of Pilmuir* pp 111–113.

26. PCM 23.

Chapter 16

1. Ross JA. *The Edinburgh School of Surgery after Lister*. Edinburgh, London, New York: Churchill Livingstone, 1978.

2. Wade H. The art of the surgeon in diagnosis and treatment. *Newcastle Med J* 1946;**23**:22–7.

3. HWP 14/12.

4. HWP 12/54.

5. HWP 14/33,34.

6. HWP 14/25.

7. HWP 8/41.

8. HWP 8/42.

9. HWP 14/8.

10. HWP 8/48.

11. HWP 8/72,73.

12. HWP 8/76.

13. HWP 8/77–84.

14. HWP 8/87.

15. HWP 8/18.

16. HWP 8/29.

17. Wade H, Dick IL. Suppression of urine and deficiency of urine secretion. *Trans Med Chir Soc Edinb* 1934;**41**:193–220.

18. Wade H. Sir David Wilkie. *Edinb Med J* 1938;**45**:726–8.

19. Wade H. JJM Shaw. *Edinb Med J* 1940;**47**:773–5.

20. Wade H. The balanced urinary system. *J Urol* 1932;**28**:381–403.

21. Wade H. Harvey in Scotland. *Edinb Med J* 1938;**45**:761–81.

22. Wade H. The Barber Surgeons of Edinburgh. *Ann R Coll Surg Engl* 1949;**5**:3–16.

23. Larrey D. *Mémoire de chirurgie militaire et campagnes*. Paris: De l'imprimerie de J Smith, 1812.

24. de Segur, General Count Philip. *History of the expedition to Russia undertaken by the emperor Napoleon in the year 1812*. London: Treuttel and Wurtz, Treuttel, jun. and Richter, 1825.

25. Anonymous. Red Cross memorandum, undated.

26. HWP 14/16/49.

27. HWP 14/16/50.

28. HWP 14/16/51.

29. HWP 14/16/52.

30. HWP 14/12/19.

31. HWP 14/16/55.

32. HWP 14/16/56.

33. HWP 14/16/57.

34. HWp 14/16/58.

35. HWP 14/16/59.

36. HWP 14/16/60.

37. Gallie W. *Essays in surgery*. Toronto: University of Toronto Press, 1950. (Presented to Henry Wade by the author).

38. Reitz D. *Commando. A Boer journal of the Boer war*. London: Faber and Faber, 1929.

39. Wood M, ed. *Extracts from the records of the burgh of Edinburgh, 1655–1665*. Edinburgh and London: Oliver and Boyd, 1940.

Appendix 1.1

Correspondence between Henry Wade and his mother and youngest brother

18th March 1922

PO Box 1694, Johannesburg

Dear Mother,

I will give you a rough idea of what has been going on since the beginning of this year. On the first of January last the coal miners in the Witbank District of the Transvaal came out on strike against a reduction in their wages of 5/– per day i.e. they were being paid 30/– per day. All a "miner" in the coal mines actually does is to look after some 20 'boys'. They do the actual mining. No one is allowed to blast the holes in a mine unless he has a blasting Certificate, only given to white men. The strikers organised themselves into 'commandos'. The public saw what their meaning was but the strike leaders stated that their purpose was to protect the women & children of the Reef from the natives. Our next defence line is our new Defence Force of officers and youths between the ages of 17 to 20 years.

We have the Burger law - every man can be called up if necessary. However, it would not have been advisable to put this law into effect. It might have meant arming the miners. There was an undercurrent of propaganda carried on by parties called 'communists'. Our shopkeepers did not want to come out but the bands were armed with cycle chains attached to stout sticks. The 'communists' next move was to start on the natives. General Smuts proclaimed Martial Law in Johannesburg & district. The Commandos were now firing on the police as well as the mine officials. I think the losses, both sides included, in killed and wounded must be at least two thousand. Our gaols are now full. It has opened the eyes of the people here that an actual Bolshevik revolution had been engineered. Goodness knows what our next troubles will be.

With fondest love to all
Your affectionate son

[signed] James R Wade

10th April 1922

Dear Harry,

Mrs Cragg, my partners' wife is leaving for a trip home this week and if she should call on you to consult you as a surgeon, I would take it as a favour if you would do what you can for her and any expense in the matter to be an item between ourselves. I have not heard from home for some 3 months now and only hope that things are going well with all at home, and that no news is good news. I had 10 days driving troops in a motor, had a good view of the scrapping, but never was in any great danger. I hope that you are keeping well and will always be pleased to have a letter from you.

Your affectionate brother,

[signed] James R Wade

Appendix 1.2

Only surviving letter to Henry Wade from his youngest sister, Margaret

Sunday (undated)
Woodcroft, Larbert

Dear Harry,

We half expected you but you did not arrive. I enclose the account of the thing you gave Mother. Will you please just pay it – the cloak is a real comfort to her. But 'Far too good, she says'. I am not doing anything about a maid for you till I hear what the result of the one you heard of in the north of England. You can let me know if you want any assistance.

[signed] Margaret C Wade

APPENDIX 2.1

Dominique Jean Larrey

Larrey was surgeon to Napoleon Bonoparte's victorious armies and one of his most trusted officers. His achievements were of the greatest interest to Wade, who arranged for a translation of Larrey's memoirs after the First World War (Chapter 16).

Larrey was responsible for the concept of flying ambulances, each comprising 340 men. A chief surgeon was in command. The ambulance was organized in three divisions. Each division had 12 light, well-sprung carriages. Eight had two wheels and were designed for use in flat country; four had four wheels and were employed in mountainous terrain.

A **small ambulance carriage** was 1.1 m wide and shaped like an elongated cube with a curved top. It was drawn by two horses, with a single driver. There were two small windows and double doors at both ends. The floor of the carriage was readily swung in or out along side beams over four central rollers. There was a horsehair mattress and bolster covered in leather. The side panels were padded up to a height of 300 mm above the floor. Four metal handles for straps, or the sashes of orderlies, allowed the floor to be used as a stretcher. The wounded could be treated within the carriage, on the sliding floor, if the weather was poor.

Large ambulance carriages were drawn by four horses. There were two drivers. The floor was longer and wider than those of the small carriages, and the mattress was fixed. The left side opened for almost the whole length of the vehicle, allowing access to up to four wounded men, whose legs, on account of the dimensions of the carriage, were necessarily drawn up. There were small windows.

Larrey wrote:

> The casualties rescued by the Flying Ambulances will be assembled at a central point where the most seriously wounded will be operated on by the Surgeon-in-Chief or (under his direction) by a competent surgeon. We will always start with the most dangerously injured without regard to their rank or distinction.

When Larrey was called upon to attend the wounded in Egypt, he was

at the disadvantage of not having flying ambulances with him. There
had only been space to bring a large number of collapsible stretchers.
It had been argued that 'local resources' would be called upon for
help. Resourceful as ever, Larrey introduced the pannier-carrying
camel ambulance – a design used again in Egypt and Palestine in
1916–17 (Chapter 8).

APPENDIX 2.2

Items held in the besieged town of Ladysmith

One hundred and thirteen pounds of tincture of opium were present, together with 65 of this tincture with chloroform. Among the instruments were 177 glass syringes, 86 male pewter syringes, 18 Higginson's syringes, 23 hypodermic syringes and three brass ear syringes. The stores contained 135 lb of carbolic acid in oil. Iodoform was used widely, and there was 14 lb of this antiseptic. There was a great deal of wool, of which 343 lb was cotton, 926 lb absorbent, 625 lb boracic, 697 lb iodoform, 560 lb salicylic, 488 lb carbolized and 212 lb 'double cyanide'. There were also 519 plasters or tins of plaster, of which 132 were in the form of 6" wide adhesive plasters and 206 of 1" width. In addition, there were 16,585 bandages, of which 4,349 were loose, 3,275 calico, 1,518 flannel, 2,531 salicylate and 2,311 triangular. Fifteen varieties of tabloid were listed, and the medical supplies included 180 lb of quinine, 289 lb of astringents and 46 lb of tincture of ipecacuanha.

APPENDIX 2.3

The Royal Commission on South African Hospitals, 1901

The publication of the notorious Burdett Coutts letters catalyzed action. The Royal Commission on South African Hospitals reported in October 1901.

Evidence to the commission began to be taken in London on 24th June 1900; at Netley on 27th July; in Cape Town on 21st August; at McKenzie's Farm, Maitland, on July 27th; on the Hospital Ship Simla on the same day; on the ambulance train at Hexham River Station on 29th August; and at the 1st Imperial Yeomanry Hospital, Deelfontein, on 30th August. The collection of evidence continued until 5th November 1900. Submissions were made by Mr W Watson Cheyne and Professor John Chiene, both of whom were consultants to the forces. Professor Chiene said there was talk of Thomas' splints but he never wanted one. The wounded men often were feeble. They had travelled for hours to hospital on ordinary trains.

The Commander in Chief was Field Marshall the Right Honourable Lord FS Roberts KP GCB. His Chief of Staff was Lieutenant General Lord HH Kitchener GCB KCMG of Khartoum. The Commander in Chief's representative at Cape Town was Colonel IJC Herbert.

APPENDIX 2.4

Evidence to the Royal Commission on the war in South Africa, 1903

Mr Alfred Downing Fripp's evidence

Mr Fripp explained how a voluntary hospital could telegraph home for supplies, whereas the Royal Army Medical Corps could not. In his opinion, the head of the medical department was 'a weak brain-piece'. Medical officers in South Africa lacked knowledge of modern surgical methods. Officers who showed keenness to learn were disliked by those in command. Fripp described how his House Surgeon had been told either to sleep in a tent with three men with typhoid fever or be shot! There was a shortage of skilled nursing care. He added 'very little surgery was in fact done, even in the base hospitals since most cases demanding difficult surgery could be sent home'. He argued that 'every Army Medical Officer should have knowledge of bacteriology although not necessarily a deep one'. Combatant medical officers should be taught the elements of hygiene: it was not understood that steam disinfection of contaminated materials was critical, or even that excreta should be destroyed.

Sir Frederick Treve's evidence

Treves, invalided home after the Battle of Ladysmith, was equally critical of the army's organization, which 'he had found unsuitable for the field of war'. He added 'Medical Officers were afraid to buy items they needed' and 'the surgeon in the field was simply an administrator'. Field hospitals, he said, carried tons of useless equipment, as the lists prepared in England had to be followed, irrespective of the theatre of war. English ambulances had been barely fit to carry the sick. Some were little different from the cumbersome, horse-drawn carts used in the Crimea.

APPENDIX 5.1

Records of the Royal Infirmary of Edinburgh

Pathological records RIE 1908 (abbreviated)

Case 94 of 1908 was carefully compiled and reveals a style that changed little in the succeeding 30 years. There is no Infirmary register number. The patient died on 1st March 1908. The *post-mortem* examination was conducted on March 12th. The reason for the long delay is not clear.

'The patient was admitted to Ward 9 (Mr Dowden). Operation Feb 29th. Suprapubic cystostomy, preliminary to a suprapubic prostatectomy. That night temperature rose to 103°. Has continued to fall upon March 9th to 100°. Complained of pain in upper part of abdomen. No other symptoms. Died suddenly on March 10th 1908. The Resident Medical Officer was John Fraser.

An elderly male, well-developed, showing commencing post-mortem decomposition in abdomen and thighs. Rigor mortis is passing off. Transverse suprapubic incision.

Urethra, penile and membranous portions, healthy, prostatic portion increased in length and re vertical in direction. **Prostate** increased in size with a nodule of prostatic substance projecting into the cavity of the bladder behind the urethral opening and forming the so-called middle lobe of the prostate. This projection is covered with ulcerating bladder mucosa. The **urinary bladder** wall is hypertrophied owing mainly to an increase in the muscular coat. The mucous membrane has undergone chronic ulceration and multiple villous like projections of indurated mucous membrane project from the surface. **Ureters** somewhat dilated, their walls are hypertrophied and their mucous membranes show evidence of recent catarrh. **Kidneys**. Both pelves are dilated and show evidence of recent acute catarrh. No evidence of suppurative nephritis. Some chronic interstitial nephritis.'

There was no summary, and no histological report was appended.

Pathological records RIE 1909 (abbreviated)

PM Register No. 23; Attendant Mr Cathcart, Ward 18; Name; Male, age 68; Date of death 23rd January 1909; Date of Section [autopsy] 23rd January 1909

History Patient admitted 11th January with acute retention. Urine drawn off with Coudé catheter. 15th Jan: suprapubic drainage established. Patient difficult to deal with. An old man. Senile dementia, pulled tubes out, etc. Drainage not satisfactory. Bladder small and contracted. He also suffers from bronchitis. 18th January: patient died at 8:20 a.m.

Abstract of record Cystitis. Enlarged prostate. Ureteritis. Pyelitis.

Arterio-sclerotic atrophy of kidney

Abdomen only examined Considerable anterior curvature in upper dorsal region. General nutrition fair. Appears older than age given. Operation wound just above symphysis pubis.

On opening abdomen, no peritonitis. Urinary bladder contracted. On removing urinary tract and opening it up the kidneys were atrophied, granular on the surface. Arteries showing patches of atheromatous degeneration. The mucous membrane of the renal pelves was congested with petechial haemorrhages and covered with a layer of thin pus. Similar condition in the ureters particularly in the lower part and cystitis was present. The walls of the bladder were thickened. The mucous membrane showed patches of congestion, and a superficial necrotic area was present on the left side of a collar like projection of the prostate into the bladder. The prostate as a whole was enlarged. The aorta, common iliacs and femoral arteries showed extensive nodular atheroma with degeneration and calcification.

Nothing of importance pathologically in the other abdominal organs.

Signed: TS [Theodor Shennan, Pathologist]

APPENDIX 5.2

Preparation of large microscopic sections

Microscopic sections were often as large as 4½ × 2 inches (112mm x 50 mm). The technique of whole organ sectioning was refined by Gough and by Gough and Wentworth, allowing sections of entire lungs to be cut and incorporated with a patient's case notes for direct comparison with radiograms. They distended lungs with a solution of formalin and sodium acetate, which was infused into the bronchi. The lungs were then cut into slices 10–30 mm thick, washed and embedded in gelatine. The gelatine was hardened either with formalin or by freezing and was cut as 0.3–0.5 mm thick sections with a special microtome. Natural colours were preserved by using monophenyl ether or ethylene glycol. The sections of expanded lung could then be mounted on paper.

APPENDIX 6.1

Financial statements of the Museum of Royal College of Surgeons of Edinburgh

Some idea of the monetary burden placed on the Royal College of Surgeons of Edinburgh by the Museum can be gained from viewing a selection of the financial statements.

In 1904, the Museum cost the College £337 from a total revenue of £5,263. From time to time, sums ranging from £500 (1902) to £300 (1909) were spent in repainting the Museum. The Annandale collection was acquired in 1908 for £60, and £20 was directed to the purchase of obstetrical specimens in 1911 after Halliday Croom's strictures of the adequacy of the displays. A new microscope stand bought in 1910 cost £20 – an expenditure that could be approved only after Council discussion. Recovering from the Great War, the College incurred a financial deficit of £301 in 1922, but it spent no less than £200 on the Museum. In 1932, a plan to accommodate Logan Turner's specimens required £150.

In 1934, the Museum costs amounted to £1,205 from revenue of £9,795. Immediately before the Second World War, the Museum was allocated £922 from a College revenue of £12,012. However, College income fell drastically during the Second World War. In 1943, it had declined to £5,957, from which the Museum was allocated £322. By 1947, there was evidence of substantial recovery. As the number of FRCSEd candidates returned to peacetime levels, the Museum absorbed only £663 from an income of £14,726.

APPENDIX 6.2

Anatomical and pathological specimens contributed by Henry Wade to the Museum

Henry Wade contributed 336 anatomical and pathological specimens to the museum of the Royal College of Surgeons of Edinburgh. A large number was collected *post-mortem*, indicating their acquisition during the years 1906–08, when Wade was Assistant Pathologist to the Royal Infirmary of Edinburgh. Of these specimens, 25 had been discarded by 2003. The number of items in each disease category in the table below is one, except where otherwise shown.

Organ/tissue	Disorder	

Heart	• Endocarditis
	   ○ Unspecified (2)
	   ○ Ulcerative (2)
		• Infarction
		• Hypertrophy
		• Pericarditis, old

Lung	• Bronchopneumonia • Carcinoma, metastatic • Empyema	• Tuberculosis (6)

Kidney	• Abscess
	• Amyloidosis
	• Artery, abnormal
	• Calculus (5)
	• Carcinoma
	   ○ Hypernephroma (22)
	   ○ Renal pelvis (4)
	   ○ Metastatic (2)
	   ○ Nephroblastoma
	     (Wilms' tumour)
	   ○ Papilloma
	   ○ Adenoma
	• Contusion
	• Cyst
	   ○ Simple
	   ○ Hydatid
	• Fatty degeneration (5)
	• Fibrosis, infarction (3)
	• Haematuria (3)
		• Hypoplasia
		• Leukaemia (2)
		• Malformation
		• Nephritis
		   ○ Septic (4)
		   ○ Acute (2)
		   ○ Subacute (2)
		   ○ Chronic (11)
		   ○ Pyaemic (5)
		   ○ Syphilitic
		   ○ Unspecified (3)
		• Pelvic ectopia
		• Polycystic disease (4)
		• Pyelonephritis (6)
		• Hydronephrosis (8)
		• Tuberculosis (34)
		• Venous congestion (2)

Urinary bladder	• Calculus (2) • Carcinoma (3) • Cystitis • Diverticulum	• Papilloma (4) • Schistosomiasis (3) • Sphincteric stenosis, congenital • Tuberculosis

Organ/tissue	Disorder	
Prostate	• Benign nodular hyperplasia (7)	
Testis, epididymis	• Gumma (3)	• Teratoma
	• Hydrocoele	• Tuberculosis
	• Seminoma (4)	
Breast	• Carcinoma	• Fibroma
	• Chronic mastitis	• Papilloma (4)
	• Dysplasia	• Tuberculosis
Ovary	• Cystic tumour	• Dermoid cyst, torsion
Uterus	• Carcinoma	• Pregnant (2)
	• Choriocarcinoma	• Prolapse
	• Fibroma	
Thyroid	• Adenoma	• Toxic goitre
	• Carcinoma	
Brain	• Depression, traumatic	• Laceration (3)
	• Extradural haemorrhage (2)	• Meningitis, meningococcal
	• Gunshot wound (2)	
Pharynx	• Carcinoma (3)	
Salivary gland	• Mixed tumour	
Teeth	• Odontome, composite (mandible)	
Tongue	• Carcinoma	
Liver	• Abscess	• Fatty
	• Actinomycosis (2)	• Haemangioma (2)
	• Carcinoma (3)	• Melanoma, metastatic (3)
	○ Metastatic	• Pernicious anaemia
	• Cirrhosis (2)	• Tuberculosis
	• Contusion	
Gall bladder	• Cholelithiasis (2)	• Cholecystitis
Bile duct	• Calculus (2)	
Pancreas	• Acute pancreatitis	
Stomach	• Carcinoma	
Colon	• Carcinoma (4)	• Ulceration (2)
	• Schistosomiasis (2)	
Intestine	• Intussusception (2)	Tuberculosis
Rectum	• Carcinoma (4)	
Omentum/ mesentery	• Fat necrosis (3)	• Fibrosis
Bone	• Absorption, skull, associated with osteolytic tumour	• Osteomyelitis, femur
	• Ankylosis, femur	• Paget's disease
	• Endothelioma	• Sarcoma (3)
	• Exostosis, cartilaginous	• Skull, chloroma
	• Foot, deformity	• Spine, cervical
	• Fracture	• Teratoma, pelvisacral
	○ Rib	• Toe, valgus deformity
	○ Pelvis	• Tuberculosis
	• Hypertrophy, toe	○ Spine (2)
	• Osteitis fibrosa cystica	○ Phalanx
	• Osteoma, scapula	• Ulcer, tibia

Organ/tissue	Disorder	
Connective tissue	• Angiosarcoma • Fibrosarcoma	• Fibroma
Skin	• Burn (of hand) (2) • Carcinoma (2) • Fibroma	• Lipoma • Sebaceous cysts, multiple
Joint	• Synovial sarcoma	
Muscle	• Rhabdomyosarcoma	
Tendon	• Fibrosarcoma (of Achilles tendon)	
Neck	• Branchial teratoma	• Fibroma
Spleen	• Infarction (2) • Leukaemia (2)	• Pyaemia • Tuberculosis (2)
Lymph node	• Carcinoma (3) • Lymphosarcoma (3)	• Silicosis (foreign body), pigmentation • Tuberculosis (2)

In addition, a number of items, indicated by their General Catalogue (GC) numbers, were not fully described. They comprised GC 5133 (organ not stated: vermiform process), GC 5169 (organ not stated: schistosomiasis), GC 5984 (organ not stated: congestive venous dilatation), GC 10019 and 10020 (endothelioma tibia), GC 4611 (spine), GC 4523 (brain), GC 9554 (colon) and GC 14049 (urogenital organs of duck-billed platypus).

APPENDIX 6.3

Collection of watercolour drawings

Tissue/organ	Disease process
Brain	• Laceration
Kidney	• Carcinoma
	• Hydronephrosis
Urinary bladder	• Bilharziasis (schistosomiasis)
Lung	• Metastatic choriocarcinoma
Testis	• Torsion
	• Gumma
Bone:	
Skull	• Fracture
	• Osteomata (2)
	• Atrophy
	• Paget's disease of bone
	• Chloroma
	• Focal atrophy with psammoma body
	• Syphilis (2)
Tibia	• Chronic varicose periostitis
	• Syphilis
Femur	• Fracture
	• Osteomyelitis, acute
Spine	• Tuberculous osteitis
Radius	• Sarcoma
Humerus	• Disuse atrophy
Joint:	
Shoulder	• Dislocation (2)
Elbow	• Tuberculosis
Spleen	• Lymphoma

APPENDIX 6.4

Miscellanous items believed to have been in the possession of Henry Wade

Pocket case of surgical instruments

A pocket case of surgical instruments was presented to the Royal College of Surgeons of Edinburgh by MJW Kerr, whose aunt was housekeeper to Sir Henry Wade at Pilmuir House. The instruments were among her possessions after her death, and it may be presumed that they were originally Wade's property. The case contains:

- plated metal case and chamois leather cover
- clinical thermometer in bayonet catch case
- two tubes of hypodermic tablets
- hypodermic metal syringe with two platino-iridium needles (one in handle), together with needle box containing 12 suture needles (sizes 12 to 14)
- dissecting forceps
- Spencer Wells forceps
- Syme's abscess knife and scalpel in metal handle
- combined aneurysm needle and director
- nine triangular, pointed, size 9 suture needles
- silver probe with corkscrew and plane ends
- one pair blunt-ended scissors
- case containing eye spud with spool of silk.

Dart and bullet from Turkish invasion of Egypt, Kantara, 1914–15

Wade's notes record:

> 'Early in 1914–1915, the Turks attempted to invade Egypt. They crossed the Sinai desert and reached the Suez Canal. The steel arrow was dropped from one of their planes. The shrapnel bullet was fired into the desert from 'our warships'.'

APPENDIX 7.1

Wade's lantern slides

Eight wooden boxes contain 383 3¼″ × 3¼″ glass lantern slides, made from Wade's original photographs after he returned to the United Kingdom in 1919. The slides provide an itinerary for his travels between 1914 and 1919.

Box A: Northumberland to Gallipoli

Location/event	Slides	
	Captain Henry Wade, Scottish Horse Mounted Brigade (SHMB) Field Ambulance	
Blagdon	SHMB Field Ambulance route march	Field day, lifting wounded
	Halt on route march	Field day, lifting wounded
	Cook with greasy pan	Field day, lifting wounded
	Ambulances in field camp	Field day, field well
	Surgical operating car	Field day, transporting wounded
	Surgical operating car (interior)	Field day, signallers
Bedlington	SHMB Field Ambulance group	Field day, on football ground
	SHMB Field Ambulance unit party	Stretcher drill, on football ground
	Morning jerks	Field day, ruined house
	Field day	Motor water cart
	Field day, with surgical car	Motor water cart showing filters
	Field day, with surgical car	Two members of horse transport
Newcastle	1st Northern General Hospital	1st Northern General Hospital ward:
	1st Northern General Hospital ward	wounded from France
	1st Northern General Hospital:	Chillingham road building
Gallipoli	Suvla Bay, SHMB Field Ambulance	Suvla Bay, SHMB Field Ambulance
	Suvla Bay, surgical car and operating hut	tents
Egypt	Alexandria hospital ships	
Naples	Aquitania as hospital ship	Aquitania transporting patients
	Neuralia transporting patients to Aquitania	
Gibraltar	Aquitania approaching Gibraltar	View from Aquitania
Alexandria	Oxfordshire hospital ship approaching Alexandria	
Suez Canal	Ismalia: Turkish positions	Sweet Water canal
	Transport of Scots unit	Sweet Water canal, Kantara
Kantara	April 1916: pontoon bridge	1916: surgical car and operating hut
	1916: SHMBFA	1916: breakfast with dead flies
	April 1916. SHMBFA surgical car and hut	1916: hospital tents

Box B: Kantara and Sinai

Location/event	Slides	
Kantara 1916 (continued)	1916 SHMB Field Ambulance dust storm stretcher bearer	Canal hospital transport
	Patients on stretcher bed	Hospital transport bathing
	Wounded from Katia	Hospital transport
	New Zealand wounded	Watering horses
	Turkish wounded: Ali and Achmed	Drawing rations
	Orderlies and patients	Army Service Corps Depot
	Inspection of sand sledge	Egyptian Labour Corps, road making
	Inspection of sand sledge	Egyptian Labour Corps, unloading barge
	SHMB race meeting	Making Palestine railway
	SHMB swimming gala	Easter morning
	Egyptian Labour Corps moving hut	Sinai Desert, 1916
	Egyptian Labour Corps	Awards for gallantry
Sinai desert 1916	Buchanan and Brown	Campbell sand sledge
	Camel transport convoy	Sledge, Campbell, patient, Buchanan
	Infantry on march	Sledge crossing railway
	Infantry on march	Sand sledge
	Field kitchens on march	Camel transports sand sledge
	Motor ambulance in sands	Camel transport of wounded
	SHMB sports	Camel transport of wounded
	Hill 40, sporting track	Lying down cacholet
	Operating hut viewed through gauze window	Lying down cacholet
	Henry Wade operating	Camel transports lying down cases
	McLauchlin, Clark, Ferguson	Transport of sitting cases
	McLauchlin gets gifts from home	Hill 40, SHMB Field Ambulance
		Turkish wounded from Romani

Box C: Cairo to Kharga

Location/event	Slides	
Cairo	Turkish wounded from Romani	Forstat, excavating ruins
	Abdin Palace, Khedive's funeral	Nile feluccas
	Funeral leaving Abdin Palace	Boat passing bridge
	Mohamed Ali street/stairs – Funeral passing.	Felucca, boy on boat
	Buried city of Forstrat, excavations	Abdazza, cloud burst
	Forstat, excavators at work	Cloud burst, train buried
Journey by water during Nile floods from Giza to Sakara	Pyramids of Giza during Nile flood	Women making dung cakes
	Pyramids of Giza during flood	The fertile delta
	Pyramids of Giza during flood	Donkey transports
	Egyptian feluccas on bank of Nile	DF at city banks of Nile
	Funeral party passing along dyke	Irregulars at head of Shadons
Visit to Sakara	Steps of pyramid	Temple of Sakara
	Sakara, entrance to tomb	Cairo, hieroglyphics
Visit to Western Oasis of Kharga	Western Oasis, railway trains	Temple of Hibis, entrance
	Western Oasis, training, drawing water	Temple of Hibis
	Oasis train transporting sick	Temple of Hibis
	SHMB Field Ambulance party in line at platform	Roman fort
	Kharga village, underground	Roman fort
	Kharga village, entrance to underground passage	Roman fort, interior
	Public well, blind water carriers	Roman fort, battlements
	Blind water carriers filling their bags	Roman fort, walls
	Kharga, mosques	Irrigation of land by amateurs
	Kharga, village gardens	Fraser and one other
	Patients with smallpox	Donkey transports
	Near city of Kharga	Collection of Pierpoint Morgan

Box D: Kharga to Beersheba

Location/ event	Slides	
Visit to western Oasis of Kharga (continued)	Road to tomb in dead city	
Life on the Sinai Desert as Consulting Surgeon	Laying pipeline Railway in desert Water tanks at railhead Water transport from railhead Watering at railhead and hospital Cycle to ambulance train Ambulance convoy in desert Stretcher (single) ambulance American tractors in desert Bedouin camp in desert	Camel transport convoy Wadi El Arish El Arish, bridge building Well at El Arish, drawing water Gate of El Arish Stationary hospital at El Arish El Arish, walking wounded from Third Battle of Gaza El Arish, walking wounded
First Battle of Gaza	Rafa, March 1917 Casualty clearing station, moving forward Casualty clearing station, encampment 52nd Division advancing Camel Corps, advancing Camel Corps ambulance Camel Corps ambulance Camel ambulance, formerly SHMB Field Ambulance	Camel ambulance, non-commissioned officers of the former SHMB Field Ambulance Camel ambulance, Sergeant Cuthbert Camel ambulance, Private Porter Camel ambulance camel transports Gaza Gaza: camel ambulance in action at the battle Quaja and Gaza
Khan Unis, at First Battle of Gaza	Khan Unis, wounded arrive at casualty clearing station	Motor ambulances arrive by train Engine derailed at Khan Unis
Third Battle of Gaza	Rafa, September 1917, casualty clearing station making shelter	Rafa, equipment of three casualty clearing stations
Amara	Zero hour, cavalry moving out Casualty clearing station, wounded arriving Casualty clearing station, wounded arriving	Turkish wounded entraining Turkish wounded Aeroplane overhead Wounded Turk British walking wounded
Capture of Beersheba	Beersheba, station in distance Ambulances, flag and mosque	Town hall, surgical car at window Street in town

Box E: Beersheba to Haifa

Location/ event	Slides	
Capture of Beersheba (continued)	Town hall Henry Wade with Field Ambulance Street in town	Well Fruit sellers Amara transport
Sinai in late 1917 and early 1918	Gaza, tank abandoned at second battle Sinai, sick convoy Conducting surgeons on wire road	Spectators Delousing train
Palestine maritime plain 1918	Palestine maritime plain: peasants	Trading out the corn
Advance on Jerusalem December 1917	Palestine road making Donkey water carriers	Judean hills, road to Jerusalem Road to Jerusalem
Jerusalem	Outside Italian Hospice Outside Jaffa Gate Temple area Mosque of Omar	Via Dolorosa Firewood Judean hills, Bedouin Solomon's wells
Raids on Amman and El Gath	Jericho – Road to Jericho Road to Jericho Field ambulance at Good Samaritan Inn Good Samaritan Inn March 1918	Australian Field Ambulance Surgical car at Jericho Wady Kelt New road down to Jericho Wounded in cavalry charge
Advanced operating unit in action during final advance	Advanced operating unit (AOU), 1918 Palestine, AOU on road Australian operational unit Captain Anderson at Field Ambulance	AUO in action, final advance AUO operating tents AUO bivouacked for funeral
In Jordean Hills in front of Jerusalem	Bir and Ramallah In Judean Hills Field ambulance bivouacked in Judean Hills	Judean Hills, destroyed village Judean Hills, hospital tent
Haifa in final advance	Haifa, from Mount Carmel Mount Carmel	Field ambulance Wade in field ambulance

Box F: Nazareth to Damascus

Location/ event	Slides	
Nazareth in final advance	Nazareth, German general headquarters	
Tiberias in final advance	Road to Tiberias, long camel convoy	
Final advance	Tulkarm: ammunition dump Approaching Acre Approaching Acre Syria, the Lebanon and Dog River Dog River, construction	Dog River cartouches: Allenby and Napoleon III Sidon Ladder of Tyre Ladder of Tyre
Beirouth [sic]	Beirouth [sic] 54th Division entering Beirouth 54th Division entering Beirouth	54th Division entering Beirouth Advance towards Tripoli
Homs	Homs Homs From window of billet	Homs After armistice
Aleppo	Blind beggar Fortune teller From bazaar Citadel Citadel from guardroom	Citadel "golden window" View from Citadel Guarding Armenian orphans Indian cavalry Indian cavalry
Baalbeck	Baalbeck Baalbeck	Bedouin convoy south of Baalbeck Aleppo railway after Armistice
Malacca	Malacca Mance and Smith	Summit of Lebanon
Journey to Damascus	Yarmack Gorge Yarmack Gorge Yarmack: trains transporting supplies	Yarmack: trains transporting supplies Yarmack: re-entraining supplies Yarmack Gorge: bridge repaired
Damascus	Damascus Damascus View from hospital	View from hospital Barada River City

Box G: Damascus to Port Said; Touring; Turkish photographs

Location/ event	Slides	
Damascus (continued)	Damascus Damascus	Damascus Damascus
Visit to Memphis and Luxor	Sphinx at Memphis Luxor Karnak Karnak	Karnak Temple on road to Valley of Kings Temple on return from Kings Colossi of Luxor
Visit to Soudan and Khartoum	Bank of Nile Nile steamer at river bank Wady [sic] Halfa Wady [sic] Halfa Desert railway train Desert railway station	Atbara Khartoum Gordon College, Khartoum Gordon's carriage, Khartoum Omdurman Mahdi's tomb, Khartoum
Further, final advance, photographs	Beyond Jenin, bombed transports Bombed transports "War"	Aleppo railway Deraa, bombed station Ambulance train on Aleppo railway
Turkish and German prisoners	Turkish prisoners on Jericho road German prisoners in Damascus	German and Turkish prisoners Prisoners
Return home	Transport at Port Said	Embarking at Port Said
Turkish photographs	Beersheba Beersheba, review of troops Mosque at Beersheba Plain of Esdraelon Desert town Sheria Hospital Turkish camel corps Turkish lines before Gaza	Turkish hospital Sheria Turkish cavalry German commander: General Kress von Kressenstein Turkish desert staff General Falkenhayn visits a mosque

Box H: Miscellaneous

Location/ event	Slides	
Kantara	Duke of Connaught and General Allenby Christmas camel Sand carts	Transport in canal Naval vessel in canal
Maps	Mediterranean Sea Eastern Mediterranean	Palestine Palestine and Syria
Third Battle of Gaza and capture of Jerusalem	Advance through Philistria Advance through Philistria Advance through Philistria Advance through Philistria Advance through Philistria Advance through Philistria Advance through Philistria Advance through Philistria	Advance into Judea Advance into Judea Occupation of Jerusalem Amman raid Amman raid Es Salt raid Esid
Final advance	Turkish Intelligence Advance into Samaria Advance into Samaria Advance into Samaria Advance through Samaria and into Galilee	Advance through Samaria and into Galilee Advance through Samaria and into Galilee Capture of Damascus Lines of communication

APPENDIX 8.1

Henry Wade's notes on war wounds

'The initial impression of the surgeon in the Great War was undoubtedly that of profound humiliation. The layman has often said to me that you must have learned a great deal from treating so many wounded during the war, suggesting that, in consequence, surgery must have made great advances from the experience gained. There is a slight element of truth in this, but frankly there is an immense difference between civil surgery and military surgery and the latter has taught the former comparatively little that is new.

Tissue damage and infection. In civilian practice, clean wounds were virtually universal. In war, foul infection and gas gangrene were common. The fundamental problem was shattered tissue devitalized by high explosive – a fertile soil for bacterial multiplication. Removal of dead tissue was the key to effective treatment. Many attempts were made to control infection. W Watson Cheyne introduced a powerful antiseptic paste into wounds to kill the organisms. The paste was a failure. Alexis Carrel, 'that great Frenchman from New York', joined Dakins from Leeds and devised a cumbersome treatment in which a wound was washed constantly by a chemical antiseptic. Eusol (Edinburgh University Solution of Lime) was made in 1916 from boric acid and bleaching powder (chlorinated lime). It was of great value when the underlying cause was appreciated, although the results were still not good and suppuration remained rife.'

Wade emphasized again and again that the surgeon must go to the wounded not the wounded to the surgeon. This was less difficult in France than in the Middle East, where mobile warfare was the rule.

'**Time**. We solved it by creating Advanced Operation Units (AOU), mobile teams with their equipment carried in light box Ford cars...The cars accompanied the cavalry and were ready to go into action immediately they were called upon. In Allenby's final advance, 12 of these teams did service. When the 5th Cavalry Division entered Damascus, they had with them an AOU under the command of Major Pirie Watson, my Edinburgh colleague. The unit was 400 miles from the railhead.

Immobilisation. I mean by this the vital importance of careful transport as a means of saving the life of a badly wounded man. To illustrate this I would give you the history of the Thomas splint. This was a simple mechanical device made by a blacksmith for the great Liverpool surgeon, Hugh Owen Thomas some 75 years ago. It is now so universally used that we are all familiar with it and there is probably not a single ambulance student who cannot apply it in the case of fracture of the thigh bone. In Edinburgh before the War, we hardly knew of this instrument. On the outbreak of War, therefore cases of gunshot fracture of the thigh that occurred in France were very badly splinted by various crude devices with the result that the poor lad jolted back in the Ambulance from the main Dressing Station to the nearest Casualty Clearing Station, arriving in a state of profound shock from the agony caused by the broken bones rubbing together. Many unfortunately died.

Before the Battle of Arras, General Allenby, in command of the 3rd Army, was approached by his consulting surgeon, Sir Henry Gray of Aberdeen, and persuaded to allow an intensive campaign to be carried out for the use of the Thomas splint in these cases. This was adopted enthusiastically with the result that these cases which had previously had a mortality of 80% dropped to a 30% mortality and many lives were saved.

Later Allenby went out to the east to command the Egyptian Expeditionary Force of which I was Consulting Surgeon. We had been conducting a campaign for the use of the Thomas' splint with only doubtful success but at his first meeting with his Staff General Allenby said he believed there was a splint known as a Thomas splint which could be used in the field and it was his instruction that every one of his men who was wounded in the thigh was to have one of these immediately. From the Base Hospital at Alexandria and Cairo right up to the Regimental Medical officer in the field every unit carried with it Thomas splints and in each Division it was looked upon as a point of honour that every case requiring it had the splint applied by the stretcher bearer in the field and I have seen cases in the 60th London Division where the splint had been applied in the hills of Moab on the other side of the Jordan and kept on undisturbed until ultimately the patient arrived in Cairo many days later.

The other aspect of the question is the type of vehicle in which the journey is made. A journey from the Hills of Moab down into Egypt demanded many different forms of transport, each with its own value. The required transport ranged from hand-bearers drawn from the Eastern Labour Corps; camel cacholets; sand carts; cycle carts; sand sleighs; horse-drawn ambulances; motor ambulances; ambulance trains; and small hospital ships on the Suez Canal. A camel cacholet was an ideal from of transport on the hills of Moab but dangerous and alarming when rain had made the roads muddy and slippery.

Sound surgical judgement. It is vitally important for the young medical officer to realise his position in the field in wartime. The keen young hospital surgeon highly trained and specialised is apt to forget that his position is subordinate to the demands of victory. He is apt to demand the impossible provision of equipment that he considers to be the minimum necessary for his work in civilian practice. If I were to be offered the choice between this highly trained and skilful specialist or the Salvation Army equipped to give hot cocoa and buns to the walking wounded, I would most assuredly choose the latter. If I were in command of the main dressing station during an important engagement...'

At this point, Wade's notes end.

Appendix 12.1

Miscellaneous Papers of Henry Wade

1. WG Richardson. *Development and anatomy of the prostate gland*. London: J & A Churchill, 1904,

2. Walker T. On the surgical anatomy of the prostate. *J Anat Physiol* 1906; 1

3. A presidential address in summary by Hugh Cabot (presumably the American Association of Urology) followed by a paper by AG Stokes (Suprapubic or perineal prostatectomy) and summaries of discussion including comments by Murphy of Chicago.

4. Wilson LB, McGrath BF. Surgical pathology of the prostate. *Surg Gynecol Obstet* 1911; 13.

5. Hugh Hampton Young. The cure of prostatic obstruction.

6. Belfield WJ. Perineo-urethral prostatectomy.

7. Squier B (Professor of Genito-urinary surgery, New York Postgraduate Medical School and Hospital). The merits of suprapubic prostatectomy.

8. Young HA. Surgery of the prostate In: Keen's *Surgery*, volume IV.

9. Derry Douglas E (MB, ChB, Assistant Professor of Anatomy, Government School of Medicine, Cairo). On the real nature of the so-called pelvic fascia. In two parts.

10. Elliott Smith G (MA, MD, ChM, FRS. Professor of Anatomy, Cairo). Studies on the anatomy of the pelvis with special reference to the fasciae and visceral supports. [in two parts].

11. Wallace CS. *Prostatic enlargement*. pp.110: Physical basis of the clinical phenomena.

12. Wilkie, Elsie, Bowman. Paget's disease of bone, with special reference to its relation to neoplasia. This appears to be a thesis. There are 15 sections. It is under the supervision of Professor Adami of McGill University and is based on the Royal Victoria Hospital, Montreal.

13. Keyes EL. *Surgical diseases of the genito-urinary organs*, pp. 259: Hypertrophy of the prostate.

14. Luciani's *Human Physiology*, volume II, Chapter VII

Appendix 14.1

Finances of the Royal College of Surgeons of Edinburgh during Henry Wade's association with the College

Income

The College's income came principally from examinations. By 1957, the fee for the primary Fellowship was 12 guineas and for the final Fellowship examination 24 guineas. Undergraduates paid a matriculation fee when they enrolled for the courses of the School of Medicine, but these fees, like those of the postgraduates, were necessarily credited to the School. The College Hall was leased frequently for dinners, meetings and other occasions. In 1957, the charge for hiring the hall for a dinner rose to £15, while to hire the Library cost £7.

The College's investments were modest but increased with the years. Their market value rose from £31,992 in 1920 to £32,821 in 1925, £40,297 in 1930, £54,106 in 1935 and £60,719 in 1940.

As time passed, a little money came from the slowly growing volume of College heritable property in and around Hill Square and Roxburgh Place, Edinburgh. In 1935, the value of this property amounted to £31,377. The College buildings themselves were of immense historical and cultural value but were in essence wasting assets, as the market value of the Playfair Hall was inevitably small. No organization or individual wished to buy it.

The Royal College of Surgeons of Edinburgh benefited indirectly from the generosity of the Carnegie Foundation. From time to time they also received other more immediate donations. DM Greig left the residue of his estate to the College in 1936. A Logan Turner bequeathed £1,000 to the College in July 1939. He had been responsible for meeting the costs of moving the old doorway from the first Surgeons' Hall to the Playfair building. The President's room in the College is named after him.

Expenditure

College expenditure centred on salaries and wages, on the insurance and upkeep of buildings and on the payment of examiners. The contributions made annually to support the Laboratory of the Royal College of Physicians of Edinburgh are explained in the main text.

Staff salaries and wages were modest and in keeping with those of the times. In 1899, the salary of the College Secretary, Mr George Robertson, was £150 per annum. Robertson, Clerk of the College for 50 years, became 'law agent' and, in 1908, was given 'a piece of plate' to thank him for his loyal service. In 1911, the salary of the College Officer, which had been £80 per annum, was raised to £150. By 1958, this figure had become £430, a figure closely similar to that of the College Librarian, Miss Francis Brown. Office bearers received generous honoraria, but, in 1914, the Conservator was granted an honorarium of only £50, a figure that rose to £100 by 1920, £300 by 1922 and £450 by 1930.

A critical factor that contributed to heavy financial outlays was the requirement to maintain and repair old buildings and to install modern facilities that included supplies of gas, electricity and water. The sanitary conditions of the College were not always modern and had been the object of criticism when the experience of the 400th anniversary of the Incorporation of Barber Surgeons was commemorated in 1905. In July 1927, flood damage, attributed to rain, required £43 of repairs. Improvements were made periodically. In July 1936, Wade, as President, approved a plan to install a revolving door at the western, Nicolson Street entrance to the College building at a cost of £384.

Local property was increasing in value, and, in 1895, the Hill Square investment was worth £28,184; five years later, the value had increased to £32,447. In 1909, eight small 'houses' (flats or apartments) were absorbed into the Museum premises. Six were modernized: three to accommodate College servants and three to be let. In time, the College also acquired buildings in Nicolson Street and Hill Place. In 1911, it was offered Roxburgh Place Church, a building with a convenient entrance at the corner of Hill Square. The asking price was £2,850, but the College secured the deal for £1,480. They were also offered the New School of Medicine, Bristo Street, and the Cinema House in Nicolson Street but declined both.

In 1932, a workman had been killed accidentally in the College building. The Council agreed a statutory payment of £350 compensation but recorded no note of sympathy to the victim's relatives.

Hospitality

It was inevitable that the President and Council should offer hospitality to their numerous visitors, as well as providing lunches, teas and dinners for great numbers of examiners, teachers and others. In 1910, a party of distinguished American surgeons was entertained at a cost of £25. A lunch held in February 1926 to commemorate the 200th anniversary of the founding of the Royal College of Physicians of Edinburgh cost £60. Anticipating the 1927 Edinburgh Meeting of the

British Medical Association, the College set aside £300 towards the cost of this important occasion, the centenary of Joseph Lister's birth.

Payments were required for many occasional purposes. In 1902, £100 was granted towards the celebrations of King Edward VII's coronation. In December 1928, the Council was sympathetic to a letter in the *Times* newspaper seeking money for the purchase of radium. In 1934, the College invested £6 in a duplicating machine. A typewriter had cost £20, one quarter of a staff salary, in 1905. In October 1928, the money available in the Francis Caird Prize fund amounted to £198/5/2s. In December 1922, the Judicial Factor for the Society of Barbers claimed £209/11/9d arising from the 1845 agreement to compensate the Barbers for the loss of rights related to the Trades Maidens Hospital. Compensatory payments so far had been made only until 1897.

War came again. In 1940, the government appealed to the nation for help with payments for the manufacture of fighter aircraft. The College responded by preferring to invest £1,000 into 3% Defence bonds and 2½% National War bonds. There were also occasional demands for donations. Responding to the national mood, the College contributed £300 in 1935 to the George V Jubilee Trust. Occasionally, the College could seem thrifty to the point of meanness. Thus, in 1942, a prisoner of war, Lieutenant Colonel Bull, asked for books to study surgery. The College Treasurer agreed a sum not exceeding £15.

Like all charities, the College received frequent appeals for financial help. In 1923, a Manchester organization invited the college to join their efforts to provide for the relief of starving Russian doctors.[6]

No organization can survive for five centuries without experiencing deception, fraud and crime. The RCSEd was no exception. In February 1929, discrepancies became apparent in the College's ledgers. In spite of considerable and sympathetic help, it became clear that the Clerk, Mr Eadie, should be dismissed. He claimed that he had been ill. In 1932, the College Attendant suffered the same fate but was allowed 10/– weekly as compensation.

APPENDIX 14.2

Bangour Hospital

Bangour Village Hospital had been constructed as a mental asylum. It was declared open in 1908. In 1913, there were 813 patients.

By the spring of 1915, the combatants on the western and eastern European fronts were exhausted. Faced with the prospect of continued, interminable conflict, the British War Office demanded a further large military hospital in Scotland. Bangour Village was selected. It had many advantages. Bangour was connected to the nearby city of Edinburgh by a rail link and it had spacious buildings and room for many more. A hutted hospital was added to the original, permanent red brick buildings. By May 1915, the mental patients from Bangour had been evacuated to nine other asylums. The Superintendent, Dr Keay, was made Officer Commanding and granted military rank. Senior resident surgeons and physicians were accompanied by residents and a resident dental officer, and a radiologist and a pathologist were appointed. The nursing staff of 200 was soon augmented by large numbers of volunteers. Additional beds were crowded into the permanent buildings: in six villas alone, 520 new beds were installed. Gradually, a series of special services came into use. A substantial X-ray unit was installed. Orthopaedic surgery, with facilities for plaster work, the fitting of artificial limbs and photography were added, and a tropical medicine unit set up.

The first trainload of war casualties – 51 surgical and 49 medical – arrived on 12th June 1915. Early in 1916, it became clear that no more patients could be accommodated. A series of marquees was therefore erected, allowing a total of 1,838 casualties to be housed. Even this figure proved inadequate. A tented hospital of 1,000 beds was added. As the war drew to its end, the total number of patients at Bangour reached the astronomical figure of 3,036.

Throughout 1919, the number of military patients at Bangour was steadily reduced. The last patient was discharged on 31st December 1921 and the hospital returned to civilian use on 1st January 1922. A Report on the work of the hospital was published in 1923. By 1929, the work of the hospital had returned entirely to normal peacetime proportions, and there were now no more than 1,000 patients.

Appendix 16.1

Henry Wade: original papers and communications

Carmichael EWS, Wade H, A case of primary sarcoma of the liver in a child aged four months. *Lancet* 1907;**i**:1217–19.

Wade H. *A contribution to the problem of cancer research, based upon the results of an experimental investigation of infective sarcoma of the dog* [MD thesis]. Edinburgh: University of Edinburgh, 1907.

Wade H. An experimental investigation of infective sarcoma of the dog, with a consideration of its relationship to cancer. *J Path Bacteriol* 1908;**12**:384–425.

Wade H. Experimental acute interstitial nephritis: the renal changes induced by the toxins of infective sarcoma in dogs. *J Path Bacteriol* 1908;**12**:138–9.

Wade H, Watson BP. The anatomy and histology of an early tubal gestation, with lantern demonstration. *Lancet* 1908;**i**:1844–5.

Wade H. Excision of ulna for infective osteomyelitis; nephropexy for moveable kidney. *Lancet* 1910;**ii**:1834.

Wade H. Treatment of simple fractures. *Lancet* 1912;**i**:798.

Wade H. Some points in the surgical pathology of the prostate gland. *J Path Bacteriol* 1912;**17**:107. [Title of paper presented to the Pathological Society of Great Britain and Ireland.]

Wade H. Nephrectomy for acute consecutive suppurative nephritis; cellulitis and osteomyelitis. *Lancet* 1912;**i**:97–8.

Wade H. Tissue reactions to foreign bodies. *J Path Bacteriol* 1912:**17**:107. [Title of paper presented to the Pathological Society of Great Britain and Ireland.]

Wade H. Intussusception of the stomach and duodenum due to a gastric polypus. *Surg, Gynecol Obstet* 1913;**20**:184–90.

Wade H. Intussusception of the stomach and duodenum due to a gastric polypus. *Lancet* 1913;**ii**:1204.

Wade H. Prostatism: the pathological basis of the operative treatment. *Lancet* 1913;**ii**:299-300.

Wade H. An endemic febrile illness. *Lancet* 1913;I:246.

Wade H. Treatment of prostatism. *Intl Clin* 1914;**ii**:1–12.

Wade H. Prostatism. The surgical anatomy and pathology of the operative treatment. *Ann Surg* 1914;**37**:321–59.

Wade H. Report of patient six years after the implantation of a homoplastic bone graft. *Edinb Med J* 1920;NS24:37–9.

Wade H. Student life in the Scottish Horse Field Ambulance. *The Student* 1920:43–6.

Wade H. The diagnosis and treatment of calculus in the pelvic portion of the ureter. *Edinb Med J* 1920;**24**:392–401.

Wade H. The influence of the war on the modern treatment of fractures. *BMJ* 1921;**I**:1–12.

Wade H. The choice of methods employed in the surgical diagnosis of renal disease. *Medico-Chirurgical Trans* 1922;**36**:8–13.

Wade H. Surgical work in Palestine, Mesopotamia and Macedonia. In: MacPherson W, Bowlby A, Wallace C, English C, editors. *History of the Great War, based on official documents. Medical Services: Surgery of the War.* London: Stationery Office, 1922: 310–27.

Wade H. The clinical significance of the form and capacity of the renal pelvis. *Trans Med Chir Soc Edinb* 1924;**38**:13–19.

Wade H. The treatment of tumours of the urinary bladder. *Trans Med Chir Soc Edinb* 1926-27;**41**:1–19.

Wade H. The surgical pathology of tuberculous disease of the urinary tract. *Irish J Med Sci* 1928;**6**:245–58.

Wade H, Band D. Uroselectan: excretion urography. *Trans Med Chir Soc Edinb* 1929–30;**44**;203–20.

Wade H. The treatment of malignant tumours of the urinary bladder. *Surg, Gynecol Obstet* 1931;**52**:312–23.

Wade H. The significance of haematuria. *BMJ* 1932;**1**:1–12.

Wade H. The balanced urinary system. The Ramon Guiteras Lecture. *J Urol* 1932;**28**:381–403.

Wade H. The role of excretion urography in the diagnosis of disease. *BMJ* 1933;**i**:353–5.

Wade H. The treatment of tuberculous disease of the kidney from the standpoint of the surgeon. *Edinb Med J* 1933;NS**40**:166–75.

Wade H, Dick IL. Suppression of urine and deficiency of renal secretion. *Trans Med Chir Soc Edinb* 1934;**41**:193–220.

Wade H. Renal tumours. *Aust NZ J Surg* 1935;**5**:3–17.

Wade H. The diagnosis of renal and vesical disease in general practice. *Clin J* 1935;**64**:66–71.

Wade H. The treatment of ureteric calculi. *Proc R Soc Med* 1935;**28**:582–-90.

Wade H. Vesical exclusion. *Proc R Soc Med* 1937;**31**:277–84.

Wade H. Sir David Wilkie. *Edinb Med J* 1938;**45**:726–8.

Wade H. Harvey in Scotland. *Edinb Med J* 1938;**45**:761–81.

Wade H. The expectancy of life after ureteral transplantation. *Edinb Med J* 1939;**46**:61–82.

Wade H. J.J.M. Shaw. *Edinb Med J* 1940;**47**:773–5.

Wade H. Urological reflections. *Proc R Soc Med* 1946;**39**:751–4.

Wade H. The art of the surgeon in diagnosis and treatment. *Newcastle Med J* 1946;**23**:22–7.

Wade H. The barber surgeons of Edinburgh. *Ann R Coll Surg Engl* 1949;**5**:3–16.

Unpublished

Wade H. *Lymphadenoma: experimental research.* 1909.

Index

Readers' note: HW = Henry Wade; page numbers in *italics* indicate an illustration or table; page numbers such as *n335E* indicate an entry in the End Notes.